To my dearest wife Joyce
who sadly did not live to see
the book completed.
L.L.A.

The World's Show

Coincraft's Catalogue of
Crystal Palace Medals and Tokens
1851-1936

Leslie Lewis Allen

Coincraft

London 2000

First published in 2000
by Standard Catalogue Publishers Ltd for
Coincraft
44 & 45 Great Russell Street
London WC1B 3LU

Series editor: Eleni Calligas

British Library Cataloguing in Publication Data
A catalogue record for this book is available from the British Library

ISBN 0 9526228 90

Database typeset by Polestar Whitefriars Ltd
Printed and bound by Polestar Wheatons Ltd

Contents

About the Author

Leslie Lewis Allen was born in North London in 1927. At the outbreak of World War II, he was evacuated to Hertfordshire, which effectively brought his education to a halt. As a result, he was soon brought back to war-torn London, and at the age of 13, was pushed out to work as a pawnbroker's assistant, where he received the magnificent sum of 14/- (70p) for a 54 hour working week; this would not buy a Sunday newspaper today. One of his duties, which was at the forefront of technology, was to operate a device which wrote three pawn tickets simultaneously. Called up for war service in 1945, he served nearly three years in the Royal Army Service Corps, of which, thankfully, 'only one day' was wartime service, but during that period he was forced to endure a lengthy 'overseas' posting on the Isle of Wight. On return to 'civvy street', he studied accountancy at evening classes, and up until his retirement in 1983, spent the last 33 years of his working life on management accounting within the National Health Service. He met and married his loving wife Joyce in 1958, whilst they were both working at the same hospital in London. They moved out to Clacton in 1966. He took up coin collecting soon after, but by the early 1970s had moved on to collecting Coronation and Jubilee medals. In 1974 he acquired from a colleague a London Coronation medal (SY-1911 /001). It had been given to his colleague on 30 June 1911 when, as one of 100,000 London schoolchildren, he was taken to the Crystal Palace (wearing the medal) to greet the newly crowned King and Queen who were at the Palace to open the 'Coronation Fete'. This acquisition re-awakened the author's interest in the Crystal Palace, which must have lain dormant since the catastrophic night of 30 November 1936, when as a boy, in North London, he had witnessed that awful red glow in the night sky.

Acknowledgements

The author is very grateful to Richard Lobel who kindly offered to publish this work for him. It was awesome to see Coincraft swing into action and, thanks to the expertise, dedication, understanding and kindness shown by Eleni Calligas and John Medlin, reality has exceeded his wildest dreams.

The author owes a great deal to many friends and acquaintances who have been ready and willing to assist him in the compiling of this book, and who drew his attention to various publications and articles of which he was unaware. Thanks are also extended for the generous help and encouragement given so readily by many kind people who were, previously, complete strangers. This is particularly true of two very good new friends in the United States of America: Jim Allen, his namesake, who contributed enormously by his constant support and unselfishness in providing details and illustrations from his own collection, and, likewise, Jim Sweeny who has been a constant source of inspiration and encouragement by providing a regular flow of expert information relating to tokens. The author thanks them both for their friendship, generosity and kindness. Regretfully, our thanks to Jim Allen must be posthumous as he has sadly left us before this book was completed. We lost a good, generous and kind friend and feel much richer for having known him.

Grateful thanks also go to Clive Hickson, the author's brother-in-law, who corrected the draft and steered him in the right direction; to John Whitmore, for generously allowing us to make extensive use of his numismatic expertise; to Siegfried Schwer, for suggesting the author should undertake this project, and generously allowing the use of his extensive library; to Douglas Pearson, for his warm friendship, constant interest and advice; to John R.P. King, for introducing the author to the realm of Crystal Palace tokens; to Eric Price and Melvyn Harrison of the Crystal Palace Foundation, for the generous loan of medals and other material for illustration purposes; to Dr William J. Mira of New South Wales, for providing the information relating to Australian tokens; to Paul & Bente Withers, who provided a large proportion of the numismatic photographs; to Barry Kaizer who helped to scan the photographs and to Jonathan Newson for keeping the computer going. In addition our thanks to the dealers who have found so many interesting pieces for us over the years. These include Mrs Neddy Allen, A. H. Baldwin

& Son Ltd, Christopher Eimer, Alan Judd, Ian Jull, Reg Lomas, Simon Monks, Robert Pratt, Siegfried Schwer, Mark Stevens, Howard & Frances Simmons, Noel Warr and John Whitmore. Our special thanks also to Laurence Brown for allowing us to quote descriptions of the following medals from his excellent catalogue *British Historical Medals 1837–1901*. This includes medals numbered 2441, 2450, 2451, 2551, 2555, 2610, 2722, 2727, 2730, 2732, 2734, 2753, 2755, 2799 and 3116. We would be remiss were we not also to thank the chief librarian and staff at the University of Essex; the staff at the British Library; the curators and their staffs at the British Museum, the Crystal Palace Museum, the Museum of London, the Victoria & Albert Museum and the other museums which were visited or contacted.

Finally, my love and thanks go to my late wife, Joyce, who suffered with patience and humour through the many years during which I pursued my 'hobby' (there are those who would consider 'obsession' to be a more appropriate word), as I traced the history of the fairy-tale Crystal Palaces as shown to me in medallic form. My thanks to you all.

Introduction

'The Crystal Palace': in 1851 Douglas Jerrold of *Punch* magazine, bestowed this magical name on one of the foremost architectural and technological wonders of its age. Designed, not by a professional architect, but instead by Joseph Paxton, a humble landscape gardener, and constructed almost entirely of the newest materials available, glass and iron, the magnificent, glittering building has captured the hearts and imaginations of generations of British people. Originally intended as a fitting venue for the 'Great Exhibition' of 1851, it soon symbolised the imperial greatness and international prestige of Great Britain and her dominions during the reign of Queen Victoria and her beloved consort, Prince Albert.

The Crystal Palace came to be seen as a hallmark of success when it was quickly realised that the enormous popularity of the Great Exhibition was due in large part to the actual Crystal Palace building; such recognition rapidly led to other 'Crystal Palaces' being built in many other major cities around the world. Numerous medals and tokens were struck to commemorate most of them, but, as it would take more than a lifetime to locate many of these pieces, this book dedicates itself to just the four English buildings, i.e. the original built for the 'Great Exhibition'

Hyde Park, view from the northwest by Ackerman. Reproduced by permission of Eric Price.

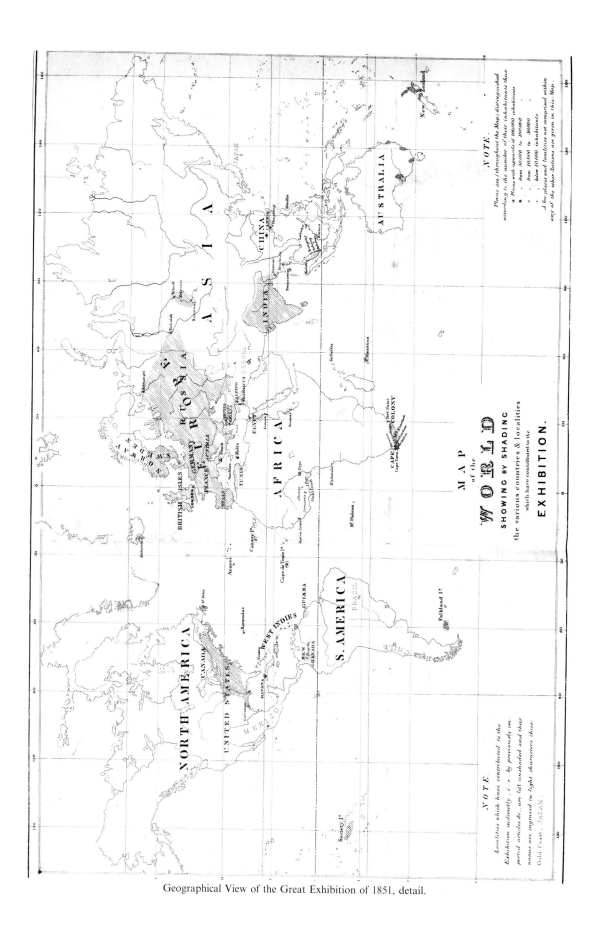

Geographical View of the Great Exhibition of 1851, detail.

at Hyde Park, London (1851); its successor at Sydenham (1854); that for the 'Exhibition of Art Treasures of the United Kingdom' at Manchester (1857), and the final building for the 'International Exhibition' at South Kensington (1862). Unfortunately, none of these buildings has survived.

During the first half of the twentieth century, almost everything Victorian was distinctly unpopular, so it was not until 1951, when the Festival of Britain was held to celebrate the centenary of the Great Exhibition, that considerable interest was again aroused in a subject which had largely been forgotten for so many years. One direct result of the Festival has been the attraction of an increasing number of collectors to the Crystal Palace series, making it not only a popular medallic theme, but also one of the few areas of numismatics not to have been adversely affected by the depressions suffered since the late 1980s. Most medal dealers now have both British and foreign collectors on their books, which fact has encouraged prices to move steadily upwards. A survey of dealers' prices since the early 1950s confirms that they have risen at a much sharper rate than normal inflation, and, particularly so, in the past five years.

This volume has been produced because of the growing interest in this legacy of Victorian enterprise, and, hopefully, it will be useful to collectors and dealers alike. It is not the first publication to list materials of this type, but it will be the first work devoted entirely to Crystal Palace medals and tokens covering the whole period from the opening of the Great Exhibition in 1851, to the destruction by fire of the Sydenham Crystal Palace in 1936. As such, the author hopes, it will provide a sound basis for any later works upon the subject. Nor does this volume claim to be definitive, particularly with regard to the Sydenham Crystal Palace, where, it will be seen, there are still a number of years for which no medals have been recorded. Yet, as the lifetime of this Palace coincided with the most prolific period of medal production in British history, it is difficult to believe that no medals were struck during any of these years, except, possibly, for those of 1915–1918, during World War I. Accordingly, there should still be many exciting pieces just 'sitting out there' waiting to be discovered, and, with this in mind, the numbering system in this book has been devised in a style that is not strictly sequential, in order to allow new material to be easily inserted without causing the work to become disordered. In fact the author would be delighted to hear from any readers who know of any items not recorded here, as these could possibly be included in either a supplement or a revised edition, at a later date. Sources of information would, of course, be gratefully acknowledged and quoted in any further works. This, or any other correspondence, should be sent to the author, c/o Coincraft, 44 & 45 Great Russell Street, London WC1B 3LU.

Values have not been quoted alongside each entry because experience has shown that, immediately they become outdated, the credibility of the catalogue begins to suffer. To compensate for this, readers will find that a price guide has been added at the end of the catalogue. A degree of rarity has been defined for each medal (in EF condition), based on a knowledge of rarity which has been acquired from collecting these particular pieces over a period spanning more than twenty years. As, however, the author is a newcomer to the world of tokens, he has, in this area, gratefully used the values and rarity ratings by John Whitmore, from *Bell's*

Unofficial Farthings, A Supplement by Robert Bell, John Whitmore & James O. Sweeny. Finally, the creation of this book has been a labour of love by a keen collector seeking simply to record these beautiful pieces for posterity.

Sydenham, Tram Terminus c. 1908. Reproduced by permission of Eric Price & Melvyn Harrison

Using the Catalogue

Entries are catalogued by medallist and size, in number and date order. The information is presented in the following sequence:

Identification:

> Catalogue number — Subject, or name if the entry is a token
>
> Medallist or issuer — Metals in which the piece has been found & size in millimetres
>
> The catalogue number is prefixed by an abbreviation of the relevant Crystal Palace Exhibition: HP – the Great Exhibition of the Works of Industry of all Nations at Hyde Park, 1851; SY – Sydenham, 1854–1936; MA – the Exhibition of Art Treasures at Manchester, 1857; SK – the International Exhibition at South Kensington, 1862.
>
> HP and SK entries are further classified into: A – Official medals, B – Unofficial medals, C – Trade tokens and D – Associated pieces. SY entries are prefixed by the date. MA entries are not prefixed.

Illustration.

Description:

> of the obverse and reverse, as well as the rim design and, if applicable, the edge inscription. All the symbols and devices found upon the medals and tokens are shown, except for the dots or dashes sometimes found beneath the superscript text. An oblique (/) indicates the start of a new line.

Collecting Information: (see below for further details and the abbreviations used)

> Rarity value, which refers to specimens in Extremely Fine condition only. Other works which cite the entry. If an entry is not illustrated herein, another volume containing the illustration is cited if known. 'Unrecorded' indicates that the piece is not listed in any of the reference works mentioned. Collections where specimens may be found.

Notes.

A general index and a price guide are to be found at the end of the catalogue.

Abbreviations

Metals

Ae	bronze or copper
Aeg	gilt bronze or copper
Aes	silvered bronze or copper
Al	aluminium
Alg	gilt aluminium
Ar	silver
Av	gold
Br	brass
Brg	gilt brass
Brs	silvered brass
Wm	white metal
Wmb	bronzed white metal
Wmg	gilt white metal

Rarity

Medals

Dealers judge rarity from the number of items which flow through their hands. By contrast, because collectors do not see anywhere near the same number of pieces, their judgement of rarity is usually measured by the length of time it takes them to find the particular pieces they are looking for. This can differ from one locality to another, since their place of residence may sometimes play an important part in their ability to find specimens. Consequently, the author would not expect everyone to agree precisely with his interpretation of rarity for each piece, but, by drawing on the knowledge acquired from searching for these particular pieces for more than 20 years, his conclusions, which are shown in each of the individual entries in the catalogue, accord with the table set out below. As mentioned earlier, the rarity rating refers to a specimen in Extremely Fine condition only, and should not be used to describe a specimen which is in an inferior state. Based on this criteria the author maintains that there are no common Crystal Palace medals in EF condition; while a few have been rated as normal or scarce, it will be seen from the entries that the majority are rated as rare, very rare or extremely rare:

N	Normal, frequently seen
S	Scarce, less frequently seen
R	Rare, difficult to find
RR	Very rare, very difficult to find
RRR	Extremely rare, extremely difficult to find
RRRR	Highest rarity, virtually impossible to find

Tokens

The rarity ratings used for unofficial farthings are those to be found alongside the individual entries in *Bell's Unofficial Farthings, A Supplement* by R.C. Bell, J. Whitmore and J.O. Sweeny. Like Crystal Palace medals, there are no common Crystal Palace tokens; while a few have been rated as normal or scarce most of them are rare, very rare or extremely rare.

Numismatic References

Batty	Batty, D.T., *Catalogue of the Copper Coinage of Great Britain, Ireland, British Isles and Colonies*, Manchester: 1868-1898.
Bell	Bell, R.C., *Unofficial Farthings 1820-1870*, London: 1975.
Bell et al	Bell, R., J. Whitmore & J.O. Sweeny, *Bell's Unofficial Farthings, A Supplement*, Whitmore: 1994.
Brown	Brown, L., *British Historical Medals 1760-1960*, Vol. I *1760-1837*, London: 1980; Vol. II *1837-1901*, London: 1987; Vol. III *The Accession of Edward VII to 1960*, London: 1995.
Carlisle	Carlisle, L.J., *Australian Commemorative Medals & Medalets from 1788*, Sydney: 1983.
Davis	Davis, W.J., *The Token Coinage of Warwickshire*, Birmingham: 1895.
Davis et al	Davis, W.J. & A.W. Waters, *Tickets and Passes of Great Britain and Ireland*, London: 1974.
Eidlitz	Eidlitz, R.J., *Medals & Medallions relating to Architects*, New York: 1927.
Eimer (I)	Eimer, C., *British Commemorative Medals and their values*, London: 1987.
Eimer (II)	Eimer, C., *An Introduction to Commemorative Medals*, London: 1989.
Fearon (I)	Fearon, D., *Spink's Catalogue of British Commemorative Medals, 1558 to the present day, with valuations*, London: 1984.
Fearon (II)	Fearon, D., *Victorian Souvenir Medals*, Aylesbury: 1986.
Gunstone	Gunstone, A., 'Records of the Birmingham Mint', in Spink's *Numismatic Circular*, April-June 1978.
Minnet et al	Minnet, S.C., J. Durrell & A. Gunstone, *Somerset Public House Tokens*, Bridgewater: 1995.
Pinches	Pinches, J.H., *Medals by John Pinches, A Catalogue of works struck by the company from 1840 to 1969*, London: 1987.
Rulau	Rulau, R., *U.S. Merchant Tokens 1845-1860*, 2nd edition, Iola, WI (no date).
Sabo	Sabo, D.E., 'Exposition 1851', *The Numismatist*, January 1968.
Seaby	Seaby, W.A., 'Catalogue of Ulster Tokens etc.', *Ulster Journal of Archaeology* 1971.
Taylor	Taylor, J., *The Architectural Medal, England in the nineteenth century*, London: 1978.

| Todd | Todd, N.B., *Tavern checks from Liverpool & vicinity*, Liverpool Museum Occasional Papers No. 1, 1987. |
| Withers | Withers, P., *Catalogue of the collection of Coins, Medals, Medallions, Tokens, Dies, etc. in the Assay Office Birmingham*, Birmingham: 1985. |

Collections Cited

Most of the medals and tokens listed in the catalogue have been seen by the author. There are however some which he has not yet seen, that have been included for the sake of completeness. In all such cases, their provenance will be found in a note to the entry.

AM	Ashmolean Museum, Oxford
BM	British Museum, London
BG	Birmingham Museum & Art Gallery
BR	Bromley Museum, Orpington.
CP	Crystal Palace Museum, London
FM	Fitzwilliam Museum, Cambridge
LV	Liverpool Museum
LM	Lincoln Museum
ML	Museum of London
PC	Private collections
RC	Royal collection, Windsor Castle, Windsor
RM	Royal Mint Museum, Llantrisant
UM	Ulster Museum
VA	Victoria and Albert Museum, London

Price Guide

Medals

The values shown are a guide to the price a collector can expect to pay when buying from a dealer, and refer to specimens in Extremely Fine condition. This means there is little actual wear except on the highest points, and they are free from nicks, scuffs, scratches and other defects. Accordingly a specimen in uncirculated condition in its original case or paper packet will attract an additional premium, as will those awarded to VIPs. Also, due to the passage of time, it is often extremely difficult, and in some cases nigh impossible, to find certificates and other types of paperwork such as descriptive leaflets which were sometimes presented with the medals. The presence of any of these items will automatically attract an additional premium.

Tokens

The values shown are a guide to the price a collector can expect to pay when buying from a dealer, and refer to specimens in Extremely Fine condition. This means there is little actual wear except on the highest points, and they are free from any nicks, scuffs, scratches and other defects. Accordingly, a specimen in uncirculated condition will attract a premium. However, readers should appreciate that while most medals were made just to be looked at, tokens were made to be used; consequently, most of them did get some degree of wear and are, therefore, less often found in EF condition.

View from the south side. (Lithograph by Brannan)

Bibliography

Batty, D.T., *Catalogue of the Copper Coinage of Great Britain, Ireland, British Isles and Colonies*, Manchester: 1868–1898.

Beaver, P., *The Crystal Palace*, London: 1970.

Bell Knight, C.A., *The Crystal Palace 1851 Exhibition*, Bath: 1983.

Bell, R.C., *Unofficial Farthings 1820–1870*, London: 1975.

Bell, R., J. Whitmore & J.O. Sweeny, *Bell's Unofficial Farthings, A Supplement*, Whitmore: 1994.

Bird, A., *Paxton's Palace*, London: 1976.

Bristow, M., *The Postal History of the Crystal Palace 1851–1936*, London: 1983.

Brown, L., *British Historical Medals, 1760–1960*, Vol. I *1760–1837*, London: 1980; Vol. II *1837–1901*, London: 1987; Vol. III *The Accession of Edward VII to 1960*, London: 1995.

Carlisle, L.J., *Australian Commemorative Medals & Medalets from 1788*, Sydney: 1983.

Cassell, J., *Art Treasures Exhibition*. London: 1858.

Chadwick, G.F., *The Works of Sir Joseph Paxton, 1803–1865*, London: 1965.

Cole, H., *Fifty years of Public Life*, London: 1884.

Concanen, E., *Remembrances of The Great Exhibition*

Crystal Palace I.B.C., *90 years of Indoor Bowling*, London: 1995.

Davis, W.J. & A.W. Waters, *Tickets and Passes of Great Britain and Ireland*, London: 1974.

Davis, W.J., *The Token Coinage of Warwickshire*, Birmingham: 1895.

de Mare, E., *London 1851 The year of the Great Exhibition*, London: 1972.

Dean, Thomas & Son., *The Worlds Fair; Or Children's Prize Gift Book*, London: 1851.

Eidlitz, R.J., *Medals & Medallions relating to Architects*, New York: 1927.

Eimer, C., *An Introduction to Commemorative Medals*, London: 1989.

Eimer, C., *British Commemorative Medals and their values*, London: 1987.

Fay, C.R., *Palace of Industry 1851*, Cambridge: 1951.

Fearon, D., *Spink's Catalogue of British Commemorative Medals, 1558 to the present day, with valuations*, London: 1984.

Fearon, D., *Victorian Souvenir Medals*, Aylesbury: 1986.

French, Y., *The Great Exhibition 1851*, London: 1950.

Gibbs-Smith, C.H., *The Great Exhibition of 1851. A Commemorative Album*, HMSO, London: 1950.

Gunstone, A., 'Records of the Birmingham Mint Limited', *The Numismatic Circular*, April-June 1978

Hawkins, R.N.P., *A Dictionary of makers of British metallic tickets, checks, medalets, tallies, and counters, 1788–1910*, London: 1989.

Hobhouse, C., *1851 and the Crystal Palace*, London: 1937.

Howarth, P., *The year is 1851*, London: 1951.

Markham, V., *Paxton and the Bachelor Duke*, London: 1935.

McKean, J., *Crystal Palace, Joseph Paxton and Charles Fox*, London: 1994.

Minnet, S.C., J. Durrell and A. Gunstone, *Somerset Public House Tokens, by Somerset*, Bridgewater: 1995.

Musgrave, M., *The musical life of the Crystal Palace*, Cambridge: 1995.

Pinches, J.H., *Medals by John Pinches, A Catalogue of works struck by the company from 1840 to 1969*, London: 1987.

Pinches, J.H., *The Family of Pinches*, London: 1981.

Reeves, G., *Palace of the People*, 1986.

Royal Commissioners of 1851, *Official Descriptive and Illustrated Catalogue*, London: 1851.

Royal Commissioners of 1851, *Reports & documents in the Victoria & Albert Museum*, London: 1851.

Royal Commissioners of 1851, *Reports by the Juries*, London: 1851.

Rulau, R., *U.S. Merchant Tokens 1845–1860*, 2nd edition, Iola, WI (no date).

Ruskin, J., *The Opening of the Crystal Palace*, London: 1854.

Sabo, D.E., 'Exposition 1851', *The Numismatist*, January 1968.

Seaby, W.A.,'Catalogue of Ulster Tokens etc.', *Ulster Journal of Archaeology* 1971.

Tallis, J., *History and Description of the Crystal Palace*, London: 1851.

Taylor, J., *The Architectural Medal, England in the nineteenth century*, London: 1978.

Todd, N.B., *Tavern checks from Liverpool & vicinity*, Liverpool Museum Occasional Papers No. 1, 1987.

Victoria and Albert Museum, *The International Exhibition of 1862*, HMSO 1962.

Vincent, B., *Haydn's Dictionary of Dates 1895*, London: 1895.

Warwick, A., *The Phoenix Suburb*, London: 1982.

Withers, P., *Catalogue of the collection of Coins, Medals, Medallions, Tokens, Dies, etc. in the Assay Office Birmingham*, Birmingham: 1985.

Yglesias, J.R.C., *London Life & the Great Exhibition 1851*, London: 1964.

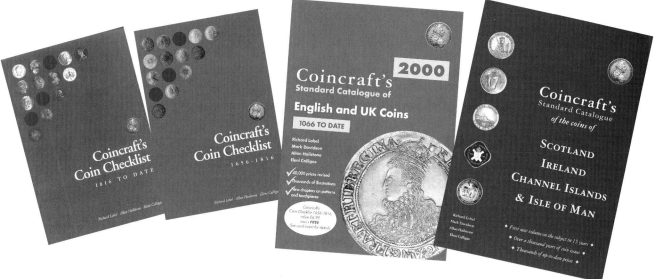

Part I
Great Exhibition
Hyde Park
1851

Introduction

During the late 1840s, and quite unlike today, Britain led the world in industrial expansion. In order to consolidate that position, and to enable the British Empire to capture the lion's share of the new markets which were gradually opening up, the Society of Arts, with HRH Prince Albert as its president, was striving to improve industrial design. To encourage this development, a series of small exhibitions of art manufacture began in 1847. These proved to be so popular that they led to the proposal of a National Exhibition, planned to be held in 1851. However, when members of the Society visited the Paris Exposition of 1849, they found that the French government had tried desperately to make this exhibition an international event. These efforts had been totally thwarted because the French manufacturers, being greatly protected by countless trade tariffs, could not be persuaded to co-operate.

Prince Albert painted on Sevres porcelain (Tallis, *History & Description of the Crystal Palace*)

By contrast, it was quickly realised by Society members, that the system of free trade operating in Britain presented an ideal climate in which to launch an international competition. Therefore the opportunity to turn the proposed 1851 national event into the first 'Exhibition of the Works of Industry of all Nations', and for London to be shown as the shop window of the world, was too good to miss and not to be wasted. Prince Albert proposed that a Royal Commission would be needed to plan and manage such an important display, so, during the delay in its formation, the Society of Arts agreed to appoint a Committee to perform executive functions; the most important of which would be to visit the principle manufacturing districts nationwide to encourage the setting up of 299 local committees, whose task it would be to disseminate information and gather suitable exhibits for the great occasion.

Everything pointed to 1851 witnessing the biggest and best show the world had ever seen, since it was calculated that nearly one million square feet of floor space would be needed to house the thousands of exhibits which were expected to arrive from far and wide. After much acrimonious debate, Parliament eventually gave approval for a building to be erected in Hyde Park, albeit, only for the duration of the Exhibition.

It was at this point that the Commissioners made a near-disastrous error by appointing a high-powered Building Committee consisting of three architects and three engineers. The architects were Charles Barry, C.R. Cockerell, and T.L. Donaldson, whilst the engineers were I.K. Brunel, W. Cubitt, and Robert Stephenson. Any one of these men, acting on his own initiative, could easily have undertaken the responsibility alone, but, collectively, it was a classic case of 'too many cooks', the result being disputes and unbearable delays which seriously jeopardised the entire project.

When designs for an exhibition building were invited from architects world wide, 245 plans were received by the Commissioners for their consideration. The Building Committee took far too long digesting this mass of architectural ingenuity, and, after picking all of these eminent brains, cheekily declared that, even though eighteen of them were of the highest distinction, none of them was regarded as suitable. Instead it recommended the adoption of its own monstrous plan, for a building comprising fifteen million bricks and surmounted by a dome larger than that on St Paul's Cathedral. Although this would have been impossible to erect within the specified time, the Commissioners, reluctantly accepted their proposal. However, as soon as news of this reached the press, a public outcry ensued, causing the fate of the Exhibition to hang in the balance yet again.

Sir Joseph Paxton (de Mare, *London 1851*)

Fortunately a gentleman who was not an architect came to the rescue just in time. Mr Joseph Paxton, landscape gardener at Chatsworth House and personal advisor to His Grace the Duke of Devonshire, presented his idea for a building constructed of glass and iron which, after modification, was accepted for consideration. As specifications for contractors to tender were at that time in the course of preparation, a simple clause was added permitting those who tendered to also submit a design different to that recommended by the Building Committee. Within ten days Paxton prepared and presented detailed drawings to the Commissioners, who were very impressed, but who, in the face of opposition from their Building Committee, regretfully announced that his design could not, after all, be accepted. Undismayed, Paxton took his plan to *The Illustrated London News* and persuaded them to publish an engraving of his design, along with details, not only of how quickly and cheaply his building could be constructed, but also of how quickly it could be dismantled; the latter point being of great importance in view of the fact that the tenure at Hyde Park was, by decree of Parliament, to be of limited duration only. The overwhelming support for Paxton's spectacular design soon forced the Building Committee to relent, and he was told that, if he sent in a priced tender, it would receive sympathetic consideration. Due to the unforeseen delays, time was fast running out, so, in the space of less than a week, Paxton's contractors had to calculate the cost of every pane of glass, every pound of iron and every inch of wood. This remarkable achievement did not go unnoticed because in an article referring to the Crystal Palace in *Household Words*, Charles Dickens wrote:

There is no one circumstance in the history of manufacturing enterprise of the English nation which places in so strong a light as this its boundless resources in materials, to say nothing of the marvellous arithmetic skill in compiling at what cost and in how short a time they can be converted to a special purpose. What was done in those few days? Two parties in London, relying on the accuracy and goodwill of a single Ironmaster, the owners of a single Glassworks in Birmingham, and of one master Carpenter in London, bound themselves for a certain sum of money and in the course of some months to cover eighteen acres of ground with a building upwards of a third of a mile long; 1851 [1] feet (the exact date of the year), and some 450 feet broad.

Erecting the transept roof, *Illustrated London News*, Dec. 1850.

The Paxton design was unique, novel and notable for its number of 'firsts', e.g. among its many such claims it was:
a) The first building to host an international exhibition.
b) The first to accommodate 100,000 people in one day.
c) The first large building to have been constructed almost entirely from glass and iron, both of which were the most modern building materials available at that time.
d) The first example of the use of what would come to

---

1. This is the outside measurement, most medals record the dimension as 1848 feet, which is the inside measurement.

be seen as mass production techniques. This innovation had enormous implications for all future enterprise; producing thousands of parts elsewhere and assembling them on site, is suggestive of twentieth century techniques being applied in the middle of the nineteenth century. This was obviously visionary thinking, far ahead of its time.

To add to this peep into the future, most of the materials were interchangeable; the columns, girders, gutters and sash bars were of identical size throughout, whilst the timber, which was originally erected as an eight-foot-high fence around the building site, was later used as flooring (Paxton had also calculated that the long dresses of female visitors would brush the dust down the gaps between the floorboards, therefore, during its lifetime, the Crystal Palace was never swept). As the building was divided by rows of slender iron columns into avenues and aisles, with galleries rising in tiers which were supported by columns linked together by lattice work girders, construction was enormously simplified. Consequently, once the first column had been put into place, on 26 September, the building seemed to grow, as if by magic. The magnificent structure, comprising 3,320 columns, linked by 2,244 girders, and walled by 400 tons of glass, rose at a rate that amazed the huge crowds which gathered daily in Hyde Park to watch its triumphant progress.

Understandably, Paxton's success was very unpopular in certain professional quarters, as two hundred and forty five competitors, including many highly distinguished persons, had seen their own designs spurned and the Very Prestigious Prize awarded to a mere landscape gardener.

The exhibition was a huge success, and, as a show, it paved the way for the development of education and entertainment on a very large scale. Nearly 14,000 exhibitors showed over 100,000 items in almost a mile of galleries covering close to one million square feet of floor space. Opening times were:

Monday to Friday: 10.00 a.m. till dusk or 6.00 p.m., whichever came first.

Saturday: 12.00 noon till dusk or 6.00 p.m., whichever came first.

Sunday: closed all day.

The only items licensed for sale within the building were official catalogues, refreshments, flowers, and the medals struck by W.J. Taylor and his screw press. The only other items which could be taken out of the building were exhibitors leaflets, handbills and any other free handouts. Cloakroom charges were 2d. Alcohol, smoking and animals were prohibited.

In a period of five months more than six million visitors viewed the exhibition. This, despite the fact that the cost of admission was astronomical compared with similar charges today. For example:

a) Season tickets cost 3 guineas for gentlemen and 2 guineas for ladies. Season ticket holders were also privileged to attend the Grand Opening Ceremony. Season ticket prices were reduced by 50% at the beginning of August.

b) Daily entry charges were £1 for the two days following the Grand Opening and 5/- daily thereafter until 24 May, by which time, the Commissioners had calculated, all of their costs would have been recovered, so...

c) Prices were reduced to 1/- from Monday to Thursday, changed to 2/6d on Friday, but left at 5/- on Saturday, until the beginning of August, when it was reduced by 50%.

Serpentine During Winter by Ackerman. Reproduced by permission of Eric Price

d) To avoid accusations of 'jobbery', the commissioners decided that exhibitors, members of the Executive Committee and themselves should pay for admission to the Exhibition.

The cost of admission was deliberately set at these very high prices to ensure that the guarantors would not be called upon to make good any losses which might have otherwise been incurred. Accordingly, a huge profit of £186,000 accrued. Today this sum would equate to about £50 million.

The following chart has been compiled from the official lists published daily by Mr Wade, the Registrar to the Executive Committee, and shows the estimated weekly number of visitors, and the amount of money taken at the doors, from Thursday 1 May 1851 until the last public day, Saturday 11 October 1851.

The sale of more than 25,000 season tickets raised £67,500. The cash taken at the 18 turnstiles exceeded £356,000, of which £275,000 was in silver, and weighed in at a staggering 35 tons. The rapid flow of visitors through the turnstiles prevented every coin from being closely examined, and, as a consequence, £90 worth of bad silver was taken. Interestingly, only one bad gold coin, a sovereign, was presented, though many gold coins accepted were so badly worn that their true value by weight was less than their face value. Many foreign coins

were also accepted and this, too, resulted in a certain loss in turnstile receipts. In total there was a loss of £540 in cash receipts, and these can be summarised as follows:

		£
value of defaced coins		1452
recouped from the bank		1220
actual loss		**232**

Spurious coins	£	£
crowns	3	
half-crowns	33	
shillings	52	
sixpences	2	
actual loss		90
loss on light gold		218
total loss		**540**

It was particularly noticeable that a very high proportion of the bad money and light gold was taken on the days when 2/6d and 5/- were the prices for daily admission!

In order to facilitate an orderly transfer of money from the Exhibition site to the bank, four money porters were

Week Ending	Number of persons paying at the doors	Amount received at the doors £ s d	Estimated number of persons using season tickets	Total number Includes exhibitors, staff & the press	Largest number of persons in the building at any one time, as estimated by the police
3 May	1,042	1,042 0 0	49,000	56,042[1]	
10 May	41,194	10,298 10 0	77,056	118,250	
17 May	53,386	13,346 10 0	80,121	145,507	
24 May	89,458	22,189 0 0	91,440	192,869	
31 May	160,857	11,123 5 0	61,257	222,114[2]	
7 June	218,799	13,694 2 0	27,129	245,928	Fri. 6 June at 4 pm — 21,606
14 June	206,233	12,943 12 0	32,352	238,585	Mon. 9 at 3 pm — 46,167
21 June	267,800	16,421 3 0	35,215	303,015	Tues. 17 at 3 pm — 54,422
28 June	262,464	16,177 8 0	30,245	292,709	Mon. 23 at 3 pm — 55,379
5 July	225,503	14,073 0 0	21,436	246,739	Thurs. 3 July at 3 pm — 44,890
12 July	265,319	16,427 5 0	23,108	288,427	Tues. 8 at 3 pm — 54,016
19 July	283,400	17,516 0 0	22,453	305,853	Tues. 15 at 3 pm — 61,640
26 July	255,768	15,761 4 0	18,371	274,139	Mon. 21 at 2 pm — 58,451
2 Aug.	270,900	16,315 17 6	15,617	288,519	
9 Aug.	266,770	15,440 14 6	20,001	286,771	
16 Aug.	236,096	14,050 18 6	15,961	252,057	Tues. 12 Aug. — 51,736
23 Aug.	226,502	13,360 12 6	10,037	236,539	
30 Aug.	202,808	11,860 7 6	8,636	211,446	Mon. 25 — 45,035
6 Sept.	204,171	11,833 17 0	10,452	214,623	Mon. 1 Sept. — 43,170
13 Sept.	238,656	13,937 18 0	15,376	254,032	Tues. 9 — 50,651
20 Sept.	225,715	15,084 17 0	17,615	273,330	Tues. 16 — 54,127
27 Sept.	254,552	15,288 16 6	20,815	275,367	Tues. 23 — 50,246
4 Oct.	298,837	18,726 19 6	24,011	322,848	Tues. 30 — 60,039
11 Oct.	478,773	29,794 11 6	39,504	518,277	Tues. 7 Oct. — 93,224

1. This includes 25,000 persons who were present at the Grand Opening Ceremony on 1 May, 19,000 of whom were season ticket holders.
2. Monday 26 May was the first shilling day, when 18,402 persons paid at the doors, and 7,000 season ticket holders were present.
Total number of visitors from 1 May to 11 October: 6,063,986.
The largest amount taken at the doors on any of the five-shilling days was £5,078 on 24 May.
The greatest half-crown day was Saturday 11 October when £4,845 was received.
The greatest shilling day was Tuesday 7 October when £5,283 was taken.
The receipts in August and September were affected by the harvesting operations.

engaged to pick up the takings from the turnstiles and transfer it on trolleys to four collectors, who sorted it out and counted it. From the collectors it was transferred to two tellers, who verified the count before passing it on to the Chief Financial Officer, whose duty it was to lock it in iron chests and store it in his office overnight. The following morning it was placed in boxes, each of which contained £600, and taken away in a hackney cab by a clerk and a porter employed by the Bank of England!

In addition to the cost of entry to the Exhibition, it is estimated that visitors spent £503,000 on refreshments in the building; £657,000 on the railways; £800,000 on buses; £250,000 on cabs; and a further £1,000,000 on accommodation and other personal expenses. If the cost of admission to the Exhibition is added to these, it is estimated that visitors spent a sum similar to that spent in the UK each year on alcohol!

Weekdays would have been a shilling collector's paradise, particularly in the final week when nearly 100,000 were taken on each of three consecutive days. In hindsight one can picture the tellers unconcernedly accepting hundreds of shillings in mint condition, 'dated 1850', oblivious to the fact that by the year 2000, the year of the new millennium, these very coins would have become extremely rare and be one of the hardest-to-come-by, most sought after and, often, the most valuable acquisition in many a collection.

During the Exhibition more than five thousand items were lost or mislaid in the building. 1,697 were reclaimed by their owners leaving 3,347 unclaimed items in the hands of the police, amongst them were the following:

750 handkerchiefs, 85 bracelets, 281 brooches, 322 parasols, 177 shawl pins, 173 umbrellas, 9 umbrella cases, 46 veils, 77 catalogues and hundreds of other books and papers, 65 bunches of keys, 49 neck ties, a pair of galoshes, 34 victorines, 3 campstools, 28 lockets, a pair of slippers, 30 ladies' cuffs, 1 pendulum, 52 coats, 3 card cases, 25 neck-chains, 31 knives, 3 pincushions, 188 pairs of gloves, 25 walking sticks, 39 pairs of spectacles, 22 eye-glasses, 16 pencil cases, 7 rings, 23 fans, 1 silver watch, 1 opera glass, 59 baskets, 84 shawls, 2 pairs of ladies' shoes, 2 petticoats and 2 bustles, a carpenter's tool-basket with tools, 3 scent bottles and more than a hundred purses including one containing £5 9s. 4d.

Her Majesty Queen Victoria made thirty four visits to the Crystal Palace, of which eight were during construction, and, by all accounts, was very impressed by the medal-making machinery. During her last visit, she was greeted by an old lady who had walked all the way from Cornwall to London to see her Queen and the Exhibition. The Duke of Wellington, at age 82, was a constant visitor to his favourite entertainment, at times attending every day of the week.

Countless foreign visitors came, but the real secret of

Queen Victoria painted on Sevres porcelain (Tallis, *History & Description of the Crystal Palace*)

the enormous success enjoyed by the Exhibition can be traced to the 'shilling days', which encouraged nearly four million of the working classes to save up their precious pennies and take advantage of the cheap excursions arranged through the railway companies. Thomas Cook, founder of the travel company which still bears his name, made a fortune out of them, and for more than a century his organisation popularised organised railway travel.

Sir Henry Cole (*Illustrated London News, July 1873*)

In his memoirs, Sir Henry Cole, acknowledged as the executive who did the most to ensure the success of the Exhibition, wrote:

> The history of the world, I venture to say, records no event comparable in its promotion of human industry, with that of the Great Exhibition of the Works of Industry of all Nations in 1851. A great people invited all civilised nations to a festival, to bring into comparison the works of human skill. It was carried out by its own private means; was self-supporting and independent of taxes and employment of slaves, which great works had

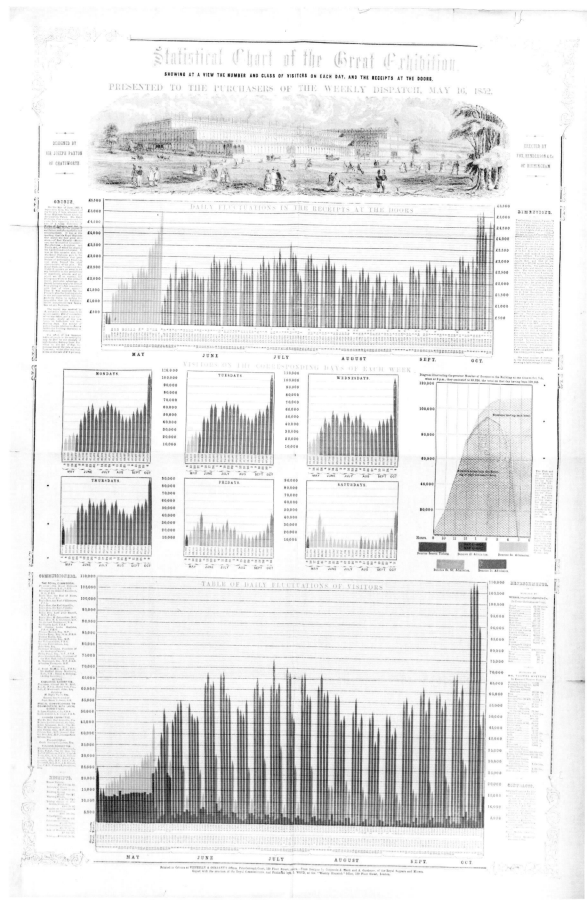

Statistical Chart of the Great Exhibition. (*Weekly Dispatch*, 1852)

exacted in ancient days. A prince of pre-eminent wisdom, of philosophic mind, sagacity, with power of generalship and great practical ability, placed himself at the head of the enterprise, and led it to a triumphant success. The Sovereign of that people gave to the work of her husband and subjects, her warmest sympathy, fondly watched its progress, and witnessed its triumph among a multitude of 25,000 persons, all assembled under one glass roof of 1850 feet in length, an event which had never happened before. In the history of the world, it may perhaps be safely said, that no monarch before Queen Victoria, had ever personally assisted a work like this. Her Majesty watched it with daily solicitude, and herself wrote a record of it.

As a fitting tribute, knighthoods were bestowed upon Joseph Paxton, William Cubitt and Charles Fox. Eleven other officials were presented with gold medals by Prince Albert (see HP-D001).

During the course of the Exhibition the Royal Commissioners earned a great deal of criticism regarding some of their decisions, a few of those which caused most condemnation were:

a) Their very strange decision to prohibit pictorial art caused an uproar, particularly when it was found that statuary had readily been included. Most of the visitors attending the exhibition were astounded by its absence.

b) By selling the rights of the catalogue to a consortium of Messrs Spicer Brothers (stationers) and William Clowes & Sons (printers) for £3,200 plus a royalty of twopence for each copy sold in the building, the Commissioners were accused of selling their birthright in the catalogue for a mess of pottage. The first edition, which cost a shilling, was found to be unintelligible, as was the second edition; the corrected second edition, and each succeeding corrected edition, all of which cost a shilling each, were of a similar standard so, after spending all that money regular visitors were still rushing hopelessly about looking for this, that, or the other.

Eventually it was announced that approved and qualified persons would act as guides conducting visitors throughout the building. The cost of using this service amounted to a further charge of two shillings for the first hour and one shilling for every other hour for parties not exceeding three; or sixpence per person for the first hour and fourpence per person for every other hour for parties not exceeding six.

As soon as this service was introduced, a visitor could not ask for directions from a functionary or one of the thousand extra policemen employed in the building, without it being regarded as an infringement of the rights and privileges of the guide company, and such a request met with the reply 'There are guides appointed, and if you want information you must pay for it.'

c) The prohibition on prices being affixed to exhibits caused a great deal of resentment from the exhibitors since the catalogue contractors, Messrs Spicer & Clowes, demanded a shilling per line for the insertion of prices and descriptions into their catalogue. Most exhibitors overcame this problem by distributing leaflets and price lists advertising their wares, and apparently the printing presses on display in the exhibition were kept hard at work producing a multitude of advertising documents.

d) The decision to charge exhibitors an entrance fee brought forth angry protests from exhibitors throughout the whole of the Exhibition.

A. Official Medals

The Commissioners proposed that three medals of different size and design should be awarded as prizes. Bronze was selected as being the metal most suited for the development of superior skill and ingenuity in medallic art, and the most likely to constitute a lasting memorial to the Exhibition, it being felt that recipients would be less tempted to melt them down for their intrinsic value. It was also proposed that, in order to enhance the prestige of the medals, Her Majesty should be asked to award them. William Wyon was chosen to produce a design containing portraits of both the Queen and Prince Albert, which would grace the obverse of the medals. Artists worldwide were invited to submit designs for the three reverses, and rewards of £100 each were offered for the winning three designs. Additionally, the three next-best designs not chosen to be used were each to be awarded a prize of £50.

In answer to this invitation one hundred and twenty nine designs were submitted, and publicly displayed at the premises of the Society of Arts. To demonstrate that the selection procedure was impartial, the name of the artist was submitted in a sealed envelope attached to the design; which was not opened until after the Medal Committee had made its choice. The £100 winning entries chosen to grace the reverses of the medals were submitted by Hyppolite Bonnardel of Paris (The Council Medal), Leonard Charles Wyon of London (The Prize Medal) and George Gammon Adams of London (The Jurors Medal). The £50 'runner-up' prizes awarded for designs not used on the medals were submitted by John Hancock of London, L. Wiener of Brussels and M. Gayrard of Paris. The latin inscriptions on the medals were chosen by a committee comprising Gladstone, Macaulay, Lord Lyttleton, Dr Liddell and the Dean of St Pauls Cathedral.

The exhibition was divided into thirty different classes, with a separate Jury appointed for each class. When, however, it was found that some classes were too large for a single jury to manage, four additional juries were formed. Each panel of Jurors was made up of an equal number of British and foreign members. The Chairmen of each of the panels were formed into a Council, the object of which was to determine the way in which the juries would perform, and the conditions under which medals would be awarded. The most difficult problem which they faced was of awarding three medals without giving the perception that they were being awarded for different degrees of success, so they asked for one of the medals to be withdrawn. The Commissioners readily agreed with this proposal as this meant that there would

Summary of awards made by the Jurors

Groups	Council Medal			Prize Medal			Honourable Mention		
	British	Foreign	Total	British	Foreign	Total	British	Foreign	Total
Raw Materials *class I-IV*	6	16	22	125	437	562	131	535	666
Machinery *class V-X*	52	36	88	301	191	492	51	114	165
Textile Fabrics *class XI-XX*	1	2	3	337	498	835	185	277	462
Metallic, Vitreous & Ceramic Manufactures *class XXI-XXV*	14	21	35	312	214	526	208	199	407
Miscellaneous Manufactures *class XXVI-XXIX*	4	10	14	142	232	374	100	154	254
Fine Arts *class XXX*	2	2	4	27	60	87	41	47	88
Unclassified	1	7	8						
Totals	**80**	**94**	**174**	**1244**	**1632**	**2876**	**716**	**1326**	**2042**

According to the report of the Commissioners there were 170 Council medals and 2918 Prize medals awarded, this differs slightly with the above analysis of the Reports of the Juries, which reveals there were 174 Council medals and 2876 Prize medals awarded by the Jurors.
While Britain received the highest proportion of the medals, France received more per capita.

be a medal available for presentation to the jurors, in recognition of their Herculean labours. Of the other two medals, it was decided that a 77 mm Prize medal would be conferred by the juries when a certain standard of excellence in workmanship, beauty, utility, and adaptability had been attained, whilst an 89 mm Council medal would be reserved as a reward for remarkable invention, to be awarded only by the council of chairmen, on the recommendation of the juries.

The Commissioners report is sketchy regarding the number of medals awarded. While it mentions 170 Council medals and 2,918 Prize medals, it says nothing at all about the other three medals. These being the Jurors medal mentioned above, the Exhibitors medal and the one presented as a recognition For Services rendered. The latter two medals would appear to have been an afterthought on the part of the Commissioners, since no earlier reference to these two medals has been found. It is possible to determine the number of Jurors medals awarded by adding up the number of jurors; we also know that there were roughly 14,000 exhibitors who should have received the Exhibitors medal. It was originally thought that the For Services medals were awarded to just the Secretary of each of the 299 Local Committees, plus a few other VIPs; but it appears that approximately another 700 were awarded to officials representing the police, military and other local public services. A source giving the exact number of medals awarded in each of the five categories has not yet been found.

In addition to the medals noted above, the governments of all participating countries, the twenty seven Commissioners, and an unspecified number of other senior officials each received a magnificent presentation case containing a complete set of the five official medals. Again an official document recording the number issued has not yet been found. The Commissioners also permitted certain firms to purchase duplicate medals at a cost of seven shillings each on production of a letter from the Secretary of the Executive Committee, but, here again, it does not appear that an official record of the number sold has survived.

An extract from a letter addressed to Leonard Charles Wyon from Matthew Digby Wyatt reads [1]:

> I am directed by the Executive Committee to inform you that Messrs ... have made a formal declaration that they are a firm consisting of ... partners. You are hereby therefore empowered to furnish them with ... extra medals of the kind awarded to them on the payment by that firm of the cost thereof.

This facility will have been available to eligible firms awarded one of the official medals. It is thought they would not have been inscribed on their edge and, if this is so, it could account for the un-named medals which have been seen in each of the five categories.

The Royal Mint Catalogue indicates that four of the official medals were struck there, but, since they were supplied by William Wyon as a private commission, there is no further information about them on Mint records. As Chief Engraver, apparently one of William Wyon's perquisites was permission to use the minting machinery after hours; but when ill health forced his retirement, the same facility was not extended to his son, Leonard Charles Wyon, who took over the position of Chief Engraver.

This meant that although Leonard Charles Wyon was in possession of the dies (which are now on display at the Victoria and Albert Museum), he had no machinery or premises on which to strike the 14,000 Exhibitors medals, presentation sets and duplicate medals which had been ordered by firms with a number of partners. Indeed, the last named may have been considerable in number because, in a letter sent to exhibitors at the 1862 exhibition by Leonard Charles Wyon offering them the same facility, he mentioned that many such medals had been provided in 1851 [2]. Fortunately for him all was not lost because, due to a long-standing close relationship between the Wyon and Pinches families, he was able to use the minting facilities at the Oxendon Street premises of Messrs Pinches to fulfil his father's contractual obligation to the Royal Commissioners.

Distribution of the medals at the Closing Ceremony of the Exhibition was thwarted by the ill health of William Wyon, and by his untimely death just two weeks later; which caused the inscribing of them to become seriously delayed. The Jurors medal was the first to be completed and became available for distribution by mid-November 1851. The Council medal was ready next and the Prize medal followed soon after. The For Services medal, however, was not ready until April 1852.

Because it took the juries a considerable length of time to produce their one thousand page report, it was not until 12 July 1852 that a notice was eventually sent to exhibitors informing them that they could collect their medal, certificate and report of the juries, from the offices of the Commissioners in Old Palace Yard. Alternatively, they could accept them at a public ceremony organised either by their local committee or their municipal authority.

The medals cost the commissioners £4,657, while their cases cost a further £583. The printing, and distributing of the reports of the juries cost an additional £9,268.

Although all medals issued by the Commissioners were

---

1. 1851 Exhibition documents held in the Victoria and Albert Museum.

2. 1862 Exhibition documents held in the Victoria and Albert Museum.

struck in bronze, some specimens are known to exist in other metals. The author has seen what would appear to be a pattern of the Prize medal, unsigned on its reverse, and in a glazed frame (HP-A030). He has also seen two specimens of the Jurors medal in white metal. Laurence Brown records having seen a specimen of the Prize medal in silver. Is it possible that specimens of the other medals may also have been struck in soft metal? The most likely explanation for the existence of these pieces is that they are trial specimens, struck in a soft metal to test the dies prior to annealing; a process carried out to strengthen and harden the metal from which the dies were made. Gilded and silver plated specimens of the Prize medal, For Services medal and Exhibitors medal are known, but all of those seen by the author, were awarded, which implies that they had been coated some time after being presented by the Commissioners.

Mr Hensman, Superintendent of Classes V, VI and

The Hensman Testimonial (*Illustrated London News* 1851)

VII, and the gentleman who was in charge of the distribution of the official medals, was presented with a handsome silver plated vase of Greek design. On one side of the vase there is a view of the Crystal Palace above a representation of the obverse of the Council medal, on the other side of the vase there is an inscription. On the handles are representations of the reverses of the other four official medals.

The Great Exhibition by Bibby. Contemporary steel engraving

HP-A001　Council Medal
by W. Wyon, H. Bonnardell & J.F. Domard　　　Ae 89 mm

ETIAM IN MAGNO QUAEDAM RESPUBLICA MUNDO
In exergue: MDCCCLI *Signed* H.BONNARDELL INV.
DOMARD SCULP.
Rim　Beaded obverse, plain reverse.
Edge　*Inscribed at the top* with the name of the recipient and
class number; *at the base:* COUNCIL MEDAL OF THE
EXHIBITION.

RRRR	*Brown 2461, Eimer (I) 1455, Fearon (I) 302.4*	BM PC
VA		

The medal derives its name from the way it was awarded, i.e.
by the Council of Chairmen, on the recommendation of the
juries. The commissioners report states that 170 medals were
awarded to exhibitors, but that figure does not include the
medals struck for the presentation sets, or the duplicates sold
to firms with a number of partners. A certificate accompanied
the medal when it was awarded, and the author would be
pleased to hear from any reader who has a specimen. Both the
obverse and reverse dies are on display in the Victoria and
Albert Museum.

HP-A005　Council Medal
by W. Wyon, H. Bonnardell & J.F. Domard　　　Ae 89 mm

Obverse　Conjoined heads of Queen Victoria and Prince
Albert left. Dolphins in the field symbolise the naval power of
the Empire. *Inscription around the border:* VICTORIA D: G:
BRIT: REG: F:D: ✿ ALBERTUS PRINCEPS CONJUX. /
W. WYON R:A: MDCCCLI. ROYAL MINT.
Reverse　Britannia standing upon a raised platform draped
with flags of different nations bestowing wreaths on
Commerce and Industry. *Inscription around the border:* EST

HP-A010   Prize Medal

by W. Wyon & L.C. Wyon   Ae 77 mm

Obverse   Similar to obverse of HP-A001, but has a stop instead of a colon after D. of F: D:
Reverse   Similar to reverse of HP-A001.
Rim   Similar to HP-A001.
Edge   Similar to HP-A001.

RRRR   *Eimer (II)*   PC

The three medals awarded in the civil engineering and architectural class were won by Prince Albert for the design of his model lodging house (Joint medal to that granted for the original conception and successful prosecution of the Exhibition of 1851); Joseph Paxton for designing the Crystal Palace; and Messrs Fox & Henderson for constructing the Crystal Palace. Both the obverse and reverse dies are on display in the Victoria and Albert Museum.

Obverse   Similar to obverse of HP-A001.
Reverse   Britannia seated and bending forward, raising with one hand and crowning with the other, the kneeling figure of Industry, presented to Britannia by Europe, Asia, Africa and America. In the background are emblems of the four sections of the Exhibition. *Inscription around the border:* DISSOCIATA LOCIS CONCORDI PACE LIGAVIT. *In exergue, L/H side:* LEONARD C: WYON. / DES: & SC: *R/ H side:* ROYAL MINT. LONDON / 1851.
Rim   Beaded obverse, plain reverse.
Edge   *Inscribed at the top* with the name of the recipient and

class number; *at the base:* PRIZE MEDAL OF THE EXHIBITION.

R *Brown* 2462, *Eimer (I)* 1457, *Fearon (I)* 302.5 **BM ML PC**

The Commissioners report states that 2,918 medals were awarded to exhibitors, but that figure does not include the medals struck for the presentation sets, or the duplicates sold to firms with a number of partners. Laurence Brown notes that he has seen a silver specimen uninscribed. Electrotypes of this version have also been seen, one of which has been used for the above illustration. A certificate accompanied the medal when it was awarded, and the author would be pleased to hear from any reader who has a specimen. Leonard C. Wyon was awarded a medal in class XXX for medallic portraiture. Both the obverse and reverse dies are on display in the Victoria and Albert Museum.

HP-A015   Prize Medal
by W. Wyon & L.C. Wyon   Ae 77 mm

Obverse   Similar to obverse of HP-A001.
Reverse   Similar to reverse of HP-A010, but no stop after Wyon, and no stop after 1851.
Rim   Similar to HP-A010.
Edge   Similar to HP-A010.

RRR   *unrecorded*   **PC**

The author has seen a specimen with the following inscription on the edge: PRESENTED TO RICHARD SAINTHILL by L.C. WYON. Whilst no other specimens of this type have yet been seen, others could exist. Both the obverse and reverse dies are on display in the Victoria and Albert Museum.

HP-A020   Prize Medal
by W. Wyon & L.C. Wyon   Ae 77 mm

Obverse   Similar to obverse of HP-A001, but the colon after REG: is missing. There is a stop after Wyon.
Reverse   Similar to reverse of HP-A010, but the inscription is missing from the hem of Europa's gown. There is a design on the upper half of Britannia's helmet.
Rim   Similar to HP-A010.
Edge   Similar to HP-A010.

RRR   *unrecorded*   **PC VA**

The author has not seen sufficient numbers of this particular version in order to form an opinion. Both the obverse and reverse dies are on display in the Victoria and Albert Museum.

HP-A025	**Prize Medal**	
by W. Wyon & L.C. Wyon		Ae 77 mm

R   *Sabo* 50   **PC**

This is the type usually found in the Royal Commissioners presentation set. Electrotypes of this version have been seen including one in silver of the obverse of the prize medal from the set of medals presented to Sir Henry Cole. It is possible the other four medals in this set were also copied. The author would be pleased to hear from any reader who knows why this particular copy was made; it bears a 1977 hallmark. The illustration is of the medal awarded to J.E. McConnell, Locomotive Superintendent to the London and North Western Railway Company, who later became a juror in Class V at the 1862 Exhibition. Only the obverse die is on display in the Victoria and Albert Museum. The Commissioners gave all their dies to the museum in 1921, so it is surprising this reverse die is not among them.

HP-A030	**Prize Medal**	
by W. Wyon & L.C. Wyon		Pewter? 77 mm

Obverse   Similar to obverse of HP-A001, but the colon after REG: is missing.
Reverse   Similar to reverse of HP-A010, but the signature: LEONARD. C: WYON. DES: & SC: ROYAL MINT. LONDON. is in one line around the lower rim of the exergue. There is no stop after LIGAVIT.
Rim   Similar to HP-A010.
Edge   Similar to HP-A010.

Obverse Similar to obverse of HP-A020.
Reverse Similar to reverse of HP-A020, but there are no lines above or below Europa on the hem of her gown. America has a pattern on the sleeve of her dress, and the bow in her hand is shorter than normal. There is a design on the upper half of Britannia's helmet. The exergue is empty.
Rim Similar to HP-A010.

RRRR *unrecorded* **PC**

The medal is housed in a glazed frame with a suspension loop at the top, therefore the edge cannot be examined to find if it has been engraved. The piece could be a pattern or a trial specimen. The reverse die is not among those on display at the Victoria and Albert Museum.

HP-A034 Prize Medal Test or Trial pieces
by W. Wyon & L.C. Wyon   Ar Pewter 77 mm

Obverse Any one of the obverse dies from HP-A010 to HP-A030.
Reverse Any one of the reverse dies from HP-A010 to HP-A030.
Rim Beaded obverse, plain reverse.

RRRR *unrecorded* **PC**

Soft metal pieces produced to test the dies prior to annealing.

HP-A037 Prize Medal Electrotypes
by W. Wyon & L.C. Wyon   Ar Ae 77 mm

Obverse Any one of the obverse dies from HP-A010 to HP-A030.
Reverse Any one of the reverse dies from HP-A010 to HP-A030.
Rim Beaded obverse, plain reverse.

Ar RRR Ae R *unrecorded* **PC**

In effect this is an electrical equivalent of metal casting, the copper version is obtained when a wax impression of a design is treated with powdered graphite and, with copper conductor pegs attached to it, it is immersed in a solution into which an electric current is introduced. The current dissolves the copper which is deposited on the surface of the wax forming an exact impression. This process is undertaken in two parts which, when finished, are sometimes joined together to form a replica of the medal being copied. They were produced mainly for advertising purposes and may be found in one piece representing either the obverse or the reverse or, more often, in two separate unjoined pieces representing both the obverse and the reverse.

HP-A040 Jurors Medal
by W. Wyon & G.G. Adams   Ae 64 mm

Obverse   Similar to obverse of HP-A001.

Reverse   Industry seated upon a cornucopia, encouraged by Commerce and crowned by Fame. *Inscription around the border:* PULCHER ET ILLE LABOR PALMA DECORARE LABOREM *In exergue:* A steelyard, a laurel wreath and a helmeted bust. *Signed* G.G. ADAMS.

Rim   Beaded obverse, plain reverse.

Edge   *Inscribed at the top* with the name of the recipient; *at the base:* JUROR GREAT EXHIBITION 1851.

RRR   *Brown 2464, Eimer (I) 1459*   BM ML PC VA

Courtesy of Les Stevens.

There were 318 jurors appointed to the panels, 160 being from overseas. A further 97 associate members were co-opted to provide particular expertise wherever required; as 30 of these were jurors from other panels, only 67 additional medals would have been awarded to them. In addition, an unknown number were struck for inclusion in the presentation sets. A few soft-metal trial pieces are also known to exist. Both the obverse and reverse dies are on display in the Victoria and Albert Museum. Each juror received the following personal letter from Prince Albert when awarded the medal:

Windsor Castle
October 31st. 1851.

Sir,

I have the honor, as President of the Royal Commission for the Exhibition of 1851 to transmit to you a Medal that has been struck by order of the Commissioners, in commemoration of the valuable service which you have rendered to the Exhibition, in common with so many eminent men of all Countries, in your capacity of Juror.

In requesting your acceptance of this slight token on our part of the sense entertained by us of the benefit which has resulted to the interests of the Exhibition from your having undertaken that laborious office, and from the zeal and ability displayed by you in connection with it, it affords me much pleasure to avail myself of this opportunity of conveying to you the expression of my cordial thanks for the assistance which you have given us in carrying this great undertaking to its successful issue.

I have the honor to be etc. etc.

HP-A050   For Services Medal
by W. Wyon   Ae 48 mm

Obverse Bare head of Prince Albert left. *Inscription around the border:* H: R: H: PRINCE ALBERT PRESIDENT OF THE ROYAL COMMISSION. *Signed* W. WYON. R A
Reverse *Inscription within a closed laurel wreath:* FOR / SERVICES *Inscription around the border:* EXHIBITION OF THE WORKS OF INDUSTRY OF ALL NATIONS. / MDCCCLI.
Rim Plain.
Edge *Inscribed at the top* with the name of the recipient.

S *Brown 2465, Eimer (I) 1461, Fearon (I) 302.6* BM ML PC VA

A magnificent certificate 22" high by 16.5" wide accompanied the medal. The upper half has a circular engraving of a female (presumably Londinia) flanked by a lion and a lamb, standing in front of a pedestal on which are two cherubs, one with a cornucopia, the other holding an Aesculapian rod; in the background is the transept of the Crystal Palace. The lower half is inscribed: EXHIBITION OF THE WORKS OF INDUSTRY / OF ALL NATIONS. / 1851. Below this in copperplate script: *I hereby certify that Her Majesty's Commissioners / have awarded a medal to / (name of recipient) / for the services rendered to the / Exhibition.* At the bottom centre are actual-size engravings of the obverse and reverse of the medal, flanked by: Exhibition / Hyde Park, London 15th Octr

1851, and ALBERT (his signature) / President of the Royal Commission. These certificates are considerably more difficult to find than the medals; the author is indebted to Mr. J.V. Webb for providing details of his certificate which was awarded to Police Constable George Floyd.

The author is also indebted to members of the Orders and Medals Research Society whose research has disclosed that at least 500 medals were awarded to the constabulary, a further 200 to sappers and officers serving in the Royal Engineers who worked upon the Exhibition site, and an unknown number to members of the Fire Service.

There is a handsome gilded specimen named on the edge to WALTER ELLIOTT, but the shape and size of the lettering punched on the edge is quite different to that on other named specimens. Walter Elliott was an agent of the East India Company in Madras, and won a prize medal in Class IV for his exhibit of Cattimundoo resin (similar to gutta percha).

Both obverse and reverse dies are on display in the Victoria and Albert Museum.

HP-A055   Exhibitors Medal
by W. Wyon   Ae 45 mm

Obverse Similar to obverse of HP-A050, but *signed* W WYON. R A, or with a stop after the A.
Reverse Terrestrial globe within a laurel wreath, a dove resting on the top. *Inscription on a ribbon across the equator:* EXHIBITOR *Inscription around the border:* EXHIBITION

OF THE WORKS OF INDUSTRY OF ALL NATIONS. / MDCCCLI.

Rim   Plain.

Edge   Inscribed at the top: country, class number, and catalogue number.

N   *Brown* 2463, *Eimer (I)* 1462   BM ML PC VA

Nearly 14,000 exhibitors received a medal, a certificate and a copy of the reports of the juries, but that figure does not include medals struck for the presentation sets, or the duplicates sold to firms with a number of partners. Some silver-plated and also gilded specimens have been seen. In each case they were awarded, which implies they had been coated some time after being presented by the Commissioners. A certificate accompanied the medal when it was presented, and the author would be pleased be to hear from a reader who has a specimen. Both obverse and reverse dies are on display in the Victoria and Albert Museum.

HP-A060   Royal Commissioners Presentation Set

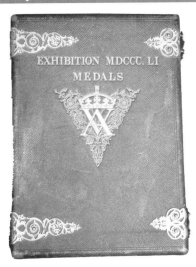

RRRR   *Brown* 2460   PC

Specimens of the five official medals were made up into sets and housed in a magnificent red Morocco case measuring approximately fourteen inches by ten inches. The medals are displayed in the case in the following positions: Council Medal at the top, Prize Medal at the bottom, Jurors Medal in the centre, Exhibitors Medal left of centre and For Services Medal right of centre. The inside of the lid is inscribed: PRESENTED BY HER MAJESTY'S / COMMISSIONERS FOR THE / EXHIBITION OF MDCCCLI / TO ... The top edge of each medal is inscribed with the name of the recipient and the office held. The lower edge is inscribed: PRESENTATION, followed by the type of medal, e.g. PRESENTATION PRIZE MEDAL OF THE EXHIBITION.

The governments of all the participating countries, the twenty seven Commissioners plus some other senior officials received one of these presentation sets. A record has not been found of the number of sets presented by the Commissioners. The set illustrated above was presented to Captain Thomas Bernard Collinson of the Royal Engineers, who was superintendent of the British side of the Great Exhibition building. One of his many responsibilities would have been supervision of the unloading and distribution of the British exhibits, by the sappers on his staff. The owner of this set wishes to remain anonymous, but the author gratefully acknowledges his generosity in allowing the medals to be examined and photographed. Sadly there are no documents with the medals, but a certificate probably accompanied the case when it was presented, and if so, the author would be pleased to hear from a reader who has a specimen.

Laurence Brown examined the set at Windsor Castle which was presented to Prince Albert, President of the Royal Commission (see *Brown* 2460). When researching his article 'Exposition 1851', Donald Sabo examined the set presented to Francis Fuller, a member of the Executive Committee, and noted that the Jurors medal was missing, believed to be lost or destroyed, but replaced in the case by an 1854 medal of the same size, i.e. SY-1854 /110. Fortunately, the Jurors medal was not actually missing because it turned up in the case of medals presented to Francis Fuller by the Crystal Palace Company, to commemorate the opening of the Sydenham Crystal Palace in 1854 (see note to SY-1854 /095).

B. Unofficial Medals

Next to royal occasions, the Great Exhibition of 1851 was by far the biggest attraction of the nineteenth century, so it is not really surprising that many medals were struck to commemorate the event. No exhibition or building before, or since, has captured the attention and imagination of the medallist to anything like the same degree. Most of the medals depict the Crystal Palace and record many of its huge dimensions. As souvenirs, they were mostly made of white metal alloys costing only a few pence to produce, and because of this, some have darkened through exposure to the atmosphere. Accordingly, it is not uncommon to find even cased uncirculated specimens which have darkened or blackened on one or both sides, and as a consequence they have lost much of their appeal, and some of their value. Very few manufacturers kept records of their output, and sadly those that did, all seem to have lost them through some unfortunate catastrophe.

Therefore, very little is known about most of them other than that they were struck by private firms as a commercial venture. Many were undoubtedly sold by street traders on every street corner along the route of the royal procession, and others in the vicinity of Hyde Park. Some were sold by advertisements placed in the press and journals of the day, but there are insufficient records available to tell us how the others were marketed.

Fortunately, we do know that the Commissioners licensed W.J. Taylor to strike and sell medals to the public within the Great Exhibition building. He used only the one design (see HP-B340). Some specimens were struck in bronze and sold in a fitted case, but huge numbers were struck in white metal, and were sold in a paper packet for one shilling. The medals were not ready until 24 June, yet during the 90 days they were on sale the Commissioners recorded an income of £865 from W.J. Taylor. It is not evident how much commission Taylor had to pay for his franchise, but readers do not need a degree in mathematics to calculate that at one halfpenny per medal, the number sold would have been 415,200, or at one penny per medal, it would have been 207,600 etc.. Each of these two figures may seem huge, but if measured against the number of visitors for the same period, they only represent a sales ratio of either one in ten, or one in twenty. We might never learn the exact number struck, but, we do know it was sufficient to make the white metal version, the most often seen Great Exhibition medal.

It is interesting to note that a number of unofficial medals bear the title Prince Consort, even though Her Majesty did not make the title official until 25 June 1857.

HP-B001
by Allen & Moore — Br 23 mm

Obverse Bare head of Prince Albert right. *Inscription around the border:* PRINCE ALBERT CONSORT OF QUEEN VICTORIA.
Reverse View of the Crystal Palace. *Inscription above:* THE CRYSTAL PALACE *In exergue:* FOR THE GREAT / EXHIBITION / IN LONDON OF / 1851 *Signed* A & M.
Rim Beaded.

RRR *unrecorded* PC

HP-B005
by Allen & Moore — Brg 23 mm

Obverse Similar to reverse of HP-B001.
Reverse *Nine line inscription:* DIMENSIONS. / LENGTH 1848 FEET, / WIDTH 456 FEET; /HEIGHT OF ROOF 66 FEET; / HEIGHT OF TRANSEPT / 108 FEET; / GLAZED SURFACE / 900,000 SUP. FEET. / OCCUPIES 18 ACRES.
Rim Beaded.

S *Brown 2434, Bell et al - /CP 16, Eidlitz 762a/85, Taylor 165a* AM BG ML PC UM

HP-B010 Medal Box
by Allen & Moore — Br 28 mm

Lid View of the Crystal Palace. *Inscription above:* THE CRYSTAL PALACE *In exergue:* MEDAL / BOX
Base Bare head of Prince Albert right. *Inscription around the border:* PRINCE ALBERT, CONSORT OF QUEEN VICTORIA.
Rim Toothed.

RRR *Brown 2428* ML PC

Medals from two different sets have been found in this type of brass box, i.e. HP-B015 to HP-B035 comprise one set of five medals, and HP-B040 to HP-B065 comprise a slightly different set of six medals. As different combinations of four from each of the sets have been found in a box, it would appear that any four constituted a set. Boxes are occasionally found with one or more medals missing, and sometimes a selection from both sets are found in a box, but it is not thought they were issued that way. Boxes are known with a depth of both 9 mm and 10 mm.

HP-B015
by Allen & Moore — Wm 26 mm

Obverse Crowned Gothic bust of Queen Victoria left. *Inscription in the field:* H.M.G.M. QUEEN VICTORIA. *Inscription around the border:* BORN MAY 24 1819. CROWNED JUNE 28 1838. MARRIED FEB: 10 1840.
Reverse View of the Crystal Palace. *Inscription above:* THE CRYSTAL PALACE *In exergue:* FOR THE GREAT / EXHIBITION / IN LONDON OF / 1851 *Inscription around the border:* LENGTH 1848 F^I, WIDTH 456 F^I, HEIGHT OF ROOF 66 F^I, HEIGHT OF TRANSEPT 108 F^I •
Rim Plain.

RR *Brown 2429* FM ML PC

One of a set of five medals. These medals are known in two sizes, 26 mm with a 2.2 mm flan and 26.5 mm with a 1.8 mm flan. On the latter medals, the O and R of VICTORIA are both indistinct. It is strange that medals in this set were produced in different sizes, possibly the larger size was marketed without the brass box. Collectors with an empty box trying to make up a set should be aware of this difference in size, and should ensure that the medals fit easily into the box, otherwise they could experience considerable difficulty getting them out of the box at a later date. See note to HP-B010.

HP-B020
by Allen & Moore   Wm 26 mm

Obverse   Uniformed bust of Prince Albert left. *Inscription in the field:* H.R.H. PRINCE ALBERT. *Inscription around the border:* BORN AUGUST 26 1819. MARRIED FEBRUARY 10 1840. *Signed* A & M.
Reverse   Similar to reverse of HP-B015.
Rim   Plain.

RR   *Brown* 2431   ML PC

One of a set of five medals, see notes to HP-B010 and HP-B015.

HP-B025
by Allen & Moore   Wm 26 mm

Obverse   Conjoined busts of Queen Victoria and Prince Albert left. *Inscription around the border:* H.M.G.M. QUEEN VICTORIA. AND H.R.H. PRINCE ALBERT *Signed* A & M
Reverse   Similar to reverse of HP-B015.
Rim   Plain.

RRR   *unrecorded*   PC

One of a set of five medals, see notes to HP-B010 and HP-B015.

HP-B030
by Allen & Moore   Wm 26 mm

Obverse   The Prince of Wales in a sailor suit seated on a foul anchor. *Inscription above:* 'BRITAIN'S HOPE' *In exergue:* THE PRINCE OF / WALES *Signed* M & A.
Reverse   Similar to reverse of HP-B015.
Rim   Plain.

RR   *Brown* 2432   ML PC

One of a set of five medals. Note the obverse signature has accidentally been transposed from A & M to M & A. The 26.5 mm specimen is signed A & M in the normal way, but the BR of BRITAIN'S HOPE is indistinct, and the inscription in the exergue is serifed. See notes to HP-B010 and HP-B015.

HP-B035
by Allen & Moore   Wm 26 mm

Obverse   Three oval medallions with portraits of the royal children divided by crowned arms and floral emblems. *Top:* conjoined heads of Prince of Wales and Princess Royal. *Left:* conjoined heads of Princess Alice and Prince Alfred. *Right:* conjoined heads of Princess Louise and Princess Helena.
Reverse   Similar to reverse of HP-B015.
Rim   Plain.

RR   *Brown* 2430   ML PC

One of a set of five medals, see notes to HP-B010 and HP-B015.

HP-B040
by Allen & Moore   Wm 27 mm

Obverse   Similar to obverse of HP-B015.
Reverse   View of the Crystal Palace. *Inscription above:* THE CRYSTAL PALACE *In exergue:* FOR THE GREAT / EXHIBITION / IN LONDON OF / 1851 *Signed* ALLEN & MOORE BIRM.
Rim   Plain.

RRR   *unrecorded*   PC

One of a set of six medals, the reverse is similar to that in the previous set, but without the dimensions around the border. See note to HP-B010

HP-B045
by Allen & Moore   Wm 27 mm

Obverse   Similar to obverse of HP-B020.
Reverse   Similar to reverse of HP-B040.
Rim   Plain.

RRR   *Taylor* 165b   BM PC

One of a set of six medals, see note to HP-B010 and HP-B040.

HP-B050
by Allen & Moore   Wm 27 mm

Obverse   Similar to obverse of HP-B025.
Reverse   Similar to reverse of HP-B040.
Rim   Plain.

RRR   *unrecorded*   PC

One of a set of six medals, see note to HP-B010 and HP-B040.

HP-B055
by Allen & Moore   Wm 27 mm

Obverse   Similar to obverse of HP-B030.
Reverse   Similar to reverse of HP-B040.
Rim   Plain.

RRR   *unrecorded*   PC

One of a set of six medals, see note to HP-B010 and HP-B040.

HP-B060
by Allen & Moore   Wm 27 mm

Obverse   Similar to obverse of HP-B035.
Reverse   Similar to reverse of HP-B040.
Rim   Plain.

RRR	*Brown* 2430A	PC

One of a set of six medals, see note to HP-B010 and HP-B040.

HP-B065
by Allen & Moore — Wm 27 mm

Obverse Similar to reverse of HP-B040.
Reverse *Eleven line inscription:* THE CONSTRUCTION IS OF / IRON AND GLASS; / 1848 F^T LONG / ABOUT HALF IS 456 F^T WIDE, / THE REMAINDER 408 F^T WIDE, / AND 66 F^T HIGH; / WITH TRANSEPT 108 F^T HIGH, / SITE UPWARDS OF 20 ACRES. / COST £ 150,000. / - - / JOS^H PAXTON ESQ^R / ARC^T.
Rim Plain.

RRR	*unrecorded*	PC

One of a set of six medals, see notes to HP-B010 and HP-B040.

HP-B070
by Allen & Moore — Wm 27 mm

Obverse View of the Crystal Palace, no trees. *Inscription above:* THE BUILDING FOR THE INTERNATIONAL / EXHIBITION *In exergue:* LONDON / 1851 *Signed* A & M.
Reverse Similar to reverse of HP-B065.
Rim Plain.

S	*Brown* 2433, *Eidlitz* 764/83, *Taylor* 165d	BM BG PC

HP-B075
by Allen & Moore — Wm 27 mm

Obverse Similar to obverse of HP-B070.
Reverse *Eleven line inscription:* THE CONSTRUCTION IS OF / IRON AND GLASS, / 1848 F^T LONG, / ABOUT HALF IS 456 F^T WIDE, / THE REMAINDER 408 F^T WIDE, / 66 F^T HIGH, / WITH TRANSEPT 108 F^T HIGH; / SITE UPWARDS OF 20 ACRES; / COST £150,000. / - - - / JOS^H PAXTON ESQ^R / ARCH^T.
Rim Plain.

R	*unrecorded*	ML PC

The reverse is similar to HP-B070, but AND is missing from line six. There are also minor punctuation differences.

HP-B080
by Allen & Moore — Wm 30 mm

Obverse Similar to obverse of HP-B070.
Reverse Similar to reverse of HP-B070.
Rim Plain.

RRR	*Eidlitz* 764/83, *Taylor* 165c

Description obtained from Taylor, because the author has not seen a specimen.

HP-B085
by Allen & Moore — Wm 31 mm

Obverse View of the Crystal Palace. *Inscription above:* THE INDUSTRIAL EXHIBITION / LONDON, 1851 *In exergue:*

PROPOSED BY PRINCE ALBERT / DESIGNED BY J. PAXTON ESQ / ERECTED BY / FOX, HENDERSON & Cᵒ. *Signed* ALLEN & MOORE BIRMM
Reverse   Thirteen line inscription: THE / MATERIALS ARE / IRON AND GLASS; / LENGTH 1848 FEET; / WIDTH 456 FEET; / HEIGHT OF ROOF 66 FEET; / HEIGHT OF TRANSEPT / 108 FEET; / GLAZED SURFACE / 900,000 SUP. FEET; / OCCUPIES 18 ACRES / OF GROUND; / VALUE £150,000.
Rim   Beaded.

RR   *Brown 2427, Eidlitz 760/83, Taylor 165e*   FM ML PC

HP-B090
by Allen & Moore   Wm 39 mm

Obverse   Crowned Gothic bust of Queen Victoria left.
Inscription in the field: H.M.G.M. QUEEN VICTORIA.
Inscription around the border: BORN MAY 24 1819.
CROWNED JUNE 28 1838. MARRIED FEB: 10 1840. ✠
Signed A & M.
Reverse   View of the Crystal Palace. Inscription above: THE BUILDING AT LONDON, FOR THE / INTERNATIONAL EXHIBITION / 1851 *In exergue:* Conjoined heads of Queen Victoria and Prince Albert in a crowned medallion supported by two cherubs. *Signed* J. PAXTON ESQ. ARCHITECT. ALLEN & MOORE F.
Rim   Plain.

R   *Brown 2425, Eidlitz 759/83, Taylor 165h*   AM BM ML PC

HP-B095
by Allen & Moore   Wm 39 mm

Obverse   Similar to reverse of HP-B090.
Reverse   Sixteen line inscription: THE MATERIALS ARE / IRON AND GLASS, / IN SHAPE / A PARALLELOGRAM, / 1848 Fᵀ LONG BY 408 Fᵀ BROAD, / AND 66 Fᵀ HIGH. / IT IS CROSSED MIDWAY BY / A TRANSEPT 108 Fᵀ HIGH, / ON THE NORTH SIDE IS AN / ADDITIONAL 936 Fᵀ IN LENGTH / BY 48 Fᵀ IN BREADTH; / TOTAL AREA OF SPACE / 855,360 CUBIC Fᵀ; / OR NEARLY 21 ACRES; / ESTIMATED VALUE / £150,000.
Rim   Plain.

RR   *Brown 2426, Eidlitz 757/83, Taylor 165i*   BM UM PC

HP-B100
by Allen & Moore   Ae Wm 39 mm

Obverse   Similar to reverse of HP-B090.
Reverse   Interior view of the Crystal Palace. In exergue: EXPOSITION / 1851 *signed* ALLEN & MOORE.
Rim   Plain.

Ae RRR, Wm R   *Brown 2424, Eidlitz 755/83, Taylor 165f*   AM BM BG ML PC

HP-B105	
by Allen & Moore	Wm 39 mm

Obverse View of the Crystal Palace. *Inscription above:* EXPOSITION INTERNATIONALE DE L'INDUSTRIE, / LONDRES, 1851. *In exergue:* PROPOSE PAR / SON A.R. LE PRINCE ALBERT. / LE BATIMENT A ETE DESSINE PAR / M^R JOS^H PAXTON M.S.R. / ET ELEVE PAR / MESSIEURS FOX, HENDERSON ET CIE. *Signed* ALLEN ET MOORE BIRM^M.

Reverse Similar to reverse of HP-B100.

Rim Plain.

RR *Eidlitz 758/83, Taylor 165g* BM PC

HP-B110	
by Allen & Moore	Wm 39 mm

Obverse Similar to obverse of HP-B105.

Reverse *Nineteen line inscription:* LES MATERIAUX SONT / LE FER / ET LE VERRE: / LA FORME EST / UN PARALLELOGRAMME: / IL A 1848 PIEDS DE LONG / SUR 408 DE LARGE, / ET 66 PIEDS DE HAUT, / LA PARTIE MEDIALE EST / DE 108 PIEDS DE HAUT; / AU NORD SE TROVE UN / PROLONGEMENT DE 936 PIEDS DE LONG, / SUR 48 PIEDS DE LARGE, / LA SURFACE TOTALE / DE L'ETENDUE EST DE / 855,360 PIEDS CUBES, / 21 ARPENTS: / IL EST EVALUE A 1,050,000 FRANCS.

Rim Plain.

RRR *unrecorded* PC

HP-B115	
by Allen & Moore	Wm 45 mm

Obverse Similar to reverse of HP-B090.

Reverse *Sixteen line inscription:* THE MATERIALS ARE / IRON AND GLASS; / IT IS IN SHAPE / A PARALLELOGRAM, / 1848 F^T LONG BY 408 F^T BROAD, / AND 66 F^T HIGH; / IT IS CROSSED MIDWAY BY / A TRANSEPT, 108 F^T HIGH; / ON THE NORTH SIDE IS AN / ADDITION, OF 936 F^T IN LENGTH / BY 48 F^T IN BREADTH, / TOTAL AREA OF SPACE, / 855,360 CUBIC F^T, / OR NEARLY 21 ACRES, / ESTIMATED VALUE, / £150,000. *Inscription around the border:* THERE ARE 2,244 IRON GIRDERS, 3,300 COLUMNS, 202 MILES OF SASH BARS, AND 900,000 SUP: F^T OF GLASS.

Rim Plain.

R *Brown 2423, Eidlitz 756/82, Taylor 165j* BM PC

HP-B120		**HP-B125**	
by Allen & Moore	Wm 52 mm	by Allen & Moore	Wm 52 mm

Obverse Conjoined busts of Queen Victoria and Prince Albert left within a crowned wreath of laurel and oak. *Inscription in the field:* QUEEN VICTORIA & PR: ALBERT
Reverse View of the Crystal Palace. *Inscription above:* THE INTERNATIONAL INDUSTRIAL EXHIBITION / LONDON, 1851. *In exergue:* PROPOSED BY H.R.H. PRINCE ALBERT, / DESIGNED BY JOSEPH PAXTON ESQ. F.L.S., / ERECTED BY FOX, HENDERSON & Cᵒ. / LENGTH 1848 FEET, WIDTH 456 FEET, / HEIGHT OF PRINCIPAL ROOF 66 FEET, / HEIGHT OF TRANSEPT 108 FEET, / GLAZED SURFACE 900,000 SUP FEET, / OCCUPIES 18 ACRES / OF GROUND, / ESTIMATED VALUE £150,000. *Signed* ALLEN & MOORE BIRMᴹ
Rim Plain.

S *Brown* 2419, *Eimer (I)* 1460, *Eidlitz* 748/82, *Fearon (I)* 302.2, *Taylor* 165k AM BM BG CP FM ML PC

Obverse Crowned Gothic bust of Queen Victoria left within a wreath of laurel, oak, roses, shamrock, and thistle. *Inscription in the field:* VICTORIA, QUEEN OF GREAT BRITAIN.
Reverse Similar to reverse of HP-B120.
Rim Plain.

R *Brown* 2420, *Eidlitz* 749/82, *Taylor* 165l BM UM PC

HP-B130			HP-B135		
by Allen & Moore		Wm 52 mm	by Allen & Moore		Wm 52 mm

Obverse   Bare head of Prince Albert right. *Inscription around the border:* PRINCE ALBERT, CONSORT OF QUEEN VICTORIA. *Signed* A & M
Reverse   Similar to reverse of HP-B120.
Rim   Toothed obverse, plain reverse.

Wm R   *Brown* 2421, *Eidlitz* 750, *Taylor* 165m   AM BM PC

Brown records a specimen in bronze, the author has not yet seen one in that metal.

Obverse   Bare head of Prince Albert right within an ornate border. *Inscription in the field:* PRINCE ALBERT, CONSORT OF QUEEN VICTORIA. *Signed* ALLEN & MOORE
Reverse   Similar to reverse of HP-B120.
Rim   Plain.

Wm R   *Brown* 2422, *Taylor* 165n   BM BG PC

Brown records a specimen in bronze, the author has not yet seen one in that metal.

HP-B140
by Allen & Moore — Wm 64 mm

Brown records a specimen in bronze, the author has not yet seen one in that metal.

HP-B145
by Allen & Moore — Aeg Wmg 89 mm

Obverse Similar to obverse of HP-B135, but has serif script.
Reverse View of the Crystal Palace. *Inscription above:* THE INTERNATIONAL INDUSTRIAL EXHIBITION / LONDON, 1851. *In exergue:* PROPOSED BY H.R.H. PRINCE ALBERT / THE BUILDING DESIGNED BY JOSEPH PAXTON ESQ^R F.L.S. / ERECTED BY FOX, HENDERSON & Co. / THE MATERIALS ARE IRON AND GLASS; / LENGTH 1848 FEET; / WIDTH 456 FEET; / HEIGHT OF PRINCIPAL ROOF 66 FEET; / HEIGHT OF TRANSEPT 108 FEET; / GLAZED SURFACE 900,000 SUP. FEET; / OCCUPIES 18 ACRES OF GROUND; / ESTIMATED VALUE / £150,000. *Signed* ALLEN & MOORE F. ET D. BIRM^M.
Rim Plain.

Wm RR *Brown* 2418, *Taylor* 165o BM PC

Obverse Bare head of Prince Albert right within an ornate border. *Inscription in the field:* PRINCE ALBERT, CONSORT OF QUEEN VICTORIA. *Signed* ALLEN & MOORE F. ET D. BIRM^M

Reverse Two line inscription above a three-dimensional view of the Crystal Palace within a semi circle: THE INTERNATIONAL INDUSTRIAL EXHIBITION / 1851 *In exergue:* Industry bestowing awards on the continents. *Signed* J. PAXTON ESQ. ARCHᵀ ALLEN & MOORE. F:
Rim Plain.

RRR	*Eimer (I)* 1456 PC

Usually found in a glazed frame, the two unglazed specimens seen have each had notches on the top and bottom edges, which indicates the glass has been broken and the medal has been removed from the frame.

HP-B150
by Allen & Moore — Aeg 112 mm

Obverse Similar to obverse of HP-B145.
Reverse Similar to reverse of HP-B145.
Rim Plain.

RRRR	*unrecorded* PC

Description obtained from *Spink Numismatic Circular 232 / 5816 (Sept. 1984), because the author has not seen a specimen.*

HP-B160
by J. Davis — Wm 44 mm

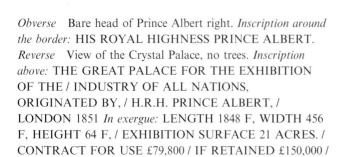

Obverse Bare head of Prince Albert right. *Inscription around the border:* HIS ROYAL HIGHNESS PRINCE ALBERT.
Reverse View of the Crystal Palace, no trees. *Inscription above:* THE GREAT PALACE FOR THE EXHIBITION OF THE / INDUSTRY OF ALL NATIONS, ORIGINATED BY, / H.R.H. PRINCE ALBERT, / LONDON 1851 *In exergue:* LENGTH 1848 F, WIDTH 456 F, HEIGHT 64 F, / EXHIBITION SURFACE 21 ACRES. / CONTRACT FOR USE £79,800 / IF RETAINED £150,000 /

DESIGNED BY / JOS PAXTON ESQ FRS. *Signed* DAVIS BIRM
Rim Plain.

RR	*Brown* 2436, *Taylor* 165p BM PC

HP-B165
by J. Davis — Wm 49 mm

Obverse Conjoined heads of Queen Victoria and Prince Albert left. *Inscription around the border:* TO COMMEMORATE THE EXHIBITION OF THE INDUSTRY OF ALL NATIONS / PROPOSED BY H.R.H. PRINCE ALBERT & PATRONISED BY H.M.G. MAJESTY THE QUEEN *Signed* DAVIS, BIRM.
Reverse View of the Crystal Palace. *Inscription above:* LENGTH OF THE BUILDING 1848 Fᵀ WIDTH 456 Fᵀ HEIGHT 66 Fᵀ TRANSEPT 108 Fᵀ / GLAZED SURFACE 900,000, Fᵀ OCCUPIES NEARLY 21 ACˢ OF GROUND / 3300, IRON COLUMNS, 2224 GIRDERS, 1128 GALLʸ BEARERS / 205 MILES OF SASH BAR, VALUE £150000. / OPENED BY H.M.G. MAJESTY VICTORIA / MAY 1. 1851. *In exergue:* Four figures representing the continents. *Signed* DESIGNED BY J. PAXTON ESQ ERECTED BY FOX HENDERSON & Co.
Rim Plain.

RR *Brown 2435, Eidlitz 752/82, Taylor 165q*   AM BM BG PC

HP-B170
by G. Dee   Wm 29 mm

Obverse   Bare head of Prince Albert left, within a tressure of arcs. *Inscription in the field:* H.R.H. PRINCE ALBERT
Signed G. DEE. F.
Reverse   View of the Crystal Palace. *Inscription above:* THE CRYSTAL PALACE LONDON /1851 *In exergue:*
COVERING AN AREA OF 18 ACRES / LENGTH 1848 F^I BREADTH / 408 F^I HEIGHT 66 F^I / TRANSEPT 108 F^I / HIGH / COST £150,000.
Rim   Plain.

RRR *Brown 2437, Eidlitz 763/83, Taylor 165r*   BM PC

Note the £.s.d. price of 10/- inscribed on the obverse in pen and ink by an over-zealous vendor.

HP-B180
by H   Ae 22 mm

Obverse   Bare head of Queen Victoria left. *Inscription around the border:* VICTORIA QUEEN OF GREAT BRITAIN
Signed on truncation with a small H
Reverse   View of the Crystal Palace. *Inscription above:* EXHIBITION PALACE. *In exergue:* LONDON / 1851
Rim   Beaded.

RR *Bell et al - /QV1, Brown 2455, Taylor 165bb (note)*   PC

Jim Sweeny attributes this to R. Heaton & Sons.

HP-B190
by HB   Ae 22 mm

Obverse   Similar to reverse of HP-B180.
Reverse   Similar to reverse of HP-B180, but signed HB in the exergue.
Rim   Beaded obverse, plain reverse.

RR *Bell et al - /CP 3, Brown 2456, Eidlitz 764/85 (ill.), Sabo 25 (ill.), Taylor 165bb*   BM PC

Jim Sweeny attributes this to R. Heaton & Sons.

HP-B195
by HB   Ae 22 mm

Obverse   Similar to reverse of HP-B190.
Reverse   Blank.
Rim   Plain.

RRR *Batty 404, Bell et al - /CP 3, Sabo 26*

Description obtained from Sabo, because the author has not seen a specimen. Jim Sweeny attributes this to R. Heaton & Sons.

HP-B200
by R. Heaton & Sons   Wm 31 mm

Obverse   View of the Crystal Palace. *Inscription above:* THE CRYSTAL PALACE *In exergue:* FOR THE / WORLD'S SHOW / IN / LONDON / 1851 *Signed* HEATON. BIRM.
Reverse   *Nine line inscription:* DIMENSIONS / - - - / LENGTH 1848 F^T / WIDTH 408 F^T / HEIGHT OF ROOF

66 F^T / HEIGHT OF TRANSEPT 108 F^T / GLAZED
SURFACE / 900,000 S^Q F^T / AND / OCCUPIES 18 ACRES
Rim Plain.

N	*Brown 2440, Eidlitz 761/83, Taylor 165s*	AM BM BG ML PC UM

HP-B205
by R. Heaton & Sons — Ae 31 mm

Obverse Similar to obverse of HP-B200.
Reverse Blank.
Rim Plain.

RRR	*Sabo 34 (ill.)*	PC

HP-B210
by R. Heaton & Sons — Wm 31 mm

Obverse Similar to obverse of HP-B200.
Reverse Ten line inscription: THIS UNIQUE
STRUCTURE / HAS 3320 / CAST IRON COLUMNS / 358
WROUGHT IRON TRUSSES / 8 MILES OF EXHIB^N
TABLES / 34 MILES OF GUTTERS / 202 MILES OF
SASH BARS / 400 TONS OF GLASS / AND / COST
£150,000.
Rim Plain.

RRR	*Gunstone 104 (ill.)*	BG

HP-B215
by R. Heaton & Sons — Wm 34 mm

Obverse View of the Crystal Palace. *Inscription above:* THE
CRYSTAL PALACE / DESIGNED BY / MR PAXTON *In
exergue:* FOR THE GREAT / EXHIBITION / IN LONDON
OF / 1851 *Signed* HEATON BIRM
Reverse Nine line inscription: DIMENSIONS / LENGTH

1848 FEET / WIDTH 408 FEET / HEIGHT OF ROOF 66
FEET / HEIGHT OF TRANSEPT 108 F^T / GLAZED
SURFACE / 900,000 FEET / AND / OCCUPIES 18 ACRES
Rim Plain.

S	*Brown 2439, Taylor 165t*	BM BG PC UM

HP-B220
by R. Heaton & Sons — Wm 38 mm

Obverse View of the Crystal Palace. *Inscription above:* THE
GREAT EXHIBITION PALACE / LONDON / 1851 *In
exergue:* PROPOSED BY H.R.H. PRINCE ALBERT /
DESIGNED BY JOS^H PAXTON. F.L.S / ERECTED BY /
FOX HENDERSON & Co / OCCUPIES 18 ACRES *Signed*
HEATON. BIRM.
Reverse Eleven line inscription: LENGTH 1848 FEET / 408
F^T WIDE / ROOF 66 F^T HIGH / HEIGHT OF TRANSEPT
108 F^T / 900,000 S^Q F^T GLAZED SURFACE / 3320 CAST
IRON COLUMNS / 358 WRO^T IRON TRUSSES / 8 MILES
EXHIBITION TABLES / 202 MILES OF SASH BARS / 400
TONS OF GLASS / VALUE £150,000.
Rim Plain.

R	*Brown 2438, Gunstone 99/100, Sabo 43, Taylor 165u*	BM ML PC

HP-B230
by J. Hinks — Wm 39 mm

Obverse Bare head of Prince Albert right. *Inscription around the border:* HIS ROYAL HIGHNESS PRINCE ALBERT. *Signed* J. HINKS F.
Reverse View of the Crystal Palace, no trees. *Inscription above:* THE CRYSTAL PALACE, FOR THE / EXHIBITION OF ALL NATIONS / LONDON 1851 *In exergue:* COVERING AN AREA OF 18 ACRES, / LENGTH 1848 F^T, BREADTH / 408 F^T. HEIGHT 66 F^T. / TRANSEPT 108 F^T / HIGH. / COST £150,000.
Rim Plain.

RRR   *Brown* 2445   PC

HP-B235
by J. Hinks   Ae Wm 45 mm

Obverse Similar to obverse of HP-B230.
Reverse View of the Crystal Palace. *Inscription above:* THE CRYSTAL PALACE, FOR THE / EXHIBITION OF ALL NATIONS / LONDON 1851. *In exergue:* PROPOSED BY H.R.H. PRINCE ALBERT. / DESIGNED BY J. PAXTON ESQ. F.L.S. / ERECTED BY FOX, HENDERSON & Cº. / LENGTH 1848 F^T BREADTH 408 F^T / HEIGHT OF PRINCIPAL ROOF 66 F^T / HEIGHT OF TRANSEPT 108 F^T / GLAZED SURFACE 900,000 F^T / OCCUPIES 18 ACRES / OF GROUND.
Rim Plain.

Ae RRR, Wm RRR   *Brown* 2444   BG PC

HP-B240
by L.C. Lauer   Wm 22 mm

Obverse Conjoined heads of Queen Victoria and Prince Albert left. *Inscription around the border:* VICTORIA ALBERT *Signed* L. LAUER
Reverse View of the Crystal Palace. *Inscription above:* THE CRYSTAL PALACE / DESIGNED BY / MR PAXTON. *In exergue:* FOR THE GREAT / EXHIBITION / IN LONDON OF / 1851.
Rim Plain.
Edge Milled.

RRR   *Bell et al* - /CP 12   PC

See HP-D020 to HP-D030 for similar pieces by L.C. Lauer.

HP-B245
by L.C. Lauer   Ae 22 mm

Obverse Similar to obverse of HP-B240.
Reverse Partial view of the Crystal Palace. *Inscription above:* GLAS PALLAST *In exergue:* FUR DIE GROSSE / AUSTELLUNG / IN LONDON. /1851.
Rim Plain
Edge Milled.

RRR   *unrecorded*   PC

Courtesy of Melvyn Harrison.

HP-B250
by Neveux | Ae 34 mm

Obverse Three line inscription within a laurel wreath:
REIGN / OF / VICTORIA *Inscription around the border:*
UNIVERSAL EXPOSITION OF LONDON / 1ST MAY
MDCCCLI
Reverse Ceres scattering seed, her right foot is upon a wheel.
Maritime symbols are to her right, art symbols to her left.
Inscription above: UNION OF ALL NATIONS *In exergue:*
GENIUS AND LABOUR / GAIN THE SAME / END
Signed NEVEUX
Rim Plain.

RRRR *unrecorded* PC

Appears to be of French origin.

Obverse Bare head of Prince Albert left within a wreath of
laurel and oak. *Inscription around the border:* HIS ROYAL
HIGHNESS PRINCE ALBERT. *Signed* OTTLEY, BIRMᴹ
Reverse View of the Crystal Palace, no trees. *Inscription
above:* THE BUILDING FOR THE GREAT EXHIBITION
IN LONDON, 1851 *In exergue:* PROPOSED BY H.R.H.
PRINCE ALBERT. / DESIGNED BY JOSEPH PAXTON
ESQ. F.L.S. / ERECTED BY FOX, HENDERSON & Cº /
LENGTH 1848 FEET. WIDTH 456 FEET. / HEIGHT OF
PRINCIPAL ROOF 66 FEET. / HEIGHT OF TRANSEPT
108 FEET. / GLAZED SURFACE 900000 FEET. /
OCCUPIES 18 ACRES / OF GROUND.
Rim Beaded obverse, plain reverse.

RR *Brown 2452, Taylor 165x* BM BG PC

Brown records a specimen in bronze, the author has not yet
seen one in that metal.

HP-B260
by T. Ottley | Wm 54 mm

HP-B265
by T. Ottley | Wm 54 mm

Obverse Bare head of Prince Albert right. *Inscription around the border:* HIS ROYAL HIGHNESS PRINCE ALBERT.
Reverse Similar to reverse of HP-B260.
Rim Plain.

RR *Brown* 2453, *Eidlitz* 753/82, *Taylor* 165v   AM BM PC

Brown records a specimen in bronze, the author has not yet seen one in that metal.

HP-B270
by T. Ottley   Wm 54 mm

Obverse Similar to reverse of HP-B260.
Reverse Britannia supported by Peace and Plenty, to the right a Briton is beating the sword into a pruning hook. St Paul's in the distance. *Signed* OTTLEY, MEDALLIST, BIRM^M
Rim Plain.

RRR *Brown* 2454, *Eidlitz* 754/82, *Taylor* 165w   AM PC

The copper plate inscription on the inside of the case reads: Britannia / supported by Peace & Plenty / inviting the Nations of the World / to partake of the / Hospitality of England / and to share in the / Honorable Competition of Industry. / A Briton on the right beating / the Sword into a pruning hook, / St Paul's in the distance. / 1851.

HP-B275
by T. Ottley   Wm 74 mm

HP-B280

by T. Ottley   Wm 74 mm

Obverse Bare head of Prince Albert left within a wreath of laurel and oak. *Inscription around the border:* HIS ROYAL HIGHNESS PRINCE ALBERT. *Signed* OTTLEY BIRM^M
Reverse View of the Crystal Palace. *Inscription above:* THE BUILDING FOR THE GREAT EXHIBITION IN LONDON 1851 *In exergue:* PROPOSED BY H.R.H. PRINCE ALBERT. / DESIGNED BY JOSEPH PAXTON ESQ. F.L.S. / ERECTED BY FOX, HENDERSON, & C° / --DIMENSIONS - - / LENGTH 1848 FEET, WIDTH 456 FEET, / HEIGHT OF PRINCIPAL ROOF 66 FEET, / HEIGHT OF TRANSEPT 108 FEET, / GLAZED SURFACE 900 000 FEET. / OCCUPIES 18 ACRES / OF GROUND
Rim Plain.

> **R** *Brown 2446, Eimer (I) 1458, Eidlitz 747/83, Fearon (I) 302.1, Taylor 165y* AM BM BG BR FM PC UM

Brown records a specimen in bronze, the author has not yet seen one in that metal.

Obverse Similar to obverse of HP-B275.
Reverse View of the Crystal Palace. *Inscription above:* THE CRYSTAL PALACE FOR THE GREAT EXHIBITION OF THE / INDUSTRY OF ALL NATIONS; IN HYDE PARK LONDON / OPENED BY H.M.G. MAJESTY VICTORIA / MAY 1ST 1851. *In exergue:* PROPOSED BY H.R.H. PRINCE ALBERT. / DESIGNED BY JOSEPH PAXTON ESQ. F.L.S. / ERECTED BY FOX, HENDERSON, & C° / -- DIMENSIONS - - / LENGTH 1848 FEET, WIDTH 456 FEET, / HEIGHT OF PRINCIPAL ROOF 66 FEET, / HEIGHT OF TRANSEPT 108 FEET, / GLAZED SURFACE 900 000 FEET, / OCCUPIES 18 ACRES / OF GROUND. *Signed* OTTLEY MEDALLIST BIRM^M

Rim   Plain.

RR	*Brown* 2448	AM FM PC

Brown records a specimen in bronze, the author has not yet seen one in that metal.

HP-B285
by T. Ottley   Ae Wm 74 mm

Obverse   Heads of Queen Victoria and Prince Albert vis-à-vis in oval medallions divided by royal arms and scrolls above a view of the Crystal Palace. *Inscription beneath:* PROPOSED BY H.R.H. PRINCE ALBERT. / DESIGNED BY / JOSEPH PAXTON ESQ^RE F.L.S. / ERECTED BY / FOX, HENDERSON, & Cº *Inscription around the border outside an*

open floral wreath: EXHIBITION OF INDUSTRY OF ALL NATIONS. LONDON. 1851 *Signed* OTTLEY BIRM.
Reverse   Britannia standing on the seashore flanked by symbols of art industry and transport. *In exergue: Signed* OTTLEY. BIRM:
Rim   Plain.

Ae RRR, Wm RR	*Brown* 2447, *Eidlitz* 746/83, *Taylor* 165z	
AM BM PC		

White metal specimens were sold in a pink card box with an engraving of the building on the lid, and inscribed: A MEDAL OF THE BUILDING FOR THE GRAND EXHIBITION OF LONDON 1851.

HP-B290
by T. Ottley   Ae Wm 74 mm

Obverse Similar to reverse of HP-B280.
Reverse Four female figures seated upon clouds surrounding a terrestrial globe.
Rim Plain.

RRR *Brown 2449* AM PC

HP-B295
by T. Ottley   Ae Wm 74 mm

Obverse Similar to obverse of HP-B285.
Reverse Similar to reverse of HP-B290, but inscribed: PUBLISHED BY HYAMS 57 PALL MALL & 59 CORNHILL
Rim Plain.

RRR *Brown 2450* BG

Description obtained from Brown, because the author has not seen a specimen.

HP-B300
by T. Ottley   Ae 74 mm

Obverse Similar to obverse of HP-B275.
Reverse Similar to reverse of HP-B285.
Rim Plain.

RRR *Brown 2451* PC

Description obtained from Brown, because the author has not seen a specimen.

HP-B305
by T. Ottley   Ae 74 mm

Obverse Similar to obverse of HP-B290.
Reverse Similar to reverse of HP-B285.
Rim Plain.

RRR *unrecorded* PC

Courtesy of C.E.

HP-B310
by T. Pope & Co   Ae Br 22 mm

Obverse Bare head of Queen Victoria left, no inscription.
Reverse View of the Crystal Palace, no trees. *Inscription above:* THE CRYSTAL / PALACE. *In exergue:* LONDON / 1851 *Signed* POPE & Co. BIRM.
Rim Plain.

R *Bell et al 850/CP 10, Brown 2457* PC

HP-B320
by T. Pope & Co   Ae 22 mm

Obverse Bare head of Queen Victoria left. *Inscription around the border:* VICTORIA QUEEN OF GREAT BRITAIN.
Below truncation: 1852
Reverse Similar to reverse of HP-B310.
Rim Toothed obverse, plain reverse.

RR *Bell et al 860/CP 10, Brown 2507* BM PC

The Crystal Palace should have been dismantled at the close of the Great Exhibition in October 1851. However, the attempts to get the building permanently retained, managed to preserve its life until the summer of 1852. Pope may have struck this piece to commemorate the survival of the Crystal Palace into the following year.

HP-B330	
by J. Taylor	Wm 39 mm

Obverse Bare head of Prince Albert left within a beaded circle. *Inscription in four concentric circles:* THE BUILDING IS CONSTRUCTED OF IRON & GLASS COVERING AN AREA OF 18 ACRES / LENGTH 1848 F^T BREADTH 408 F^T HEIGHT 66 F^T CROSSED BY A TRANSEPT 108 F^T HIGH / TOTAL CUBIC CONTENTS 33,000,000 F^T ESTIMATED COST £150,000 / PROPOSED BY H.R.H. PRINCE ALBERT / 1849

Reverse View of the Crystal Palace. *Inscription above:* THE CRYSTAL PALACE / FOR THE EXHIBITION OF ALL NATIONS / 1851 *In exergue:* Royal arms *Signed* J. PAXTON ESQ. ARCHITECT. / J. TAYLOR. BIRM.

Rim Plain.

RRR	*Brown* 2458	ML PC

HP-B340	
by W.J. Taylor	Ae Wm 38 mm

Obverse Bare head of Prince Albert left. *Inscription around*

the border: H.R.H. PRINCE ALBERT / STRUCK IN THE BUILDING OF THE EXHIBITION *Signed* W.J. TAYLOR MEDALLIST / LONDON

Reverse Royal arms. *Inscription around the border:* GREAT EXHIBITION OF THE INDUSTRY OF ALL NATIONS / + LONDON 1851 +

Rim Plain.

Ae S, Wm N	*Brown* 2459, *Eimer (I)* 1463, *Eidlitz* 751/82,
Taylor 165aa	AM BM BG BR CP FM ML PC

The white metal version came in two quite different paper packets, the first is a plain printed packet with a ten line inscription: MEDAL / TO COMMEMORATE / THE EXHIBITION OF INDUSTRY / OF ALL NATIONS. / THE ONLY MEDAL STRUCK / and SOLD in the BUILDING / By Command of the / EXECUTIVE COMMITTEE. / W.J. TAYLOR, MEDALLIST, & c., / 33, Little Queen Street, Holborn, Londn. The second has a blue centre circle inscribed with raised white letters: W.J.TAYLOR / MEDALLIST / BY APPOINTMENT / TO THE / GREAT EXHIBITION / 1851 / 33 LITTLE QUEEN S^T HOLBORN *in border around:* CRYSTAL PALACE MEDAL PRESS / MANUFACTURING COURT. As large quantities of white metal specimens were struck the dies needed constant attention, consequently many minor differences may be found in the design, in the signature, and in the size and positioning of the lettering. This Great Exhibition medal is seen more often than all the other types.

HP-B350	
by J. Wiener	Ae 37 mm

Obverse *Seven line inscription:* EXHIBITION / OF THE / INDUSTRY / OF ALL / NATIONS / 1851 / LONDON

Reverse View of a sailing boat between two buildings. *Signed* GEZ. v. OPPERMANN / GEST. v. J. WIENER BRUSSEL

Rim Beaded obverse, toothed reverse.

RRRR	*unrecorded* PC

The reverse die is inverted.

HP-B360	
by ?	Brg 20 mm

Obverse Bare head of Queen Victoria left. *Inscription around the border:* VICTORIA QUEEN OF GREAT BRIT:
Reverse View of the Crystal Palace, no trees. *Inscription above:* THE CRYSTAL PALACE / LONDON 1851 *In exergue:* PROPOSED BY / H.R.H. PRINCE ALBERT
Rim Plain obverse, beaded reverse.
Edge Milled.

RRR	*unrecorded* PC

HP-B365	
by ?	Aeg Brg 23 mm

Obverse Bare head of Queen Victoria left. *Inscription around the border:* VICTORIA QUEEN OF GREAT BRIT.
Reverse View of the Crystal Palace, no trees. *Inscription above:* THE CRYSTAL PALACE / LONDON 1851 *In exergue:* PROPOSED BY / H.R.H. PRINCE ALBERT
Rim Beaded obverse, plain reverse.
Edge Milled.

RRR	*Bell et al - /CP 18, Brown 2443* PC

The horizontal bar of the figure 5 is missing on all the specimens seen by the author.

HP-B370	
by ?	Wm 27 mm

Obverse View of the Crystal Palace. *Inscription above:* THE CRYSTAL PALACE / LONDON 1851 *In exergue:* PROPOSED BY / H.R.H. PRINCE ALBERT
Reverse Similar to reverse of HP-B200.
Rim Plain.

RRR	*Brown 2441* BM

Description obtained from Brown, because the author has not seen a specimen.

HP-B375	
by ?	Br Wm 26 mm

Obverse View of the Crystal Palace, no trees. *Inscription above:* THE CRYSTAL PALACE LONDON 1851. *In exergue:* PROPOSED BY / PRINCE ALBERT
Reverse Nine line inscription: DIMENSIONS / — . - / LENGTH 1848 F^T / WIDTH 408 FT / HEIGHT OF ROOF 66 F^T / HEIGHT OF TRANSEPT 108 F^T / GLAZED SERFACE / 900,000 S$^Q.$ F^T / AND / OCCUPIES 18 ACRES
Rim Plain.

RRR	*Brown 2442, Sabo 37 (ill.), Taylor 165cc* BM BG PC

Note that surface has been spelt with E instead of U.

HP-B380	
by ?	Wm 26 mm

Obverse Bare head of Prince Albert right. *Inscription around the border:* HIS ROYAL HIGHNESS PRINCE ALBERT.
Reverse View of the Crystal Palace, no trees. *Inscription above:* THE GREAT EXHIBITION OF ALL NATIONS / LONDON 1851 *In exergue:* ORIGINATED BY / H.R.H. PRINCE ALBERT / LENGTH 1848 F^T / BREADTH 408 F^T / HEIGHT 66 F^T
Rim Plain.

RRR	*unrecorded* PC

Courtesy of Jim Allen.

HP-B385	
by ?	Br 27 mm

Obverse View of the Crystal Palace. *Inscription above:* THE CRYSTAL PALACE / FOR THE *In exergue:* EXHIBITION / OF / 1851

Reverse *Nine line inscription:* DIMENSIONS / LENGTH 1848 FEET / WIDTH 456 FEET / ROOF 66 FEET HIGH / TRANSEPT 108 F^T HIGH / GLAZED SURFACE / 900 000 FEET / & / OCCUPIES 18 ACRES

Rim Plain.

RRR *Brown* 2470 BG PC

HP-B390	
by ?	Ae Aeg Br 28 mm

Obverse Bare head of Queen Victoria left. *Inscription around the border:* VICTORIA REGINA.

Reverse View of the Crystal Palace. *Inscription above:* THE CRYSTAL PALACE / LONDON 1851 *In exergue:* PROPOSED BY / H.R.H. PRINCE ALBERT / - - - / COST L. 150000.

Rim Plain.

Edge Milled.

RRR *Brown* 2469, *Taylor* 165dd BM PC

HP-B395	
by ?	Wm 30 mm

Obverse Diademed head of Queen Victoria left. *Inscription around the border:* VICTORIA QUEEN OF GREAT BRITAIN.

Reverse View of the Crystal Palace. *Inscription above:* THE CRYSTAL PALACE / LONDON 1851. *In exergue:* COVERING AN AREA OF 18 ACRES / LENGTH 1848 F^T BREADTH / 408 F^T HEIGHT 66 F^T / TRANSEPT 108 F^T / HIGH / COST £150,000.

Rim Plain.

RRR *Brown* 2468, *Taylor* 165ee BM BG PC

All specimens seen by the author have an inverted reverse die.

HP-B400	
by ?	Wm 31 mm

Obverse Interior view of the Crystal Palace, trees each side. *Inscription above:* INTERIOR VIEW / OF THE *In exergue:* CRYSTAL PALACE / LONDON / 1851.

Reverse Similar to reverse of HP-B210.

Rim Plain.

RRR *Brown* 2467, *Taylor* 165ff AM BM BG PC

Brown records a specimen in bronze, but the author has not yet seen one in that metal.

HP-B405
by ?   Aeg 35 mm

Obverse   Bare head of Queen Victoria left. *Inscription around the border:* VICTORIA REGINA

Reverse   View of the Crystal Palace, no trees. *Inscription above:* THE CRYSTAL PALACE, FOR THE / EXHIBITION OF ALL NATIONS / LONDON 1851. *In exergue:* COVERING AN AREA OF 18 ACRES. / LENGTH 1848 F^T, BREADTH / 408 F^T, HEIGHT 66 F^T, / TRANSEPT 108 F^T / HIGH. / COST £150.000.

Rim   Plain.

Edge   Milled.

RRR   *Brown* 2466, *Taylor* 165gg   BM PC

C. Trade Tokens

When this catalogue was first begun, the existence of most of these little gems was unknown to the author, because his collecting interests had been centred entirely upon commemorative medals. How pleasing therefore that John R.P. King introduced them to him, otherwise this volume would have been less than complete.

The number of pieces known to have been issued by a variety of tradesmen, in sizes ranging from 18 mm up to 54 mm, is virtually identical to the number of medals issued. Most of the pieces depict the Crystal Palace, but, as very few of these advertisers actually displayed their merchandise at the Great Exhibition, it is surprising to find that so many of them used the Crystal Palace as a way of attracting custom. Undoubtedly a number of shrewd token manufacturers foresaw the immense popularity of the Palace and were able to convince these particular trades people, and hopefully some others yet to be discovered, of the value of linking their particular merchandise or services to one of the greatest attractions of the century.

The tokens do not display a value as they were not issued as a substitute for money. That being so they did not circulate in the same way as the other nineteenth century tokens, which were issued specifically for that purpose. Nevertheless, they are still regarded as tokens within the numismatic trade; some being described as advertising tickets, others as pub, tavern or refreshment tokens. However, the majority, which are approximately 22 mm in diameter, are usually referred to as 'unofficial farthings'. Most of the pieces have been recorded and depicted in the splendid books by R.C. Bell and entitled *Unofficial Farthings 1820–1870* and *Bell's Unofficial Farthings, A Supplement*. In the following extract from the latter book, John Whitmore describes how these pieces developed:

> Even in Dickensian Britain, the lowest value coin in normal circulation, the farthing or quarter penny, had little purchasing power. It took almost a thousand of them to equal a gold sovereign, yet some traders needed a regular supply, partly because it was habitual to price many everyday goods at a farthing less than the silver sixpence or shilling. To avoid the inconvenience of running out of small change, and to advertise their businesses, more than five hundred traders in Great Britain and Ireland had their own farthings made, some in as many as ten varieties. While token coins of this nature were illegal, there seems to have been little

From the Cascade by Ackerman. Reproduced by permission of Eric Price.

effort to suppress even those copying the head of Queen Victoria from the official coins. The supremacy of the Queen as a popular symbol was temporarily eclipsed during the Great Exhibition of 1851, and many unofficial farthings display the Crystal Palace in Hyde Park.

There seems to have been a difference of opinion regarding the provenance of certain unsigned pieces, and also those pieces signed with just H or HB. Thankfully James O. Sweeny has removed most of the doubts surrounding these pieces in his 'Attribution of the Crystal Palace and Related Tokens', (*Bell's Unofficial Farthings, A Supplement*, Appendix 2). Readers will, of course, need to refer to both books by R.C. Bell to fully appreciate Jim Sweeny's conclusions.

The tokens have been grouped largely in accordance with Jim Sweeny's article, and are listed mainly by the inscription which appears above the view of the Crystal Palace. Two indices have been provided for cross reference purposes, i.e. alphabetical and geographical.

In this volume only those pieces bearing the name of an advertiser have been regarded as trade tokens. Consequently, there are a few unnamed pieces recorded as medals, which, 'in-the-trade', are usually referred to as tokens.

One final note of interest. Considering that tradesmen from at least five different countries outside the United Kingdom commissioned Crystal Palace tokens, it is surprising that none has yet been found from tradesmen in Scotland.

Alphabetical Index of Token Issuers

Geographical Index of Token Issuers

HP-C001 James Lee, Devonport
by R. Heaton & Sons   Ae 24 mm

Obverse View of the Crystal Palace with people in the grounds, flags upon each storey. *Inscription above:* EXHIBITION PALACE which starts above roof level. *In exergue:* LONDON / 1851 *Signed* HEATON BIRM.
Reverse *Five line inscription:* JAMES LEE / HATTER / 110 / FORE STREET / DEVONPORT.
Rim Beaded.

R   *Batty 51, Bell et al 1560/CP1, Sabo 12*   PC

HP-C005 John Pease, Plymouth
by R. Heaton & Sons   Ae 24 mm

Obverse Similar to obverse of HP-C001.
Reverse *Seven line inscription:* JOHN PEASE / HATTER / OPPOSITE / THE / MARKET GATE / EAST STREET / PLYMOUTH.
Rim Beaded.

RRR   *Bell et al 4290/CP1, Sabo 15*   PC

HP-C010 B. Hadley, Hay-on-Wye
by R. Heaton & Sons   Ae 22 mm

Obverse View of the Crystal Palace with people in the grounds, flags upon the roof and transept. *Inscription above:* EXHIBITION PALACE which starts below roof level. *In exergue:* LONDON / 1851.
Reverse *Five line inscription:* B. HADLEY / GROCER / & / TEA DEALER / HAY.
Rim Beaded obverse, plain reverse.

RRR   *Bell et al 7570/CP2*   PC

Details and illustration courtesy of John Whitmore.

HP-C015 W. Taylor, Ledbury
by R. Heaton & Sons   Ae 22 mm

Obverse Similar to obverse of HP-C010.
Reverse *Five line inscription:* W. TAYLOR / FAMILY GROCER / TEA & COFFEE DEALER / POST OFFICE / LEDBURY.
Rim Beaded.

RR   *Batty 87, Bell et al 1890/CP2, Sabo 19*   PC

HP-C020 Bowen, Kington
by R. Heaton & Sons   Ae 22 mm

Obverse View of the Crystal Palace with people in the grounds, flags upon the roof and transept. *Inscription above:* EXHIBITION PALACE which starts below roof level. *In exergue:* LONDON / 1851 *Signed* H B just below exergue line.
Reverse *Five line inscription:* BOWEN / FAMILY GROCER / & / TEA DEALER / KINGTON.
Rim Plain.

RRR   *Bell et al 1880/CP3*   PC

HP-C025   Callant's, Bridgnorth
by R. Heaton & Sons   Ae 22 mm

Obverse   Similar to obverse of HP-C020.
Reverse   Six line inscription: CALLANT'S / GROCERY / & / PROVISION / WAREHOUSE / BRIDGNORTH.
Rim   Plain.

S   *Batty 659, Bell et al 1180/CP3, Sabo 10*   PC

HP-C030   R. Cooper, Oldham
by R. Heaton & Sons   Ae 22 mm

Obverse   Similar to obverse of HP-C020.
Reverse   Four line inscription: R. COOPER / TEA & COFFEE / MERCHANT / OLDHAM.
Rim   Plain.

N   *Batty 320, Bell et al 4190/CP3, Sabo 7*   PC

HP-C035   J. & E. Harding, Ludlow
by R. Heaton & Sons   Ae 22 mm

Obverse   Similar to obverse of HP-C020.
Reverse   Eight line inscription: J & E HARDING / GENERAL DRAPERS / HATTERS &c / HIGH S^T / LUDLOW / & / HIGH S^T / LEOMINSTER.
Rim   Plain obverse, beaded reverse.

RR   *Bell et al 3150/CP3*   PC

HP-C040   W. Manley's, Leighton Buzzard
by R. Heaton & Sons   Ae 22 mm

Obverse   Similar to obverse of HP-C020.
Reverse   Four line inscription: W. MANLEY'S / TEA & COFFEE / MART / LEIGHTON BUZZARD.
Rim   Plain.

S   *Batty 1, Bell et al 1990/CP3, Sabo 13*   PC

HP-C045   Parry's, Wrexham
by R. Heaton & Sons   Ae 22 mm

Obverse   Similar to obverse of HP-C020.
Reverse   Seven line inscription: EIGHT OF THESE WILL BUY / AN OUNCE / OF / TEA / AT PARRY'S / CHARLES S^T / WREXHAM.
Rim   Plain.

RRR   *Bell et al - /CP3*   PC

Courtesy of Jim Sweeny.

HP-C050   T. Pope & Co, Birmingham
by R. Heaton & Sons   Ae 22 mm

Obverse   Similar to obverse of HP-C020.
Reverse   Seven line inscription: T. POPE & Co / THE IMPROVED / COIN / & PRESS MAKERS / 56 / S^T PAUL'S SQR. / BIRMINGHAM.
Rim   Plain.

RR *Bell et al 825/ CP3, Sabo* 14   PC

This firm exhibited its presses at the Great Exhibition.

HP-C055   W. Roberts, Lynn
by R. Heaton & Sons   Ae 22 mm

Obverse   Similar to obverse of HP-C020.
Reverse   *Five line inscription:* W. ROBERTS / TEA
DEALER / No. 1 / TUESDAY MARKET / LYNN.
Rim   Plain.

S *Bell et al* 3180/CP3   PC

HP-C060   W. Taylor, Ledbury
by R. Heaton & Sons   Ae 22 mm

Obverse   Similar to obverse of HP-C020.
Reverse   *Five line inscription:* W. TAYLOR / FAMILY
GROCER / TEA & COFFEE DEALER / POST OFFICE /
LEDBURY.
Rim   Plain obverse, beaded reverse.

R *Batty* 87, *Bell et al* 1895/CP3, *Sabo* 19   PC

HP-C065   T. Underwood, Birmingham
by R. Heaton & Sons   Ae 22 mm

Obverse   Similar to obverse of HP-C020.
Reverse   *Seven line inscription:* T. UNDERWOOD /

LITHOGRAPHIC / DRAUGHTSMAN / & / PRINTER /
UNION PASSAGE / BIRMINGHAM *Signed* POPE & Co
F.
Rim   Plain.

RR *Bell et al* 1010/CP3, *Davis et al* 1017   PC

This firm exhibited its lithographic colour press at the Great
Exhibition.

HP-C070   John W. White, Ross
by R. Heaton & Sons   Ae 22 mm

Obverse   Similar to obverse of HP-C020.
Reverse   *Six line inscription:* JOHN W. WHITE / FAMILY
GROCER / & / TEA DEALER / BROAD S^T / ROSS.
Rim   Plain obverse, beaded reverse.

RR *Bell et al* 4490/CP3   PC

HP-C075   William Coker, Lynn
by R. Heaton & Sons   Wm 22 mm

Obverse   Similar to obverse of HP-C020, but without H B in
the exergue.
Reverse   *Five line inscription:* CHEAP READY MONEY
DRAPERY ESTABLISHMENT. / WILLIAM COKER / 66 /
HIGH STREET / LYNN.
Rim   Plain.

RRR *Bell et al* 3175/CP4   PC

HP-C080 Josiah Robey, Newcastle
by R. Heaton & Sons   Ae 22 mm

Obverse Similar to obverse of HP-C020, but without H B in the exergue.
Reverse Five line inscription: JOSIAH ROBEY / COUNTY / TEA / WAREHOUSE / NEWCASTLE.
Rim Plain.

| **S** | *Batty* 639, *Bell et al* 3780/CP4, *Sabo* 16 | PC |

HP-C085 H. Baldwin's, Bath
by R. Heaton & Sons   Ae 22 mm

Obverse View of the Crystal Palace with people in the grounds, flags upon the roof only. *Inscription above:* EXHIBITION PALACE which starts at roof level. *In exergue:* LONDON / 1851 there is a small H on the exergue line.
Reverse Four line inscription: H. BALDWIN'S / TEA MARKET / 3, BRIDGE S^T / BATH.
Rim Plain.

| **R** | *Batty* 679, *Bell et al* 120/CP5, *Sabo* 1 | PC |

HP-C090 J. Casson, Woolwich
by R. Heaton & Sons   Ae 22 mm

Obverse Similar to obverse of HP-C085.
Reverse Five line inscription: OPPOSITE THE CHURCH. /

J. CASSON / GROCER / &c. / WELLINGTON S^T WOOLWICH.
Rim Plain.

| **N** | *Batty* 93, *Bell et al* 5170/CP5, *Sabo* 5 | PC |

HP-C095 Richard Cockerill, London
by R. Heaton & Sons   Ae 22 mm

Obverse Similar to obverse of HP-C085.
Reverse Eight line inscription: RICHARD COCKERILL / TEA / & / COFFEE / DEALER / 92 / SHOE LANE / FLEET STREET.
Rim Plain.

| **RR** | *Bell et al* 2400/CP5 | PC |

HP-C100 V. Drayson, Gravesend
by R. Heaton & Sons   Ae 22 mm

Obverse Similar to obverse of HP-C085.
Reverse Five line inscription: V. DRAYSON / GROCER / &c / 11. KING STREET / GRAVESEND.
Rim Plain.

| **R** | *Batty* 89, *Bell et al* 1670/CP5, *Sabo* 8 | PC |

HP-C105 Alfred Light, Brompton
by R. Heaton & Sons   Ae 22 mm

Obverse Similar to obverse of HP-C085.
Reverse *Five line inscription:* ALFRED LIGHT / GROCER
&c / 47 HIGH STREET / BROMPTON / KENT.
Rim Plain.

R *Batty 88, Bell et al 1260/CP5, Sabo 11* PC

HP-C110   T. Pope & Co, Birmingham
by R. Heaton & Sons   Ae 22 mm

Obverse Similar to obverse of HP-C085.
Reverse *Seven line inscription:* T. POPE & C° / THE
IMPROVED / COIN / & PRESS MAKERS / 56 / Sᵀ PAUL'S
SQR. / BIRMINGHAM.
Rim Plain.

N *Batty 937, Bell et al 820/CP5, Sabo 14* PC

This firm exhibited its presses at the Great Exhibition.

HP-C115   Josiah Robey, Newcastle
by R. Heaton & Sons   Ae 22 mm

Obverse Similar to obverse of HP-C085.
Reverse *Five line inscription:* JOSIAH ROBEY / COUNTY /
TEA / WAREHOUSE / NEWCASTLE.
Rim Plain.

S *Bell et al 3785/CP5, Sabo 16* PC

HP-C120   J. Blackwell, Birmingham
by R. Heaton & Sons   Ae 22 mm

Obverse Similar to obverse of HP-C085, but no H on
exergue line.
Reverse *Five line inscription:* J. BLACKWELL / GROCER /
84 / SNOW-HILL / BIRMINGHAM small R.H. in front of
B of BIRMINGHAM.
Rim Plain.

R *Batty 801, Bell et al 320/CP6, Sabo 2* PC

In the Great Exhibition official catalogue, J. Blackwell is listed
as Secretary to the Dudley Local Committee.

HP-C125   J. Casson, Woolwich
by R. Heaton & Sons   Ae Aes 22 mm

Obverse Similar to obverse of HP-C085, but no H on
exergue line.
Reverse Similar to reverse of HP-C090, but has a dash
below T of Sᵀ.
Rim Plain.

R *Bell et al 5172/ CP6* PC

HP-C130   J. Casson, Woolwich
by R. Heaton & Sons   Ae 22 mm

Obverse Similar to obverse of HP-C085, but different people
in the grounds.

Reverse Similar to reverse of HP-C125.
Rim Plain.

| S | *Bell et al* 5174/CP7 | PC |

HP-C135 Bond & Co, Devonport
by R. Heaton & Sons   Ae 22 mm

Obverse View of the Crystal Palace with people in the grounds, flags upon each storey. *Inscription above:* EXHIBITION PALACE which starts above roof level. *In exergue:* LONDON / 1851.
Reverse *Five line inscription:* BOUGHT AT THE WEST OF ENGLAND / BOND & Cᵒ / 78. FORE Sᵀ / DEVONPORT / TEA MART.
Rim Beaded.

| R | *Bell et al* 1550/CP8, *Sabo* 3 | PC |

HP-C140 John Bellamy, Gloucester
by R. Heaton & Sons   Ae 22 mm

Obverse Similar to obverse of HP-C135, but different people.
Reverse *Five line inscription:* JOHN BELLAMY / FAMILY GROCER / TEA & COFFEE DEALER / 3 & 4. WESTGATE Sᵀ / GLOUCESTER.
Rim Beaded.

| R | *Bell et al* 1640/CP9 | PC |

HP-C145 T. Cordeux, Bristol
by R. Heaton & Sons   Ae 22 mm

Obverse Similar to obverse of HP-C140.
Reverse *Five line inscription:* T. CORDEUX / TEA COFFEE & / SPICE MERCHANT / 1. Sᵀ JAMES'S BARTON / BRISTOL.
Rim Beaded.

| R | *Bell et al* 1240/CP9, *Sabo* 6 | PC |

HP-C150 J. Healey, Bolton
by R. Heaton & Sons   Ae 22 mm

Obverse Similar to obverse of HP-C140.
Reverse *Six line inscription:* J. HEALEY / TEA DEALER / & / GROCER / DEANSGATE / BOLTON.
Rim Beaded.

| R | *Batty* 113, *Bell et al* 1120/CP9, *Sabo* 9 | PC |

HP-C155 Scarr Brothers, Limerick
by R. Heaton & Sons   Ae 22 mm

Obverse Similar to obverse of HP-C140.
Reverse *Five line inscription:* SCARR. BROTHERS / TEA MEN / 15 / PATRICK STREET / LIMERICK.
Rim Beaded.

| RR | *Batty* 1551a, *Bell et al* 6580/CP9, *Sabo* 17 | PC |

HP-C160   J. Schlesinger & Co, London
by R. Heaton & Sons   Ae 22 mm

Obverse   Similar to obverse of HP-C140.
Reverse   *Five line inscription:* J. SCHLESINGER & Cᵒ / 8 / OLD JEWRY / PATENTEES / LONDON.
Rim   Beaded.

S   *Batty 480, Bell et al 2770/CP9, Sabo 18*   PC

This firm exhibited its banknote printing machinery at the Great Exhibition.

HP-C165   D. Gowans & Co, New Orleans
by T. Pope & Co   Aes 22 mm

Obverse   View of the Crystal Palace with people in the grounds, flags upon the roof and transept. *Inscription above:* EXHIBITION PALACE which starts above roof level. *In exergue:* LONDON / 1851 *Signed* POPE BIRM.
Reverse   *Five line inscription:* D. GOWANS & Co / CONFECTIONERS / 97 / CANAL Sᵀ / NEW ORLEANS.
Rim   Plain.

RRR   *Bell et al - /CP15, Rulau p.31 (ill.), Sabo 29 (ill.)*

Gowans imported goods from the United Kingdom, so it is thought this token was struck to reflect that connection.

HP-C170   E. & D. Kinsey, Cincinnati
by ?   Aes 22 mm

Obverse   View of the Crystal Palace with people in the grounds, flags upon the roof and transept. *Inscription above:* EXHIBITION PALACE which starts at roof level. *In exergue:* LONDON / 1851.
Reverse   *Six line inscription:* E & D KINSEY / SILVER / WARE / MANUFACTURERS / 5TH Sᵀ / CINCINNATI.
Rim   Plain.

RRR   *Bell et al - / CP17, Sabo 27 (ill.)*

Edward and David Kinsey emigrated to the United States of America from North Wales. They started their silverware business about 1837, but dissolved the partnership in 1862, with each going into business on his own account.

HP-C175   J. Knight, Bath
by R. Heaton & Sons   Br 22 mm

Obverse   View of the Crystal Palace with people in the grounds, flags upon the roof and transept. *Inscription above:* THE CRYSTAL PALACE. *In exergue:* 1851.
Reverse   *Four line inscription:* J. KNIGHT / CRYSTAL / PALACE / BATH.
Rim   Beaded.

RR   *Bell et al - /CP11, Minnet et al 36 (ill.)*   PC

HP-C180   William MᶜCoombe, Bath
by R. Heaton & Sons   Br 22 mm

Obverse   Similar to obverse of HP-C175.
Reverse   *Four line inscription:* W. Mᶜ COOMBE / CRYSTAL / PALACE / BATH.
Rim   Beaded.

RR   *Bell et al - /CP11, Minnet et al 36a (ill.)*   PC

HP-C185   T. & F. Andrews, Wolverhampton
by R. Heaton & Sons   Ae 30 mm

Obverse   View of the Crystal Palace with people in the grounds, flags upon the roof only. *Inscription above:* THE CRYSTAL PALACE *In exergue:* FOR THE / WORLD'S SHOW / IN / LONDON / 1851 *Signed* HEATON. BIRM.
Reverse   *Five line inscription:* T & F ANDREWS / SILKS SHAWLS / CARPETS WOOLEENS / 44 & 45 DUDLEY Sᵀ / WOLVERHAMPTON.
Rim   Plain.

RRR   *Gunstone 120 (ill.)*   PC

Description obtained from Gunstone, because the author has not seen a specimen.

HP-C190 Baker's, Birmingham
by R. Heaton & Sons   Ae 30 mm

Obverse Similar to obverse of HP-C185.
Reverse Top hat surrounded by a *six line inscription:*
BAKER'S / CELEBRATED / ESTAB^D A. D.1828 / MART /
94 SNOW HILL / BIRMINGHAM.
Rim Plain.

R *Davis 832* **PC**

HP-C195 Edwards Flint & Co, London
by R. Heaton & Sons   Wm 30 mm

Obverse Similar to obverse of HP-C185.
Reverse *Six line inscription:* EDWARDS FLINT & Co /
GRAFTON / HOUSE / SOHO / SQUARE / SILK
MERCERS LINEN DRAPERS & c.
Rim Plain.

RR *Gunstone 109 (ill.)* **PC**

HP-C200 Everett's, London
by R. Heaton & Sons   Wm 30 mm

Obverse Similar to obverse of HP-C185.
Reverse Seven line inscription: SECT^N 16. CENTRAL
AVENUE OF THE / EVERETT'S / BLACKING / 51 /
FETTER LANE / LONDON / GREAT EXHIBITION.
Rim Plain.

R *Gunstone 110, Sabo 39* **PC**

HP-C205 Hamilton & Chapin, Springfield
by R. Heaton & Sons   Wm 30 mm

Obverse Similar to obverse of HP-C185.
Reverse *Eight line inscription:* HAMILTON & CHAPIN /
IMPORTERS & DEALERS / IN / CHINA GLASS
CROCKERY / AND / SOLAR LAMPS / SPRINGFIELD.
MASS.
Rim Plain.

RRR *Rulau-Massachusetts 526* **PC**

HP-C210 Macartney, Belfast
by R. Heaton & Sons   Wm 30 mm

Obverse Similar to obverse of HP-C185.
Reverse *Seven line inscription:* MACARTNEY /
OPTICIAN / JEWELLER / AND / WATCH MAKER / 6.
DONEGALL PLACE / BELFAST.
Rim Plain.

RR *Seaby-AN: B39* **PC**

HP-C215   John G. McGee & Co, Belfast
by R. Heaton & Sons   Wm 30 mm

Obverse   Similar to obverse of HP-C185.
Reverse   *Six line inscription:* JOHN. G. McGEE & Co /
CLOTHIERS / AND / HATTERS / PANTECHNETHECA /
BELFAST.
Rim   Plain.

RRR   *unrecorded*   PC

This firm won a prize medal at the Great Exhibition for its
embroidered waistcoats made from a design by J.B. Wilkinson
of the Belfast School of Design. Illustration courtesy of Howard
and Frances Simmons. The author has not seen a better
specimen.

HP-C220   Henry Moss, Lincoln
by R. Heaton & Sons   Wm 30 mm

Obverse   Similar to obverse of HP-C185.
Reverse   *Six line inscription:* CITY DRAPERY &
CLOTHING ESTABLISHMENT / HENRY MOSS /
MERCER / MILLINER / &c / LINCOLN.
Rim   Plain.

RRR   *Gunstone* 96 (ill.)   LM

Description obtained from Gunstone, because the author has
not seen a specimen.

HP-C225   Murray Greene & Lloyd, Belfast
by R. Heaton & Sons   Wm 30 mm

Obverse   Similar to obverse of HP-C185.
Reverse   *Seven line inscription:* PRESENTED / BY /
MURRAY GREENE / AND / LLOYD / 13. DONEGALL
PLACE / BELFAST.
Rim   Plain.

RRR   *Gunstone* 121 (ill.), *Seaby*-AN:B 53

Description obtained from Gunstone, because the author has
not seen a specimen.

HP-C230   Phillips, Nottingham
by R. Heaton & Sons   Ae Wm 30 mm

Obverse   Similar to obverse of HP-C185.
Reverse   *Five line inscription:* A SINGLE HAT AT THE
WHOLESALE PRICE / PHILLIPS / ROYAL HAT
DEPOT / HIGH STREET / NOTTINGHAM.
Rim   Plain.

Ae R, Wm RRR   *Gunstone* 116, *Sabo* 33   PC

HP-C235   E^D Smith, Newark
by R. Heaton & Sons   Ae 30 mm

Obverse   Similar to obverse of HP-C185.
Reverse   *Six line inscription:* PRESENTED / BY / E^D
SMITH / FAMILY GROCER / BRIDGE S^T / NEWARK.
Rim   Plain.

RRR   *Gunstone* 115 (ill.)

Description obtained from Gunstone, because the author has
not seen a specimen.

HP-C240   T. Wood, London
by R. Heaton & Sons   Ae 30 mm

Obverse   Similar to obverse of HP-C185.
Reverse   *Seven line inscription:* ADDRESS COINS / SOLD
BY / T. WOOD / DRAPERS STATIONER / 24 MILK S^T /
CHEAPSIDE / LONDON.
Rim   Plain.

RRR   *Gunstone* 113 (ill.)

Description obtained from Gunstone, because the author has
not seen a specimen.

HP-C245   Hunt & Co, Cheltenham
by R. Heaton & Sons   Ae 28 mm

Obverse   View of the Crystal Palace with people in the grounds, flags upon each storey. *Inscription above:* THE CRYSTAL PALACE *In exergue:* FOR THE / WORLDS SHOW / IN / LONDON / 1851.
Reverse   *Seven line inscription:* EIGHT OF THESE WILL BUY / AN OZ OF / TEA / AT / HUNT & C^{os} / 124 HIGH S^{T} / CHELTENHAM.
Rim   Plain.

RRR   *Gunstone 105*   PC

HP-C250   T. Probert, Newcastle
by R. Heaton & Sons   Ae 28 mm

Obverse   Similar to obverse of HP-C245.
Reverse   *Five line inscription:* THE NEW TEA WAREHOUSE / T. PROBERT / 21. SANDHILL / NEWCASTLE / BRITISH WINES.
Rim   Plain.

RRR   *Gunstone 105, Sabo 32*   PC

HP-C255   C.G. Bower's, Macclesfield
by R. Heaton & Sons   Ae 28 mm

Obverse   Similar to obverse of HP-C245.
Reverse   *Seven line inscription:* EIGHT OF THESE WILL BUY / AN OZ OF / TEA / AT / C.G. BOWER'S / 29 MILL S^{T} / MACCLESFIELD.
Rim   Plain.

RRR   *unrecorded*   PC

HP-C260   M. Lyons, Birmingham
by R. Heaton & Sons   Br 34 mm

Obverse   View of the Crystal Palace. *Inscription above:* THE CRYSTAL PALACE / DESIGNED BY / MR PAXTON. *In exergue:* FOR THE GREAT / EXHIBITION / IN LONDON OF / 1851 *Signed* HEATON BIRM.
Reverse   *Eight line inscription:* M. LYONS / EXHIBITOR / INVENTOR & PATENTEE / OF / BRIGHT / ELECTRO PLATING / 143 SUFFOLK S^{T} / BIRMINGHAM.
Rim   Plain.

S   *Davis 738*   PC

Electro-plating methods in use prior to 1847 could only produce a matt or a frosted finish, but, by introducing bisulphuret of carbon, Mr Lyons discovered that a shiny finish was attainable. He exhibited at the Great Exhibition, and illustrated his new technique by striking these tokens in both a matt and a bright finish.

HP-C265   M. Lyons, Birmingham
by R. Heaton & Sons   Ae 34 mm

Obverse Similar to obverse of HP-C260, but has people along the front and down the side of the building.
Reverse Similar to reverse of HP-C260.
Rim Plain.

R *Davis* 738   PC

HP-C270   Edmund Leach & Sons, Rochdale
by ?   Ae 26 mm

Obverse View of the Crystal Palace, no trees. *Inscription above:* THE CRYSTAL PALACE LONDON. 1851. *In exergue:* PROPOSED BY / PRINCE ALBERT.
Reverse *Four line inscription:* EDMUND LEACH & SONS / ONE PINT / OF BEER / ROCHDALE.
Rim Plain obverse, beaded reverse.

RRR *Batty* 746a, *Sabo* 40   PC

Courtesy of John R.P. King.

HP-C275   John Rigg, Liverpool
by ?   Br 28 mm

Obverse Similar to reverse of HP-B390.
Reverse *Five line inscription:* JOHN RIGG / 268 MILL STREET / TOXTETH PARK / LIVERPOOL / STAG & HOUNDS VAULTS.
Rim Plain.
Edge Milled.

RRR *Todd* 63   LV

Description obtained from Todd, because the author has not seen a specimen.

HP-C280   Thomas May, Wavertree
by ? (possibly T. Pope)   Br 32 mm

Obverse View of the Crystal Palace. *Inscription above:* THE CRYSTAL PALACE / IN LONDON / A.D. 1851. *In exergue:* TOTAL AREA OF SPACE / 855,360 CUBIC FT. OR / NEARLY 21 ACRES / HEIGHT OF TRANSEPT 108 FT.
Reverse *Three line inscription:* THOMAS MAY / ✱ LAMB INN ✱ / WAVERTREE.
Rim Beaded.
Edge Milled.

RRR *Todd* 36   LV PC

HP-C285   Henry Owen, Liverpool
by ?   Br 32 mm

Obverse Similar to obverse of HP-C280.
Reverse *Five line inscription:* HENRY OWEN / CROWN / & SCEPTRE / VAULTS / 54 CROWN ST L'POOL.
Rim Beaded.
Edge Milled.

RRR *Todd* 15 (rev. ill.)   LV

Description obtained from Todd, because the author has not seen a specimen.

HP-C290   Aranzabe Labayen YC, Matanzas
by P & C (? T. Pope)   Br 32 mm

Obverse Similar to obverse of HP-C280.

Reverse Agricultural tools and a musket. *Two line inscription around:* FERRETERIA DE ARANZABE LABAYEN Y C. / MATANZAS *Signed* P & C.
Rim Beaded.
Edge Milled.

RRR	*unrecorded*	PC

Courtesy of Jim Allen. The author has not seen a better specimen.

HP-C295   S. Jacobs, Melbourne
by T. Pope & Co   Br 32 mm

Obverse Similar to obverse of HP-C280, but, in the exergue, OR is missing from the end of the second line. *Signed* POPE & Co BIRM.
Reverse *Five line inscription:* S. JACOBS / VICTORIA / PROMENADE / BAZAAR / COLLINS S^T
Rim Beaded.
Edge Milled.

RRR	*unrecorded*	PC

S. Jacobs was in business as a draper. His advertisement in the *Melbourne Argus* mentioned that these medals would be given to customers who purchased goods from him. The illustration is from a pencil rubbing courtesy of Dr William Mira.

HP-C300   Tilly, Haynes & Co, Springfield
by ?   Ae Wm 27 mm

Obverse Similar to obverse of HP-B070.
Reverse *Nine line inscription:* TILLEY, HAYNES & Co /

GREAT / EXHIBITION OF / CLOTHING AND RICH / FURNISHING GOODS / No. 18. 20. 22. 24. 26. MAIN ST / OAK HALL ESTABLISHMENT / SPRINGFIELD / MASS.
Rim Plain.

RRR	*Rulau*-Massachusetts 129, *Sabo* 30

This token may have been struck by Allen & Moore.

HP-C305   Allan, Son & Co, London
by ?   Wm 39 mm

Obverse View of the Crystal Palace, no trees. *Inscription above.* THE GREAT PALACE FOR THE EXHIBITION OF THE / INDUSTRY OF ALL NATIONS. 1851. *In exergue:* LENGTH 1848 F^T WIDTH 456 F^T / HEIGHT 64 F^T / DESIGNED BY / JOSEPH PAXTON ESQ. F.R.S.
Reverse *Four line inscription:* ❧ ALLAN, SON & Co / 69 TO 71 / S^T PAULS / LONDON ❧
Rim Plain.

RR	*unrecorded*	PC

HP-C310   E. Grove, Lambeth
by Allen & Moore   Wm 39 mm

Obverse Similar to reverse of HP-B090.
Reverse View of Lambeth House. *Inscription above:* E. GROVE / LAMBETH HOUSE. *Inscription down L/H side:* 39. 40 & 41 LOWER MARSH / LAMBETH. *Inscription*

down R /H side: AND 113 & 115 EDGWARE / ROAD. *In exergue:* OUTFITTER TO ALL / NATIONS
Rim Plain.

RRRR *unrecorded* PC

HP-C315 Maison Corr-Vander Maeren, Brussels
by Allen & Moore   Wm 51 mm

Obverse Similar to reverse of HP-B120.
Reverse *Nine line inscription:* MAISON CORR-VANDER MAEREN & CIE / DEPOT ANGLAIS / POUR LA VENTE DES ARTICLES / DE BIRMINGHAM / & SHEFFIELD / 14 LONGUE RUE DE L'ECUYER / A / BRUXELLES / ETABLIE DEPUIS 1824.
Rim Plain obverse, toothed reverse.

RR *Sabo 47* BM CP PC

HP-C320 Price's, London
by T. Ottley   Wm 54 mm

Obverse Similar to reverse of HP-B260.
Reverse *Seven line inscription:* PRICE'S / HOPE DINING ROOMS / 8, BUCKLERSBURY, / NEAR THE MANSION HOUSE / THE CHEAPEST / & BEST HOUSE / IN LONDON.
Rim Plain.

RRRR *unrecorded* PC

The author has not seen a better specimen.

HP-C325 Brewster & Co, East Dereham
by ?   Ae 22 mm

Obverse   View of the Crystal Palace. *Inscription above:* MAY 1ST *In exergue:* 1851.
Reverse   Four line inscription: TEA DEALERS COFFEE ROASTERS & SPICE MERCHANTS / BREWSTER & Cº / MARKET PLACE / E. DEREHAM
Rim   Plain.

| R | *Batty 580, Bell et al 1540/CP14, Sabo* 4 | PC |

HP-C330   W.J. Taylor, London
by ?   Wm 26 mm

Obverse   Screw press. *Inscription around the border:* CRYSTAL PALACE PRESS *Signed* W.J. TAYLOR MEDALLIST.
Reverse   Five line inscription within a floral wreath: MADE / IN THE / CRYSTAL / PALACE / W. J. TAYLOR MEDAL PRESS.
Rim   Plain.

| RRR | *unrecorded*   PC |

Courtesy of Jim Allen.

HP-C335   W.J. Taylor, London
by ?   Ae 22 mm

Obverse   Coining press. *Inscription around:* MEDALS, COINS & TRADESMENS TOKENS STRUCK.
Reverse   Line inscription: W. J. TAYLOR MEDALLIST BY APPOINTMENT TO THE GREAT EXHIBITION OF INDUSTRY OF ALL NATIONS 1851. 33 LITTLE QUEEN ST HOLBORN.

| RRR | *Batty* 1430a |

Description obtained from Batty, because the author has not seen a specimen.

HP-C340   D. Uhlhorn, Cologne
by ?   Ae Aeg Aes 37 mm

Obverse   Seven line inscription within a wreath of oak: EXHIBITION / OF THE / INDUSTRY / OF ALL / NATIONS / 1851 / LONDON.
Reverse   A Coining press. *Inscription beneath:* NEAR COLOGNE ON / THE RHINE. *Inscription around the border:* COINING PRESS. INVENTED. 1817. AND MADE BY D. UHLHORN AT GREVENBROICH.
Rim   Toothed.
Edge   Inscribed: MAY INDUSTRY BE CROWNED WITH SUCCESS.

| RRR | *Brown 2471, Eimer (I) 1464, Sabo* 42 | AM BM PC |

This firm was awarded a Council medal at the Great Exhibition for its coining press.

HP-C345   F.C. Key & Sons, Philadelphia
by ?   Wm 18 mm

Obverse   Conjoined heads of Queen Victoria and Prince Albert left, dolphins below. *Inscription around:* VICTORIA D. G. BRIT. REG. F. D. ALBERTUS PRINCEPS CONJUX. *In exergue:* MDCCCLI.
Reverse   KEY surrounded by a ring of stars.

| RRR | *Sabo* 31 |

Description obtained from Sabo, because the author has not seen a specimen.

D. Associated Pieces

Recorded in this section are various associated pieces issued by other authorities or persons who were not necessarily involved with the Great Exhibition. The entries are in no particular order.

HP-D001 Albert Presentation medal
by W. Wyon   Av 56 mm

Obverse   Bare head of Prince Albert right. *Inscription around the border:* ALBERTUS PRINCEPS VICTORIAE REGINAE CONJUX. / 1845. *Signed* W.WYON. R:A:
Reverse   St George and the dragon. Gothic style inscription around the border: TREU UND FEST.
Rim   Plain.
Edge   Inscribed with the name of the recipient.

RRRR   *Brown* 2204 (ill.), *Eimer (I)* 1398 (ill.)   AM BM RC RM

Prince Albert, as President of the Royal Commission, presented a gold medal to the following Great Exhibition officials: Joint Secretaries to the Royal Commission, J. Scott Russell Esq. F.R.S. and Sir Stafford Henry Northcote Bart. C.B.; Acting Secretary to the Royal Commission, Edgar A. Bowring; Executive Committee, Lt Col Reid R.E. C.B. F.R.S. (Chairman), Henry Cole Esq. C.B., Charles Wentworth Dilke Esq., Francis Fuller Esq., George Drew Esq., Matthew Digby Wyatt Esq. (Secretary); Special Commissioners to communicate with Local Committees, Dr Lyon Playfair C.B. F.R.S. and Lt Col J.A. Lloyd F.R.S. The medals were unavoidably delayed due to the illness of William Wyon, and were not presented until the early months of 1852. The letter from General Charles Grey, Prince Albert's personal Secretary, to Francis Fuller apologising for this delay reads:

> Windsor Castle
> October 15, 1851.
> My dear Sir,
> The Prince was anxious on this, the closing day of the Exhibition, to have presented you with a medal, in remembrance of the active part taken by you during the early discussions on the subject, and of your zealous exertions in the cause while success was yet doubtful; and he has commanded me to express his regret that the illness of Mr. Wyon, which has delayed the completion of the medal, obliges him to postpone doing so at the moment.
>
> His Royal Highness is, however, unwilling that any delay should occur in assuring you of his sense of your services; and it gives me particular pleasure, having in the earlier steps of the Exhibition been so constantly in communication with you, that his Royal Highness should have directed me to convey this assurance to you.
>
> Believe me, my dear Sir, yours very truly,
> C. GREY.

Also, see *Brown* 2204 for details of a similar letter sent to Charles Wentworth Dilke. The medal presented to Dilke appeared on the market in May 1983, when it was offered for sale by Messrs B.A. Seaby in their *Coin & Medal Bulletin*.

HP-D005 City of London Entertainment
by W. Wyon   Ar 36 mm

Obverse Diademed head of Queen Victoria left. *Inscription around the border:* VICTORIA REGINA *Signed* W. WYON RA.

Reverse *Seven line inscription:* EXHIBITION OF THE WORKS OF INDUSTRY OF ALL NATIONS / ROYAL / ENTERTAINMENT / AT / GUILDHALL / 9ᵀᴴ JULY / 1851.

Rim Plain.

Edge Inscribed with the name of the recipient.

RRRR	*Davis et al 70/184, Eimer (I) 1465*	PC

The City of London Court of Common Council agreed to spend £5,250 on a suitable banquet to celebrate the success of the Great Exhibition. Among the 2,100 invited guests were Royal and foreign Commissioners, British and foreign jurors, Superintendents of Classes, and successful exhibitors. It was originally planned to hold the reception on 2 July, but it had to be hastily re-arranged when it was discovered that it would have coincided with the anniversary of the death of Sir Robert Peel.

HP-D010   Canadian Prize
by B. Wyon   Ae Aes 37 mm

Obverse Crowned arms within an open wreath. *Inscription above:* CANADIAN PRIZE *Inscription below:* GREAT EXHIBITION 1851.

Reverse A beaver within a laurel wreath. *Inscription around the border:* THE EARL OF ELGIN AND KINCARDINE K.T. *Signed* B. WYON. SC.

Rim Plain.

RRR	*unrecorded*	PC

James Bruce, Earl of Elgin and Kincardine (1811–1863) was Governor-General of Canada from 1846–1854. At the Great Exhibition he is not listed as a prize winner under his title or his real name, so the medal does not seem to have been struck to commemorate his own success. Possibly, as Governor-General he had it struck for presentation to Canadian prize winners. The author would be pleased to hear from any reader who knows the history of this piece.

HP-D015   Universal   Society   for   the   Encouragement of Arts & Industry
by Desaide Roquelay   Ae 63 mm

Obverse Londinia with torch and laurel wreaths standing amid symbols of art and industry. St Paul's cathedral, Mansion House, and Crystal Palace in the background, royal arms with supporters below. *Signed* DESAIDE ROQUELAY.

Reverse Radiate star within a wreath of oak and laurel. *Inscription around the border:* THE UNIVERSAL SOCIETY FOR THE ENCOURAGEMENT OF ARTS AND INDUSTRY. FOUNDED IN LONDON. A.D. 1851 ✿

Rim Plain.

RRR	*unrecorded*	PC

HP-D018   International Exhibition
by ?   Aeg 59 mm

Obverse   Similar to obverse of HP-D015 but inscribed:
INTERNATIONAL EXHIBITION / LONDON / 1911
Reverse   A naked female with flowing hair on the beach with
five children.
Rim   Plain.

RRR   *unrecorded*   PC

HP-D020   Munich Crystal Palace 1855
by L.C. Lauer   Ae 22 mm

Obverse   Similar to reverse of HP-B240.

Reverse   View of Munich Crystal Palace. *Inscription above:*
MUSIKFEST IM GLASPALASTE / ZU / MUNCHEN. *In
exergue:* ABGEHALTEN / D. 4. U. 5. OCTBR. / 1855.
Rim   Plain.

RRR   *unrecorded*   PC

HP-D025   Jeton
by L.C. Lauer   Ae 22 mm

Obverse   Similar to reverse of HP-B240.
Reverse   *Inscription within a laurel wreath:* JETON.
Rim   Plain.

RRR   *Bell et al - /CP 12*   PC

Courtesy of Jim Sweeny. Possibly a gaming counter.

HP-D030   Spiel-Pfennig
by L.C. Lauer   Aeg 22 mm

Obverse   Similar to reverse of HP-B240.
Reverse   *Two line inscription within a wreath of laurel and oak:*
SPIEL - / PFENNIG.
Rim   Plain.

RRR   *Bell et al - /CP 12*   PC

Courtesy of Jim Sweeny. A gaming counter.

HP-D035 Aucher Brothers, Paris
by Roddiet Plichon   Aeg 48 mm

Obverse   Five line inscription within a wreath of oak and laurel:
MEDAILLE / D'OR / A / AUCHER / FRERES *Signed*
RODDIET — PLICHON. *Inscription around the border:* 14
MEDAILLES — EXPOSITIONS UNIV^{lle} DE
LONDRES — NATIONALES / PARIS.
Reverse   Blank.
Rim   Plain.

RRR   *unrecorded*   PC

At the Great Exhibition Aucher & Son were awarded an
honourable mention for their two upright pianos. As this piece
is named Aucher Brothers, it was possibly not produced until
after the retirement of the father, and following the introduction
of another brother into the business. The illustration is from a
pencil rubbing courtesy of Dr Bill Mira.

HP-D040 Melbourne Exhibition 1854
by W.J. Taylor   Ae 29 mm

Obverse   Seated kangaroo. *Inscription above:*
MELBOURNE. *In exergue:* W. J. TAYLOR. MEDALLIST /
TO THE GREAT / EXHIBITION / 1851.
Reverse   Seated female holding an olive branch and a staff.
Inscription above: AUSTRALIA.
Rim   Beaded.

RR   *Sabo* 38   PC

In 1853 there was a severe shortage of gold coinage in Australia
and W.J. Taylor thought he would 'get-rich-quick' by buying
raw gold direct from the Australian gold mines with the object
of turning it into coinage for circulation. Unfortunately for him,
it was not to be because, when he arrived at Hobsons Bay in
October 1853, he found to his dismay that there wasn't a crane
strong enough to unload his coining press. Therefore, it had to
be dismantled aboard ship and carried ashore piece by piece.
This unforeseen delay ruined his opportunity, for during the
time it took to unload and rebuild the press, a large
consignment of British sovereigns arrived in Melbourne. To
recoup some of his losses, Taylor produced a number of coinage
dies, also this piece and HP-D045 to commemorate the 1854
Melbourne Exhibition.

HP-D045 Melbourne Exhibition 1854
by W.J. Taylor   Ae 29 mm

Obverse   Similar to obverse of HP-D040.
Reverse   Similar to reverse of HP-D040, but the inscription
reads: UNITED STATES
Rim   Beaded.

RR   *Bell* p.236 (ill.)

The inscription 'United States' refers to the concept of
Federation of the Australian States which did not come about
until 1900. See note to HP-D040.

HP-D050 Melbourne Exhibition 1880
by Evan Jones   Ae 22 mm

Obverse   Draped bust of Prince Albert right. *Inscription*
above: ALBERT THE GOOD. *Inscription below:* 1851.
Reverse   View of the exhibition building. *Inscription above:*
MELBOURNE *In exergue:* 1880 / EXHIBITION.

Rim Plain.

RR *Carlisle* 1880/2 (ill.) PC

Evan Jones struck half a dozen similar medalets to commemorate the Sydney Exhibition of 1879.

HP-D055 Chance's Smethwick Schools
by HT   Ae 55 mm

Obverse Draped bust right. *Inscription around the border:* JAMES. T. CHANCE. MA. JP. DL. / MDCCCLXXXXV. *Signed* H T.
Reverse *Eleven line inscription:* A.D.1895. / THE 'OLD BOYS' OF / CHANCE'S SMETHWICK SCHOOLS / TO / JAMES. T. CHANCE ESQUIRE / IN GRATEFUL COMMEMORATION OF / THE SCHOOLS JUBILEE / AND / OF THE OPENING OF THE PARK / GENEROUSLY GIVEN BY HIM / TO THE DISTRICT.
Rim Plain.

RR *unrecorded* PC

Sir James Timmins Chance (1814–1902), was a partner in the firm of Chance Brothers, the glassmakers who produced the glass to construct the Crystal Palaces at Hyde Park and Sydenham. See *New Crystal Palace Matters* No. 7, for an article about the glass provided.

HP-D060 John Green Waller
by ?   Ae 52 x 43 mm

Obverse Draped bust right. *Inscription around the border:* JOHN GREEN WALLER, F.S.A., B. SEP. 1813, D. OCT. 1905 *Signed* W. WALLER, M.I.M.E.
Reverse *Nineteen line inscription:* 1836 / FROST'S MEDALLIST / & LIFE STUDENT / ROYAL ACADEMY. / 1843 / PREMIUM FOR CARTOON / WESTMINSTER HALL / 1851 / AWARDED (WITH W. A. WALLER) / DIPLOMA & MEDAL / AT / THE GREAT EXHIBITION. / 1886 / ELECTED F.S.A. / 1896 / PRESIDENT OF / QUEKETT / CLUB / & c., & c.
Rim Plain.

RR *unrecorded* PC

The engineering firm of W. Waller, Vauxhall Walk, London S.E. was established in 1835, and specialised in the supply of tools, metal work, machines and presses. The firm was awarded a prize medal in class XXII for its exhibits of monumental brass.

HP-D065   International Exhibition of Modern Arts & Industry
by Revillon   Aeg 59 mm

The obverse design is a modification of HP-D015. With the medal in its fitted case is a 57 mm ornate gilt and enamelled cruciform attached to a gilt crown-shaped suspender on a blue and red ribbon.

HP-D070   International General Trade & Modern Homes Exhibition
by Revillon   Aeg 59 mm

Obverse   Similar to obverse of HP-D065.
Reverse   Similar to reverse of HP-D065.
Rim   Plain.

RRR   *unrecorded*   **PC**

Obverse   Londinia with torch and laurel wreaths standing amid symbols of art and industry. St Paul's Cathedral, Mansion House, and Crystal Palace, in the background. *Inscription above:* INTERNATIONAL EXHIBITION / LONDON. *Inscription on a terrestrial globe:* MODERN ARTS / AND / INDUSTRY.
Reverse   Fame above Art and Industry seated on panel *Inscription down L / H side:* MODERN ARTS. *Inscription down R / H side:* AND INDUSTRY *Signed* REVILLON
Rim   Plain

RRR   *unrecorded*   **PC**

The obverse design is a modification of HP-D015. With the medal in its fitted case is a 55 mm ornate gilt and enamelled cruciform attached to a gilt crown-shaped suspender on a blue and red ribbon.

HP-D075   Festival of Britain
by P. Vincze   Av Ar Ae 39 mm

Obverse   View of the Crystal Palace. *In exergue:* CRYSTAL PALACE / 1851 / THE GREAT EXHIBITION *Signed* P. VINCZE.
Reverse   Man and a child looking across the river Thames at the 1951 Festival buildings, the dome of discovery and the skyline can be seen in the distance. *Inscription above:* FESTIVAL OF BRITAIN. *In exergue:* 1951 *Signed* P. VINCZE.
Rim   Plain.

Av RRR, Ar RR, Ae R   *Brown* 4427   PC

Originally the Festival of Britain was intended to be a celebration in recognition of the centenary of the Great Exhibition. But its character was changed when the organisers decided it ought to become a tonic for a nation which was

reeling from the effects of the war and still suffering from extensive rationing. Consequently, it was not until the very last moment that they realised they had completely overlooked 1851. As, by that time, there was no money left in the budget, all they could afford to erect was a shabby little structure at the foot of the Shot Tower which was named the Centenary Pavilion. Fortunately, the designers of the Battersea Pleasure Gardens remembered the occasion by erecting a bamboo representation of the Crystal Palace at the end of the Grand Vista, which was floodlit and made a perfect backdrop for the fireworks displays. To the northwest of the vista the bar of the Vauxhall Beer Garden was also erected in the shape of the Crystal Palace.

HP-D080   Festival of Britain
by R. Wheen   Soap 70 mm

Obverse   View of the Crystal Palace. *Inscription around the border:* THE GREAT EXHIBITION / 1851.
Reverse   1951 Festival of Britain symbol. *Inscription around the border:* FESTIVAL OF BRITAIN *Signed* WHEEN LONDON.
Rim   Toothed.

R	unrecorded	PC

This unusual souvenir of the festival is usually found in a either a blue, or red, card box with the festival symbol on the lid. *Inscription inside the lid:* Made in England / by / RICHARD WHEEN & SONS LTD / London S.E. 8 / Makers of fine soaps / since 1769.

HP-D085	**Festival of Britain**	
by ?		Earthenware 130 mm

Obverse   End elevation of the Crystal Palace with trees, people, and a horse-drawn carriage in the foreground, Festival symbol below. *Inscription on lower rim:* THE GREAT EXHIBITION, LONDON 1851.
Reverse   Blank.
Rim   Plain.

RR	unrecorded	PC

These plaques were sold at 5/11d each. The above illustration is reduced in size.

HP-D090	**Printing Plate (obverse only)**	
by ?		Br 53 mm

Obverse   Conjoined heads of Queen Victoria and Prince Albert left, dolphins and trident in the field. *Inscription around the border:* VICTORIA: D: G: BRIT: REG: F: D: ● ALBERTUS ● PRINCEPS ● CONJUX ● / MDCCCLI
Rim   Beaded.

RRRR	unrecorded	PC

Apart from the punctuations, and the absence of the signature, this piece is a replica of HP-A001. It was possibly used for the letter heading or invoices of a firm which won a prize medal at the Great Exhibition.

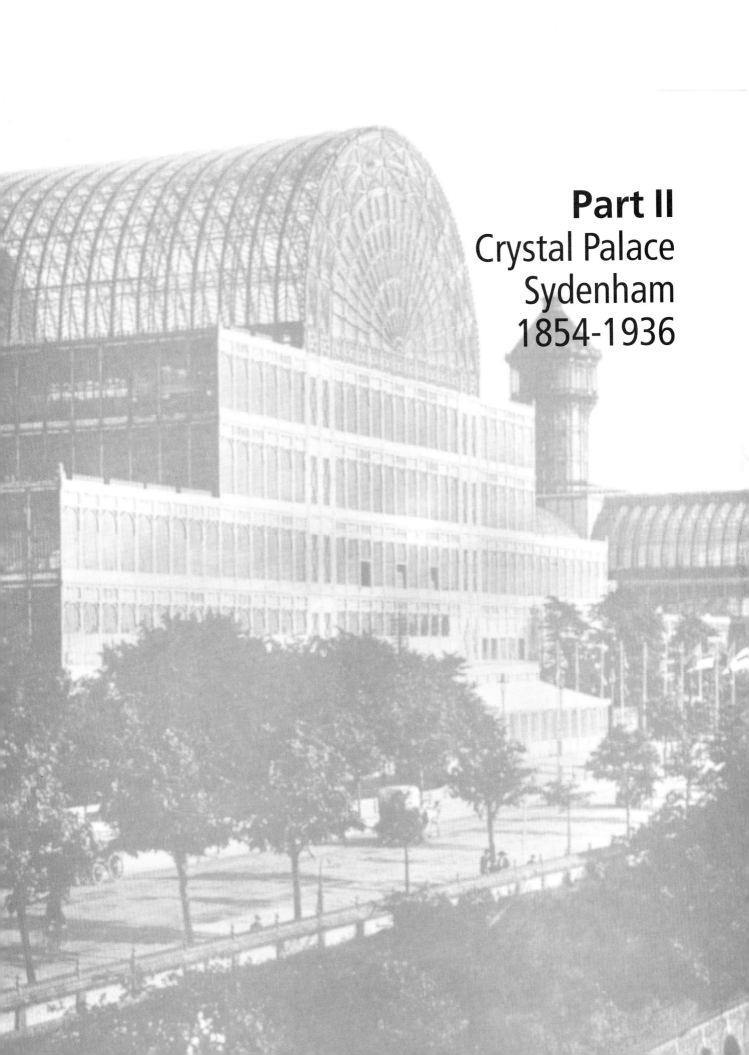

Part II
Crystal Palace
Sydenham
1854-1936

Introduction

When Parliament decreed that the Great Exhibition building had to be dismantled and the site restored to its former state, the question arose, 'what is to become of the Crystal Palace?' Fortunately, Sir Joseph Paxton, (as previously mentioned, he had been knighted on the recommendation of the Royal Commissioners) had already formulated a plan to launch a public company to take over, and rebuild, the Crystal Palace on the southern outskirts of London.

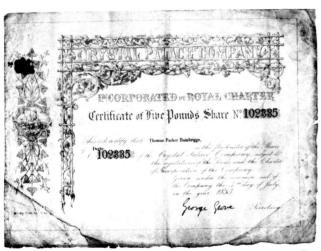

Ordinary Share Certificate, 1853. Reproduced by permission of Eric Price

In May 1852, the Crystal Palace Company was formed. It purchased the Great Exhibition building from the Commissioners for the sum of £70,000, and contracted with Messrs Fox & Henderson to dismantle and re-erect it at Penge Place, a parkland site on the summit of Sydenham Hill; a venue which had been chosen for its panoramic views of Kent and Surrey. On 5 August 1852, a foundation ceremony was held there at which Samuel Laing, Chairman of the Crystal Palace Company, erected the first column of Paxton's second masterpiece.

As forecast and planned by Paxton, dismantling the Hyde Park building was a simple operation; the bolted framework, like meccano, came apart just as easily as it had been put together. Understandably a large proportion of the glass was ruined, so an arrangement was quickly reached with the manufacturers, Chance Brothers of Birmingham, to melt and remake the damaged panes at a reasonable cost.

As there was not, at this time, a railway to the site, (the line was not opened for freight until March 1854, and to passengers, on the day the Palace opened), the task of transporting the unbroken glass, timber, and ironwork to its new home was formidable. A road journey of around twenty miles faced each of the heavily-laden horse drawn wagons, which had to thread their way through crowded London streets, across the river Thames, then negotiate countless hazards before finally reaching Sydenham Hill. This hill, which led up to the vista-giving view mentioned previously, was a real 'horse-killer' due to its long, winding, 1 in 8 gradient, and required the use of extra teams of horses and traction engines to surmount. By using many teams of horses and wagons the transfer progressed at the rate of about one hundred and fifty tons per day; yet still the last wagon load did not depart from Hyde Park until 1 November 1852.

The Italian Terrace c.1860. Reproduced by permission of Eric Price & Melvyn Harrison

Several new features were introduced into the new structure. Since the site was on a slope a basement storey was incorporated. Arched roofs were added, which increased the height by over 40 feet and transformed the new Palace into a five storey building. The addition of transepts at each end meant that the new structure measured 1,608 feet long and 312 feet wide, and the amount of glass used was almost twice that required in 1851.

The South Nave c.1860. Reproduced by permission of Eric Price & Melvyn Harrison

On the outside terraces an unrivalled collection of statuary was built to grace the magnificent ornamental fountains and cascades. Comprising 12,000 jets, these required over 7 million gallons of pressurised water per hour to operate. Sadly the first attempt by Paxton and Charles Wilde to construct twin water towers to provide the head of water needed to drive the system was a dismal failure, involving the Crystal Palace Company in a substantial financial loss, because not until the towers were almost completed was it realised they were unsafe, and would not be able to support the weight of the water. Due to shortage of time and finance, the Crystal Palace Company wanted them to be strengthened, but when Paxton called on Isambard Kingdom Brunel for advice, it was recommended they be completely demolished, re-designed, and re-built on an 11ft thick concrete base. The new water towers, each 284 feet high, had 38ft high water tanks at the top designed to hold 300,000 gallons of water, weighing 3,000 tons, which was to be circulated throughout the system by steam-driven machinery housed below. The towers which had 10 floors, and 400 steps to reach the viewing platform at the top, became a notable feature at either end of the Sydenham Crystal Palace.

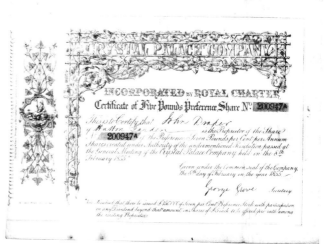

7% Share Certificate, 1855. Reproduced by permission of Eric Price

To landscape the 200 acres of grounds and gardens an enormous number of trees, shrubs and plants had to be purchased, and, since no expense seems to have been spared in this department, or any other for that matter, the total cost of the new project soared to £1,350,000. Not surprisingly, the money had run out before the work was half-finished, but fortunately the first share issue had been well over-subscribed, so there was no difficulty in raising the additional capital required to complete the project.

However, as a result of the spending spree, it took eight years for the Crystal Palace Company to become free of debt. A tragic accident occurred in August 1853, when mobile scaffolding used for erecting the central transept collapsed, killing twelve men and two horses. This misfortune, taken together with all of the other difficulties and setbacks, caused the Grand Opening to be delayed until 10 June 1854. Even at this time, however, there was a great deal of work still to be completed, both inside and outside the building.

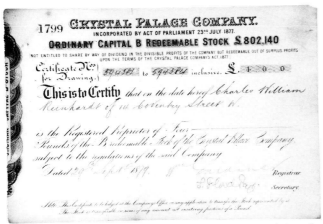

Redeemable Stock Certificate, 1879. Reproduced by permission of Eric Price

Crystal Palace Gentleman's Season Ticket valid to April 1900

The restructured Palace was opened by Her Majesty Queen Victoria at a ceremony attended by more than 40,000 people, comprised only of exhibitors, season ticket holders, and specially invited guests. To commemorate the auspicious occasion, Francis Fuller, Managing Director of the Crystal Palace Company, presented the Queen with a set of three gold medals in a red Morocco case, complete with brass hinges and clasp and inscribed 'C.P.C.' in gilt letters on the lid (see SY-1854/095).

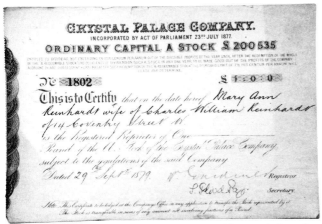

Ordinary Share Certificate, 1879. Reproduced by permission of Eric Price

Admittance to the Palace and Park was initially 1/- from Monday to Thursday; 2/6d on Friday; and 5/- on Saturday. The Palace remained closed all day on Sunday. The cost of a season ticket was set at 2 guineas. When the passenger railway was completed, the price structure was changed to combine the cost of travel and admission. From Monday to Thursday a return ticket, including admission to the Palace, could be obtained from London Bridge railway station at a cost of 1/6d for third class travel, 2/- for second class travel or 2/6d for first class travel. Children under twelve years of age travelled at half price. Season tickets including travel were now available for 4 guineas.

The new Sydenham Palace, unlike the original Hyde Park Palace, was designed, not as an exhibition site, but rather as a place of education and recreation, and, due to its enormous popularity, it was often referred to as the 'People's Palace'. The objects on display embraced a complete historical picture of the art of sculpture and architecture from the earliest known works right up to modern times, by including casts of every celebrated statue in the world, as well as many of the most remarkable monuments. In the sciences; geology, ethnology, zoology and botany received appropriate coverage. Industry was represented by a permanent exhibition in the southern half of the building, though this differed from the Great Exhibition insofar as the spaces were rented by the exhibitor, who was allowed to sell items on display; thereby making this the first large-scale trade fair to be held in the United Kingdom. This trade fair was an immediate success. In the first week the French Muslin Company (which advertised its wares in the *Illustrated London News*) sold seven hundred muslin dresses, Mr Rimmel the perfumer sold eighty pounds worth of his odoriferous compounds, and the Paris Chocolate Company were hardly able to supply the demand for its chocolates, but, by all accounts the rents were enormous because the Crystal Palace Company had publicly announced they intended to raise £150,000 per annum from the rents for exhibition space. In addition to the Picture Gallery, which opened in 1856, the Crystal Palace Company founded a School of Art, Science and Literature; a School of Engineering and a School of Physical Culture.

Pulleyn's weighing chair ticket, 1865.

SIXTH SATURDAY CONCERT.

MONDAY, TUESDAY, WEDNESDAY, THURSDAY,

November 16, 17, 18, 19.

GREAT LONDON

POULTRY, PIGEON,

AND

RABBIT SHOW.

THE LARGEST SHOW EVER HELD, THE ENTRIES NUMBERING NO LESS THAN 4,400.

ADMISSION ONE SHILLING,

OR BY GUINEA SEASON TICKET.

THE

NATIONAL MUSIC MEETINGS

WILL BE HELD

IN THE SUMMER OF 1875.

Competitions for large and small Choral Societies, Church and Chapel Choirs, Military and Brass Bands, and Solo Vocalists.

For Schedules, Lists of Pieces to be prepared, and Entry Forms, apply to the Secretary, Crystal Palace.

Crystal Palace Saturday Concert Programme Announcements, Nov. 1874.

The Palace played host to British and foreign royalty, plus countless VIPs. In addition, exhibitions, concerts, pantomimes, festivals, sporting events etc., were regularly held there. The most famous of these were the Saturday Concerts and the Great Handel Music Festivals, the latter of which were started in 1857 and were held triennially for almost seventy years. The highly popular

weekly firework displays were introduced in 1865 and continued, virtually uninterrupted, (the missing years being those of the First World War), right up to the demise of the Palace by fire in 1936.

ANNOUNCEMENTS.

THE NINTH OF THE SERIES OF

SATURDAY CONCERTS

AND

AFTERNOON PROMENADES

WILL TAKE PLACE ON

SATURDAY, DECEMBER 5TH, 1874,

When, in Memory of the Death of Mozart on Dec. 5th, 1792, the Programme will be chosen mainly from the Works of that great Composer.

VOCALISTS :

SIGNOR URIO.

MR. SANTLEY.

SOLO VIOLIN :

MONSIEUR SAINTON.

The Programme will include the following Compositions of Mozart—

OVERTURE, "FIGARO."

CONCERTO FOR VIOLIN AND ORCHESTRA, IN D (1775).
(First time in this Country.)

SYMPHONY, "JUPITER."

Also, for the first time at these Concerts,

FESTIVAL OVERTURE . . . . . *G. A. Macfarren.*

CONDUCTOR - - MR. MANNS.

Transferable Stalls for the Series of Concerts, TWO GUINEAS.
Numbered Stalls, Half-a-Crown.

Crystal Palace Saturday Concert Programme Announcements, Dec. 1874.

During the early years the Palace was not allowed to open on Sunday, therefore the Crystal Palace Company sustained an immeasurable loss in revenue which, combined with the enormous running costs, meant that the Palace was deprived, even during its heyday, of becoming a really profitable enterprise. As a consequence of this, the Crystal Palace Company was unable to build up the reserves it needed to overcome the hard times it experienced toward the end of the 19th century. At this time a change in public tastes, fuelled by the attraction of new entertainments situated closer to London, caused a dramatic decline in the number of visitors; and inevitably, the fortunes of the Company; causing it to stagger from one financial crisis to another. Eventually, in 1910, the Crystal Palace Company went into liquidation, with the court placing its affairs into the hands of Mr Ernest Husey, who was appointed Receiver and Manager of the Crystal Palace. It was decided that the building and grounds should be put up for auction, and Messrs Knight, Frank & Rutley were appointed as agents for the sale, which was to have taken place on 28 November 1911. It looked very much as if the Palace was on its way to the scrap yard when the timely intervention by the First Earl of Plymouth, who provided the £230,000 required to pay off the first debenture holders, saved it from such an inglorious end. In 1913 the Lord Mayor of London secured the Palace for the Nation when his Appeal Fund raised the sum required to repay the Earl for his unstinting generosity.

In 1914, following the start of the First World War, the Palace was requisitioned by the Admiralty for use as a naval training depot, with a School for Signallers and Wireless Operators. Although officially designated as the Royal Naval Depot, it soon became affectionately known as HMS Crystal Palace. At the cessation of hostilities it was used as an Army demobilisation centre.

Unfortunately the years of neglect, plus the ravages of military occupation, had left the Palace in a deplorable state. The Trustees, faced with the daunting task of restoration, eventually succeeded in preparing it for public use again by June 1920, at which time it was officially re-opened by their Majesties King George V and Queen Mary.

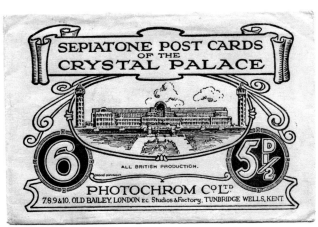

Commemorative pack of postcards

Gradually about one million visitors per year were attracted to the exhibitions and entertainments, enabling it to flourish successfully for a further sixteen years and until that fateful evening of 30 November 1936 when, in its 82nd year, and just ten days before the abdication of His Majesty Edward VIII, it burned to the ground.

Fire Souvenir, December 1936. Valentines series.

The tremendous crowds of sightseers who were attracted by the sad spectacle, so severely hampered the sixty five fire engines sent to tackle the blaze, that most arrived too late to cope with the enormous fire, the flames of which were, by then, roaring 300 feet into the air and were visible from eight counties. Sir Winston Churchill, who happened to be on his way from the House of Commons to his home, Chartwell, in Kent, was among the onlookers who watched the fire from the Crystal Palace Parade and heard the crashing of glass and iron, and, it is alleged, was heard to say 'This is the end of an age'.

The morning after. Reproduced by permission of Eric Price.

The author, himself, as a boy, standing in North London, over twenty miles away, saw the glow from the fire as a tremendous lighting up in the night sky, not realising, at that time, the interest it would awaken for him so many years later.

Fire Souvenir, December 1936. Valentines Series.

Over the years there has been much speculation as to the cause of the blaze which destroyed the Crystal Palace. It appears that, soon after 7 p.m. on the evening of 30 November 1936, Sir Henry Buckland, General Manager of the Crystal Palace, was walking towards the Palace with his daughter Crystal, when he saw a red glow in the building. Inside he found some of his staff dealing with a small fire. At first everything seemed to be under control, but as it was very windy outside, the fire suddenly started to spread, and the end result was complete devastation. The most popular theory held, is that the fire was started by an electrical fault in an office and spread at a rapid pace in the void beneath the floorboards, which by that time, held a tinder dry accumulation of 82 years of dirt and dust. Unfortunately we will never know just what destroyed this wonderful old building, we can only speculate.

Sir Henry Buckland. Reproduced by permission of Eric Price.

The palace alight, 30 November 1936. Reproduced by permission of Eric Price.

Mr Punch. 'And to think that it was I that gave you your name when I was a mere lad!' Reproduced by permission of Punch Ltd.

Crystal Palace Park is now the home of the National Sports Centre, the entrance to which is dominated by the giant bust of Sir Joseph Paxton. The sports stadium which was opened in 1964, accommodates 12,000 spectators and has gained a world-wide reputation as an important venue for international athletics. The multi-purpose sports hall, with seating for 2,000, has an Olympic-sized swimming pool and a dry-ski slope. However, facilities at the centre are not entirely suitable for modern needs and it is hoped that the funds required to upgrade the Centre will be forthcoming from its bid to the National Lottery Fund. In 1988 the former School of Engineering was opened by the Crystal Palace Museum Trust to display its photographic and other archive material. The very-popular Maze, which has been completely rebuilt by the London Borough of Bromley, is an exact replica of the original, which fell into disuse during World War II. In March 1998 Bromley council granted outline planning permission for a new leisure development to be designed on the lines of the former Crystal Palace.

The author has barely scratched the surface of this fascinating story, but readers wishing to learn more about the Palace will find a great deal of information among the general reference works cited in the bibliography (p. 18). Readers may also find of interest the following extract from a report by Barrie McKay, Chairman of the Museum Trust:

> On a rainswept day in 1979 more than 1,000 people braved the weather to view an exhibition held at the National Recreation Centre on the history of the Crystal Palace. The inspiration behind this came from a number of enthusiastic local residents who had developed something of a passion for the Palace and were keen to attempt partial restoration of the Crystal Palace site.
>
> The exhibition was a success and in response to public interest, not only in the Palace history but also in the site on which the Palace once stood, the exhibition organisors founded the Crystal Palace Foundation. Since then the Foundation, now with over 1,000 members, has devoted thousands of hours to restoring parts of the site and preserving the Victorian remains. As well as providing education and research, and publishing work concerned with the Crystal Palace, the Foundation organises regular talks, film shows and other events reflecting the importance of the Crystal Palace in our history.
>
> In 1988, the former School of Engineering was opened by the Museum Trust as a photographic display of the Crystal Palace. During this time the Museum Trust, with assistance from the Royal Commission for the Exhibition of 1851, arranged for the cataloguing and preparation of the museum collection, and on June 17th 1990 the Duke of Devonshire performed the opening ceremony of the museum.
>
> Visitors to the museum are greeted by a huge mural depicting the interior of the Crystal Palace, with the inside of the museum decorated with greenery, statues and flags of all nations to recreate the atmosphere of the old Palace. In addition to the many historical items on display, including models, porcelain, medals, trophies, books and paintings, the museum features video film of the Palace and music that once could be heard at the Crystal Palace.

Readers interested in joining the Crystal Palace Foundation, or wishing to know more about the museum, should contact CPF c/o Crystal Palace Museum, Anerley Hill, London SE19 2BA.

CARRIAGE AND HARNESS EXHIBITION.

A SPECIAL EXHIBITION of CARRIAGES and HARNESS will be held in the SOUTH NAVE, from APRIL 14TH to 23RD inclusive. The attention of both Purchasers and Manufacturers is specially requested, a very extensive collection being anticipated.

Communications to be directed to the Superintendent, Mr. WELLARD, Exhibition Department.

THE PICTURE GALLERY IS OPEN THIS DAY, with a New Collection of Pictures by British and Foreign Artists. Catalogues Sixpence each.

THE VICTORIA CROSS GALLERY, BY THE CHEVALIER LOUIS W. DESANGES.—This important Collection of FIFTY-FOUR PICTURES, illustrating the various heroic actions for which the distinguished honour of the VICTORIA CROSS was obtained, is now ON VIEW at the North End of the PICTURE GALLERY. When previously exhibited they formed a great attraction, and were sold to HARRY WOOD, Esq., who has kindly lent them for Exhibition.

THE CRYSTAL PALACE AQUARIUM, at the Northern or Tropical End of the Palace, near the Byzantine Court, is the most complete one in existence, kept in the best order. Admission—Adult, 6d.; Child, 3d. Annual Season Tickets—Adult, 5s; Child, 2s. 6d. A description of the Aquarium, and of the creatures shown, in the Official Handbook (by W. A. LLOYD, Superintendent), price 6d.

Crystal Palace Saturday Concert Programme Announcements, April 1875.

Anerley Road, c.1900. Reproduced by permission of Eric Price & Melvyn Harrison.

Crystal Palace Parade from station c. 1904. Valentines Series

The New Crystal Palace. (de Mare, *London 1851*)

Medals & Tokens

Because most Crystal Palace records perished in the great fire of 1936, we are faced with looking elsewhere for information concerning those medals struck to commemorate this Palace and the various events held there. The press reported on some of the events, but rarely mentioned any details about the prizes if they were medals. However, souvenir programmes, if they can be found, are invaluable; not only because they provide information about the event, but they also, occasionally, contain interesting details regarding the prizes. Medals found in their original box or packet, and accompanied by a descriptive leaflet, may well provide essential details not available elsewhere. Sadly, not many of these items have come this way, so all too frequently there has been little of interest to say about the medals.

The firm of Messrs Pinches was appointed as medallists to the Crystal Palace Company, who licensed them to set up their Crystal Palace medal press to strike, and sell, medals to the public within the building. John Harvey Pinches[1] mentions that the Crystal Palace medal press was set up in association with W.J. Taylor, (an uncle who taught John Pinches the art of steel engraving), and this, no doubt, explains why so many Crystal Palace medals were signed by him (Taylor).

A high proportion of the recorded white metal medals were designed to be worn on the day of the particular event, and were given mainly to the thousands of schoolchildren who attended the multitude of musical and other festivals held at the Palace over the years. Being of an ephemeral quality, many of them are now very difficult to find.

The first twenty seven medal entries relate to the construction and the opening of the new Crystal Palace. The other medals refer mainly to the many events which were held there during its lifetime. In addition to those recorded here, it is understood that medals exist for a large number of sporting activities plus countless shows and events of almost every description. This offering, therefore, should be regarded as nothing more than a preliminary checklist, which could grow considerably over the coming years. As mentioned earlier, the author would be very pleased to hear from readers who can provide details of any pieces that are not recorded in this volume.

The numbering system for this section of the book has been changed so that each entry is prefixed by its date of issue. This will enable additional material to be inserted in a correct position without fear of the work becoming disordered. The few tokens known are also listed by date, as are any associated pieces. Undated pieces appear at the end of the section, prefixed by ND.

The Fairy Archipelago, c.1930.

---

1. J.H. Pinches, *Medals by John Pinches*, London: 1981.

SY-1852 / 001	The First Column Erected	
by W.J. Taylor		Wm 45 mm

SY-1853 / 001	The Crystal Palace Erected	
by G. Dowler		Wm 74 mm

Obverse View of the Crystal Palace. *Inscription above:* DESIGNED BY SIR JOSEPH PAXTON. *In exergue:* ERECTED BY / MESS^RS FOX & HENDERSON *Signed* W.J.TAYLOR LONDON

Reverse Thirteen line inscription: THE FIRST COLUMN OF THE CRYSTAL PALACE AT SYDENHAM / DESTINED FOR / THE RECREATION AND / INSTRUCTION OF THE MILLION / WAS ERECTED ON THE / 5 DAY OF AUGUST 1852 BY / SAMUEL LAING, ESQ. M.P. CHAIRMAN / OF THE CRYSTAL PALACE COMP. / IN COMMEMORATION OF WHICH EVENT / THIS MEDAL IS PRESENTED / TO THE SUBSCRIBERS OF / THE AGE / WEEKLY NEWSPAPER

Rim Plain.

RR	Brown 2508, Eidlitz 773/84, Taylor 171j	BM BR CP PC

The Age Weekly was a short-lived periodical which ran for only 37 issues. However, it does have the distinction of being the first organisation to commission a medal depicting the new Crystal Palace. The early medals were engraved from an artists impression, and as such they did not show the two Brunel water towers which became an added feature to the original design.

Obverse View of the Crystal Palace and terraces. *Inscription above:* THE MIGHT OF INDUSTRY, THE GLORY OF PEACE *In exergue:* THE CRYSTAL PALACE / SYDENHAM / ERECTED / MDCCCLIII / FOX, HENDERSON & Co CONTRACTORS *Signed* DOWLER BIRMM

Reverse Britannia standing on a plinth holding a flag and an olive branch, attended by Industry and Commerce. Eye of providence above. *In exergue: signed* DOWLER BIRM;

Rim Plain.

RRR	Eidlitz 771, Taylor 171b	BR PC

Although the shell of the building was erected by the

contractors during 1853, the Palace did not open to the public until 10 June 1854. Even then, there was still a great deal of work still to be completed, both inside and outside of the building.

SY-1854 / 005 Crystal Palace Opened
by Allen & Moore   Wm 27 mm

Obverse Similar to obverse of Great Exhibition medal HP-B025.
Reverse View of the Crystal Palace. *Inscription above:* THE BUILDING AND GROUNDS / OCCUPY 300 ACRES. *In exergue:* LENGTH OF BUILDING / 1608 FEET, / NAVE 110 F^T HIGH, / CENTRE TRANSEPT / 194 F^T HIGH
Inscription around the border: THE PEOPLE'S PALACE SYDENHAM / OPENED JUNE 1854
Rim Plain.

RR *Brown* 2547 PC

SY-1854 / 010 Crystal Palace Opened
by Allen & Moore   Ae 39 mm

Obverse Similar to obverse of HP-B090.
Reverse View of the Crystal Palace between two statues upon columns. *Inscription above* surmounted by symbols of art, science and plenty: THE / PEOPLE'S PALACE / SYDENHAM, / OPENED JUNE 1854. *In exergue:* Symbols of industry and transport. *Inscription above:* THE BUILDING AND GROUNDS / OCCUPY 300 ACRES, / LENGTH OF BUILDING / 1608 F^T, / CENTRE TRANSCEPT / 194 F^T HIGH. *Signed* A & M
Rim Plain.

RRR *unrecorded* PC

Courtesy of Eric Price.

SY-1854 / 015 Crystal Palace Opened
by Allen & Moore   Wm 39 mm

Obverse Angel holding oval medallions with vis-à-vis portraits of Queen Victoria and Prince Albert. Crowned shields below.
Reverse Similar to reverse of SY-1854 /010.
Rim Plain.

RRR *unrecorded* PC

SY-1854 / 020 Crystal Palace Opened
by Allen & Moore   Wm 51 mm

Obverse   Draped bust of Sir Joseph Paxton bare head left, within a frame and laurel wreath. *Inscription below:* SIR JOSEPH PAXTON

Reverse   View of the Crystal Palace and terraces. *Inscription above:* THE PEOPLE'S CRYSTAL PALACE SYDENHAM. / BEING A VAST REPOSITORY OF INSTRUCTION / AND AMUSEMENT. / OPENED JUNE 1854. *In exergue:* DESIGNED BY SIR JOSEPH PAXTON F.L.S. / ERECTED BY FOX, HENDERSON & Cᵒ. / THE BUILDING AND GROUNDS OCCUPY / 300 ACRES, / LENGTH 1608 Fᵀ, NAVE 110 FT HIGH, / CENTRE TRANSEPT 194 Fᵀ HIGH, / AND 120 WIDE, / SIDE TRANSEPTS 110 Fᵀ HIGH, / AND 72 Fᵀ WIDE. *Signed* ALLEN & MOORE

Rim   Plain.

RR	*Brown 2546, Eidlitz 770/82, Taylor 171a*	BM BR CP PC

Obverse   Similar to obverse of SY-1854 /020.

Reverse   Similar to reverse of SY-1854 /020, but the date is MAY 1854.

Rim   Plain.

RRR	*unrecorded*	PC

The original plan was for the Palace to open on 1 May, but due to countless delays, the opening was deferred until 10 June. This medal is probably from a batch which was struck and distributed before the change in the official opening date was published.

SY-1854 / 025   Crystal Palace Opened
by Allen & Moore   Wm 51 mm

SY-1854 / 045   Crystal Palace Opened
by T. Ottley   Wm 54 mm

Obverse View of the Crystal Palace and terraces. *In exergue:* THE CRYSTAL PALACE / SYDENHAM
Reverse *Five line inscription within a wreath of oak and laurel:* EXHIBITION / OF / THE INDUSTRY / OF ALL / NATIONS *Signed* OTTLEY
Rim Plain.

RRR *unrecorded* PC

The medal is not dated but there is no doubt it relates to the opening of the Palace. See SY-1854 /055 for a larger, but similar, obverse design, which has an inscription above and is signed in the exergue.

SY-1854 / 050 Crystal Palace Opened
by T. Ottley — Wm 74 mm

Obverse Similar to obverse of SY-1854/055.
Reverse Similar to reverse of HP-B285.
Rim Plain.

RRR *unrecorded* PC

Courtesy of C.E.

SY-1854 / 055 Crystal Palace Opened
by T. Ottley — Wm 74 mm

Obverse View of the Crystal Palace and terraces. *Inscription above:* EXHIBITION OF THE INDUSTRY OF ALL NATIONS *In exergue:* THE CRYSTAL PALACE / SYDENHAM *Signed* OTTLEY BIRM^M

Obverse View of the Crystal Palace and terraces. *Inscription above:* EXHIBITION OF THE INDUSTRY OF ALL NATIONS *In exergue:* THE CRYSTAL PALACE / SYDENHAM *Signed* OTTLEY BIRM[M]
Reverse Four females seated upon clouds surrounding a terrestrial globe.
Rim Plain.

RRR *Brown* 2548 FM PC

The obverse is similar to SY-1854 /045 but has an inscription above and is signed in the exergue. Ottley used this reverse in 1851 to commemorate the opening of the Great Exhibition (see HP-B290), and again, for the reverse of a 74 mm white metal medal to commemorate the opening of the New York Crystal Palace in 1853.

SY-1854 / 060   Crystal Palace Opened
by Messrs Pinches   Wm 42 mm

Obverse   Diademed draped bust of Queen Victoria left.
Inscription around the border: VICTORIA REGINA *Signed* PINCHES. LONDON
Reverse   Corner elevation of the Crystal Palace. *Inscription above:* DESIGNED BY SIR JOSEPH PAXTON *In exergue:* THE FIRST COLUMN ERECTED / BY SAM^L LAING ESQ^RE M.P. / AUG^T 5TH 1852 / OPENED JUNE 10TH 1854 *Signed* T.R.PINCHES LONDON
Rim   Plain.

RRR   *unrecorded*   PC

The obverse design was used again in 1857 to commemorate the Art Treasures Exhibition in Manchester.

SY-1854 / 065   Crystal Palace Opened
by Messrs Pinches   Ae Wm 42 mm

Obverse   Similar to reverse of SY-1854 /060.
Reverse   Britannia holding a caduceus and a key, opening the doors to the exhibition. A lamb and her helmet are at her feet. *In exergue: Signed* PINCHES
Rim   Plain.

RRR   *unrecorded*   ML PC

SY-1854 / 070   Crystal Palace Opened
by Messrs Pinches   Wm 42 mm

Obverse   Similar to reverse of SY-1854 /060.
Reverse   Arms of the Ancient Order of Foresters, eye of providence above. *Inscription around the border:* THE ANCIENT ORDER OF FORESTERS
Rim   Plain.

RR   *Brown 2554, Taylor 171e*   FM UM PC

By 1859 these visits had become so popular that attendances exceeded 63,000. The date of this visit is not shown on the medal.

SY-1854 / 075   Crystal Palace Opened
by Messrs Pinches   Brass case 42 & 63 mm

Lid   *Seven line inscription:* PINCHES & Co / BY / APPOINTMENT / — . - / CRYSTAL / PALACE / SYDENHAM / MEDALLISTS
Base   Similar to obverse. There is usually a blue circular label stuck to the inside of the case inscribed: T. R. PINCHES & Co / DIE / SINKERS / SEAL / ENGRAVERS / AND / ENVELOPE / MAKERS / 27 OXENDON STREET. LONDON
Rim   Plain.

63 mm R, 42 mm S   *Brown* 2549

Every type of white metal medal dated 1854, plus many others struck on later dates by Messrs Pinches at their Crystal Palace press, have been seen in one of these brass cases.

SY-1854 / 080   Crystal Palace Opened
by Messrs Pinches   Wm 42 mm

Obverse   View of the Crystal Palace with five flags upon the roof. *Inscription above:* CRYSTAL PALACE *In exergue:* OPENED. MDCCCLIV *Signed* PINCHES LONDON
Reverse   Similar to reverse of SY-1854 /065.
Rim   Plain.

N   *Brown* 2549, *Eimer* (I) 1487, *Eidlitz* 768/84, *Taylor* 171i
AM BM BG FM LM PC UM

Specimens are often found in a circular brass case, see SY-1854 /075.

SY-1854 / 085   Crystal Palace Opened
by Messrs Pinches   Ae 42 mm

Obverse   Similar to obverse of SY-1854 /080, only three flags on the roof, one on each of the transepts.

Reverse   Similar to reverse of SY-1854 /065.
Rim   Plain.

S   *Brown* 2549, *Eimer* (I) 1487, *Eidlitz* 768/84, *Taylor* 171i   AM
BM BG FM LM PC UM

Bronze medals were sold in two types of leatherette case. One is plain, the other, which is much more difficult to find, is gilt embossed FROM THE / CRYSTAL / PALACE.

SY-1854 / 090   Crystal Palace Opened
by Messrs Pinches   Ae Wm 63 mm

Obverse   Similar to obverse of SY-1854 /085, but has stops after PINCHES. and LONDON.
Reverse   Similar to reverse of SY-1854 /065.
Rim   Plain.

S   *Brown* 2549, *Eimer* (I) 1487, *Eidlitz* 767/84, *Taylor* 171h
AM BM BG CP FM ML PC UM

The bronze version is one of the set of three sold in a red Morocco case inscribed C.P.C. on the lid, see SY-1854 /095. Also see notes to SY-1854 /075 and SY-1854 /085.

SY-1854 / 095   Crystal Palace Opened
by Messrs Pinches   200 x 125 mm

RRR *Brown* 2544 PC

The above illustration is reduced in size.

The Crystal Palace Company commissioned a set of three bronze medals to be housed in an attractive red Morocco case with a brass clasp and hinges, inscribed C.P.C. in gilt capital letters on the lid (see SY-1854 /090, SY-1854 /110 and SY-1854 / 135 for detailed descriptions). At the opening ceremony a set of these medals (in gold) was presented to Queen Victoria. The directors and other VIPs connected with the project received a set in bronze. Unlike 1851, the edge of the medals and the lid of the case were not inscribed with the name of the recipient. An official record showing the actual number struck and to whom they were presented has not yet been found.

In November 1996, Christie's held a sale of autograph letters and personal effects belonging to Isambard Kingdom Brunel. Amongst this material were two sets of these medals, one in bronze and the other in white metal. The bronze set would no doubt have been the one presented to Brunel by the Crystal Palace Company at the opening of the Crystal Palace in 1854. Although the author had not previously seen a set of white metal medals in one of these cases, there is no reason to assume that the Crystal Palace Company did not sell souvenir sets of these medals to the public. Alternatively, the set may have been made up in a spare case by a dealer or a collector.

The case illustrated above belonged to Francis Fuller the first Managing Director of the Crystal Palace Company, who was also a member of the Executive Committee of the Royal Commission of 1851. When Noel Warr purchased this set of medals he found that instead of SY-1854 /110, it contained Fuller's Great Exhibition Jurors medal (HP-A040), which rightly belonged in the presentation case of medals Fuller received from the Royal Commissioners in 1851. When researching his article, 'Exposition 1851', Donald Sabo examined Fuller's presentation set and noted in the text of his article that the Jurors medal was either lost or destroyed, and had been replaced by an 1854 medal of the same size (SY-1854 / 110). This misplacement probably occurred accidentally while both sets of medals were being examined at the same time. If the present owner of the 1851 presentation set reads this, he / she might be pleased to learn that the Jurors medal has not been destroyed. See note to HP-A060.

SY-1854 / 100   Crystal Palace Opened
by Messrs Pinches   155 x 82 mm

RRR *Brown* 2549 & 2552A PC

The above illustration is reduced in size.

A specimen set of two white metal medals in a plain fitted case (see SY-1854 /090 and SY-1854 /130 for detailed descriptions). These medals are usually found singly in either a fitted leatherette case or a circular brass case. This is the first cased pair of this type seen by the author, hopefully some of the other different types of medal may also have been paired.

SY-1854 / 105 Crystal Palace Opened		SY-1854 / 110 Crystal Palace Opened	
by Messrs Pinches	Ae 63 mm	by Messrs Pinches & G.G. Adams	Ae Wm 63 mm

Obverse Eleven line inscription: DIRECTORS / ARTHUR ANDERSON / EDMUND S. P. CALVERT / THOMAS NEWMAN FARQUHAR / FRANCIS FULLER. MANAGING DIRECTOR / CHARLES GEACH / SAMUEL LAING. CHAIRMAN / CHARLES LUSHINGTON / JOHN SCOTT RUSSELL / JOSEPH LEECH / SOLICITOR / GEORGE GROVE / SECRETARY

Reverse Similar to reverse of SY-1854 /065.

Rim Plain.

RRR	*Brown* 2550 (ill.)	AM

Obverse Conjoined heads of Queen Victoria and Prince Albert left, he bare head, and she crowned. *Inscription around the border:* VICTORIA D: G: BRITANNIARUM REGINA F: D: ALBERTUS PRINCEPS CONJUX / MDCCCLIV. *Signed* G.G. ADAMS.

Reverse Distant view of the Crystal Palace. Britannia attended by Plenty and Learning, Fame with trumpet overhead. *Inscription around the border:* ORNATUR PROPIIS INDUSTRIA DONIS *In exergue:* MDCCCLIV *Signed* G.G. ADAMS.

Rim Plain.

Ae R, Wm S	*Brown* 2545, *Eimer (I)* 1485, *Pinches* 34/35	AM
BM PC		

Bronze specimens were sold in two types of leatherette case. One is plain, the other, which is much more difficult to find, is gilt embossed FROM THE / CRYSTAL / PALACE. The bronze version is one of a set of three bronze medals sold in a red Morocco case inscribed C.P.C. on the lid, see SY-1854 /095.

SY-1854 / 115   Crystal Palace Opened
by Messrs Pinches & H. Brown   Wm 42 mm

Obverse   Similar to reverse of SY-1854 /060.
Reverse   *Six line inscription within a border of laurel:*
STRUCK IN THE / BUILDING / BY / H. BROWN / MEDAL PRESS / COURT
Rim   Plain

RRR   *unrecorded*   PC

H. Brown appears to have been a very difficult man to trace. Even Bell, in *Unofficial Farthings* and Hawkins in his *Dictionary of Medalet and Check Makers* could not establish his whereabouts. Neither of them could find him listed in any city directory between 1850 and 1865, and, while Hawkins said 'all attempts to trace him had failed', it did not deter him from assuming that H. Brown was actually a medal designer working in Birmingham. However, the discovery of this and other medals by Brown, and the advertisement placed by him in *The Times* on 3 March 1863, which obviously neither Bell or Hawkins had seen, proves beyond doubt that from 1854 to 1864, H. Brown was engaged on medal production for Messrs Pinches in their Medal Press Court at the Crystal Palace, Sydenham. He may have resided in Perry Hill, Lower Sydenham. Unfortunately his whereabouts prior to 1854 are still a mystery.

SY-1854 / 120   Crystal Palace Opened
by Messrs Pinches & W.J. Taylor   Wm 42 mm

Obverse   View of the Crystal Palace. *Inscription above:*
CRYSTAL PALACE SYDENHAM / THE /PALACE / OF THE PEOPLE *In exergue:* DESIGNED BY SIR J. PAXTON / 1ST COLUMN ERECTED AUG. 5. 1852 / OPENED / JUNE 10TH 1854

Reverse   Eye of Providence above a shield in the centre of trefoil on which is a cross, a foul anchor and a heart, a rose either side of lower leaf. *Inscription around the border:*
GRAND LODGE OF ENGLAND + INDEPENDENT. ORDER. OF. GOOD. TEMPLARS.
Rim   Plain.

RRR   *Brown* 2551

Description obtained from Brown, because the author has not seen a specimen. For obverse illustration see SY-1866 /001, for reverse illustration see SY-1881 /005.

SY-1854 / 125   Crystal Palace Opened
by Messrs Pinches & L.C. Wyon   Ae Wm 42 mm

Obverse   Bare head of Sir Joseph Paxton left. *Inscription around the border:* SIR JOSEPH PAXTON *Signed* L.C. WYON.
Reverse   Similar to reverse of SY-1854 /060.
Rim   Plain.

RR   *Brown* 2553, *Eidlitz* 769/84, *Taylor* 171c   AM BM PC

SY-1854 / 130   Crystal Palace Opened
by Messrs Pinches & L.C. Wyon   Wm 63 mm

SY-1854 / 135   Crystal Palace Opened
by Messrs Pinches & L.C. Wyon   Ae 63 mm

Obverse   Bare head of Sir Joseph Paxton left. *Vertical downwards inscription behind head:* PAXTON *Signed* L.C. WYON.

Reverse   *Six line inscription above crossed laurel sprigs:* THE / CRYSTAL PALACE / DESIGNED BY / SIR JOSEPH PAXTON / OPENED / JUNE . 10 . 1854

Rim   Plain.

RRR   *Brown* 2552A, *Eidlitz* 765/84, *Taylor* 171f   PC

This is also one of the set of two white metal medals sold in a fitted case. See SY-1854 /100.

Obverse   Similar to obverse of SY-1854 /130.

Reverse   Similar to obverse of SY-1854 /090.

Rim   Plain.

RR   *Brown* 2552, *Eimer (I)* 1486, *Eimer (II)* 90 (ill.), *Eidlitz* 766/84, *Taylor* 171g   AM BM FM ML PC

Two types of leatherette case were used, one is plain, the other, which is much more difficult to find, is gilt embossed FROM THE / CRYSTAL / PALACE. It is also one of a set of three sold in a red Morocco case inscribed C.P.C. on the lid. See SY-1854 /095.

SY-1854 / 140   Crystal Palace Opened
by Messrs Pinches & L.C. Wyon   Ae 63 mm

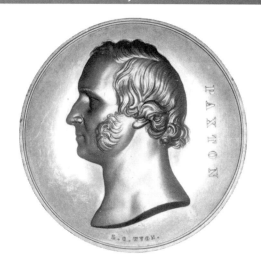

Obverse   Similar to obverse of SY-1854 /130.
Reverse   Blank.
Rim   Plain.

RRRR   *Brown 2552*   AM PC

Brown describes this as a uniface trial striking.

SY-1854 / 145   Crystal Palace Opened
by ?   Wm 30 mm

Obverse   Diademed head of Queen Victoria left. *Inscription around the border:* VICTORIA QUEEN OF GREAT BRITAIN
Reverse   View of the Crystal Palace and grounds. *Inscription above:* THE NEW CRYSTAL PALACE / SYDENHAM *In exergue:* THE BUILDING AND GROUNDS / OCCUPY 300 ACRES / LENGTH 1608 F^T / 110 F^T HIGH / OPENED JUNE 10. 1854

RRR   *Brown 2555*   BG

Description obtained from Brown, because the author has not seen a specimen.

SY-1854 / 150   Grand Military Fete
by Messrs Pinches   Wm 42 mm

Obverse   Similar to reverse of SY-1854 /060.
Reverse   Similar to reverse of SY-1854 /070, but, *in exergue:*

VISITED THE CRYSTAL PALACE / SYDENHAM / OCTOBER 28. 1854
Rim   Plain.

RRR   *Eidlitz 777/84, Taylor 171e*   BM

Struck at the Palace and sold to the public in aid of the widows and orphans of H.M. Forces engaged in the Crimean war.

SY-1854 / 155   Grand Military Fete
by Messrs Pinches   Ae Wm 42 mm

Obverse   End elevation of the Crystal Palace. *Inscription above:* TO COMMEMORATE THE VISIT OF THE / BAND OF THE IMP: REG: OF GUIDES *In exergue:* TO THE CRYSTAL PALACE / SYDENHAM / OCTOBER 28. 1854
Reverse   The French eagle in a medallion superimposed on a union flag above a scroll on a trophy of musical instruments, two crowns above. *Inscription around the border:* JUNGIMUS HOSPITIO DEXTRAS *Signed* PINCHES. LONDON
Rim   Plain.

Ae RR, Wm R   *Brown 2557, Eidlitz 776/84, Taylor 171d*   AM PC

A contingent of 46 musicians were sent by the Emperor of France to play at the Grand Military Fete held on 28 October in aid of the sick, wounded, widows and orphans of HM Forces engaged in the Crimean war. See note to SY-1854 /150.

SY-1854 / 160   Grand Military Fete
by Messrs Pinches   Wm 42 mm

Obverse   Five line inscription within a wreath of laurel:
STRUCK AT / THE / CRYSTAL / PALACE / OCTR 28. 1854 *Inscription around the border:* IN AID OF THE WIDOWS AND ORPHANS OF OUR BRAVE SOLDIERS SAILORS & MARINES *Signed* PINCHES. LONDON
Reverse   A trophy of flags. *Inscription around the border:* VICTORY OF ALMA / SEPT^R 20TH 1854 / BY THE UNITED FORCES OF ENGLAND & FRANCE
Rim   Plain.

RR   *Brown* 2538   BG PC

The Alma is a river in the south-west of the Crimea which gave its name to the first battle of the Crimean war fought between the British and the French under Lord Raglan and Marshal St. Arnaud, and the Russians under Prince Menshikov. The Russians held a strong position on the heights overlooking the river but, in a blood-thirsty battle during which both sides suffered heavy casualties, the allies pushed across the river and stormed and captured the heights from the enemy. See note to SY-1854 /150. Brown records a specimen in bronze, the author has not yet seen one in that metal.

SY-1854 / 165   Crimean War: Battle of the Alma
by Messrs Pinches   Ar Ae Wm 42 mm

Obverse   Troops advancing behind standard bearer. ALMA

incuse on rock below. *Inscription above:* SEPTEMBER 20TH 1854 *Signed* PINCHES
Reverse   Eighteen line inscription listing the Regiments participating in the battle.
Rim   Plain.

Ar RRR, Ae R, Wm S   *Brown* 2539 (ill.), *Eimer (I)* 1490, *Fearon (II)* p.13   AM BM PC

Pinches produced a cased set containing a bronze specimen of each of the three medals struck to commemorate the battles of Alma, Balaclava and Inkermann. A cased set of three in top condition is extremely rare. See note to SY-1854 /150.

SY-1854 / 170   Crimean War: Battle of Balaclava
by Messrs Pinches   Ar Ae Wm 42 mm

Obverse   Dragoons charging against the enemy. *Inscription above:* BALAKLAVA *Signed* PINCHES
Reverse   Sixteen line inscription listing the Regiments participating in the battle.
Rim   Plain.

Ar RRR, Ae R, Wm S   *Brown* 2540 (ill.), *Eimer (I)* 1491, *Fearon (II)* p.13   AM BM FM PC

The charge of the Six Hundred took place during this battle on 25 October. Twenty one years later, on 25 October 1875, a banquet was given to the survivors at London's Alexandra Palace. See notes to SY-1854 /150 and SY-1854 /165.

SY-1854 / 175 Crimean War: Battle of Inkermann
by Messrs Pinches   Ar Ae Wm 42 mm

Obverse British grenadiers advancing into enemy lines.
Inscription above: INKERMANN
Reverse The names of the participating Regiments listed in the shape of a rose.
Rim Plain.

Ar RRR, Ae R, Wm S *Brown 2541, Eimer (I) 1492, Fearon (I) 305.10 (ill.), Fearon (II) p.13*   AM BM BG FM PC

This battle was fought in thick fog when, before daybreak on 5 November, the Russians attacked the British forces near the old fort of Inkermann. See notes to SY-1854 /150 and SY-1854 / 165.

SY-1854 / 180 Crimean War: Battle of Inkermann
by Messrs Pinches & W.J. Taylor   Wm 35 mm

Obverse Four line inscription within a floral wreath: MADE / IN THE / CRYSTAL / PALACE *Signed* W.J. TAYLOR. MEDAL PRESS
Reverse Allied troops astride captured fortifications. *Inscription around the border:* UNITED THUS, WHAT FOE HAVE WE TO FEAR? *Signed* W.J. TAYLOR. LONDON
Rim Plain.

RRR *unrecorded*   PC

See note to SY-1854 /150.

SY-1855 / 001 Visit of Napoleon III
by Messrs Pinches   Ae Wm 42 mm

Obverse French eagle supporting oval medallions with vis-à-vis portraits of Queen Victoria and Napoleon III, floral emblems around. *Inscription below:* WELCOME / TO / ENGLAND *Signed* T. R. PINCHES. LONDON.
Reverse Crossed flags of England and France behind fasces. *Inscription around the border:* TO COMMEMORATE THE VISIT OF THEIR IMPERIAL MAJESTIES THE EMPEROR AND EMPRESS OF FRANCE / APRIL. 1855
Rim Plain.

Ae S, Wm N *Brown 2564*   AM BM FM ML PC

Queen Victoria and Prince Albert took their Imperial guests to the Palace on Friday 20 April, this medal was sold there as a souvenir of the royal visit.

SY-1855 / 005 Death of Lord Raglan
by Messrs Pinches   Ae Wm 42 mm

Obverse Funerary plinth with portrait medallion of Lord Raglan in the centre *inscribed:* PENINSULA / WATERLOO / CRIMEA *Inscription around the border:* FIELD MARSHAL LORD RAGLAN *In exergue:* BORN A.D. 1788
Reverse View of an encampment in the Crimea. *Inscription*

above: DIED IN THE SERVICE / OF HIS COUNTRY *In exergue:* AT HEADQUARTERS / BEFORE SEBASTOPOL / JUNE 23ʀᴅ 1855
Rim Plain.

Ae RR, Wm R	*Brown* 2570, *Eimer (I)* 1495, *Fearon (I)* 306.6 (ill.) PC

Fifth Baron Raglan (1788–1855), lost an arm at Waterloo. Commander of the British Forces in the Crimea, he was made the scapegoat for the privations suffered by the British troops during this campaign. The medal was sold at the Palace in aid of widows and orphans of H.M. Forces engaged in the Crimean War. The white metal version is sometimes found in a Pinches brass case.

SY-1855 / 010   Visit of Ancient Order of Foresters
by Messrs Pinches   Wm 42 mm

Obverse Similar to reverse of SY-1854 /060.
Reverse Similar to reverse of SY-1854 /070, but *in exergue:* AUG 28ᵀᴴ 1855
Rim Plain.

RR	*Eidlitz* 777/84 PC

Description obtained from Eidlitz, because the author has not seen a specimen.

SY-1856 / 001   Treaty of Paris
by Messrs Pinches   Wm 42 mm

Obverse MARCH 30TH / 1856 within a wreath bearing shields of the four allies, Britain, Austria, France and Turkey.
Inscription around the border: PEACE WITH RUSSIA AND THE ALLIED POWERS SIGNED AT PARIS
Reverse Altar engraved with a caduceus, Holy Dove depositing an olive branch on the altar, a cornucopia inscribed PEACE — PLENTY either side of the altar. *In*

exergue: PEACE COMMERCE AND / FRIENDSHIP / WITH ALL NATIONS *Signed* PINCHES LONDON
Rim Plain.

R	*Brown* 2580 AM BM PC

Under this peace agreement, the Black Sea was neutralised, and the Danube was placed under international control and opened up to all shipping. See note to SY-1855 /150.

SY-1856 / 005   Florence Nightingale
by Messrs Pinches   Ae Wm 42 mm

Obverse Florence Nightingale seated reading a book within a beaded oval frame. *Inscription in the field:* FLORENCE NIGHTINGALE sprays of roses thistle and shamrock at either side. *Signed* PINCHES. LONDON.
Reverse Oval badge in palm fronds with crowned V R upon a cross, CRIMEA on ribbon below, three stars above. *Inscription around the border:* • AS A MARK OF ESTEEM AND GRATITUDE FOR HER DEVOTION TO / THE QUEEN'S BRAVE SOLDIERS •
Rim Plain.

Ae RRR, Wm RR	*Brown* 2668A, *Eimer (I)* 1493, *Fearon (I)* 305.11 PC

Florence Nightingale (1820–1910), English nurse and pioneer of hospital reform. Her absorbing interest in the alleviation of suffering led her to visit countless civilian and military hospitals across the continent of Europe. At the outbreak of the Crimean war she was the Superintendent at a Hospital for Invalid Gentlewomen in West London. When news came of the desperate plight of the British wounded following the battle of the Alma in September, she was invited by Sidney Herbert, the Secretary of War, to take out a party of nurses and they reached Scutari on 4 November 1854. Largely by determination, in the face of considerable official resistance, she succeeded in removing the unsanitary conditions which were mainly responsible for the high mortality rate among the servicemen. Her nightly visits to the wards earned her the title 'Lady with the Lamp'. After the evacuation of the British army from

Turkey, she arrived back in England on 8 September 1856 and, with the £50,000 raised by public subscription in her honour, founded nurse training schools at St Thomas's Hospital and King's College Hospital in London. Despite ill health, following her return to England she wrote extensively on nursing, hospital reform and army medical services, and was instrumental in the formation of the International Red Cross movement and many other nursing organisations.

The medal is undated but was struck in 1856 and sold at the Palace in May of that year, at the unveiling of the Scutari Monument which was erected there to immortalise the 'Lady with the Lamp'. The unveiling ceremony was performed by Queen Victoria in the presence of Crimean veterans and detachments from every regiment of the army.

SY-1856 / 010   Florence Nightingale
by Messrs Pinches   Wm 42 mm

Obverse Similar to obverse of SY-1856 /005, but the frame is not beaded, and the floral sprays have been replaced by Florence Nightingale's name.
Reverse Similar to reverse of SY-1856 /005.
Rim Plain.

RRR	*Brown* 2668A, *Eimer (I)* 1493, *Fearon (I)* 305.11 PC

Sometimes found in a circular brass case. See note to SY-1856 / 005.

SY-1856 / 015   Wine Duties International Festival
by Messrs Pinches   Wm 51 mm

Obverse Royal arms and the French eagle on crossed flags, with crowned arms at each side. *Inscription above:* ESTO PERPETUA *Inscription below:* TO COMMEMORATE / THE GREAT INTERNATIONAL / FESTIVAL / HELD IN THE CRYSTAL PALACE / JULY 9TH 1856 *Signed* PINCHES LONDON
Reverse Arms within a ten line inscription: WINE DUTIES REDUCTION COMMITTEE / 1250 IN NUMBER / BENJAMIN OLIVEIRA F.R.S. M.P. / PRESIDENT / IN THE CHAIR / - - - - / WILLIAM WHITE / PRESIDENT / IN THE VICE CHAIR / - - - - - / 1500 IN NUMBER / ANGLO FRENCH FREE TRADE ASSOCIATION STAFFORDSHIRE POTTERIES
Rim Plain.

RRR	*unrecorded* PC

During the year ending 31 March 1856, the customs duties on about 10 million gallons of wine produced £1,856,120. In 1860, by the French Treaty of Commerce, wine duty was reduced from 5/9d per gallon, to 2/6d and 1/- , according to the alcoholic strength.

SY-1857 / 001   The Great Handel Festival
by Messrs Pinches   **Ae 42 mm**

Obverse Draped bust of George Frederick Handel wearing cap left. *Vertical inscription behind head reading upwards:* HANDEL *Signed* PINCHES. LONDON. on shoulder.
Reverse A lyre. *Inscription around the border:* ✣ CRYSTAL • PALACE ✣ HANDEL • FESTIVAL / JUNE • 1857 ✣
Rim Beaded.
Edge Named to a performer, a Judge, or a Steward.

S   *Brown* 2597, *Davis et al* 133/255   **AM BM BG BR FM LM PC**

As the centenary of the death of Handel approached, the Sacred Harmonic Society announced it intended to commemorate the event by holding a music festival in 1859. The central transept of the Crystal Palace was the only arena capable of accommodating the desired number of instrumentalists, so it was decided a preliminary festival entitled 'The Great Handel Festival' should be held there in 1857, to test the suitability of the building for musical purposes. The principal vocalists engaged were Madame Clara Novello, Madame Rudersdorff, Miss Dolby, Mr Sims Reeves, Mr Monem Smith, Mr Weiss and Herr Formes. The chorus numbered 2,000, and the instrumentalists 386; the conductor was Michael Costa. The works selected were the oratorios of *Messiah*, *Judas Maccabaeus*, and *Israel in Egypt*.

The medal was struck for the Sacred Harmonic Society to commemorate the Great Handel Festival held on Monday 15, Wednesday 17 and Friday 19 June 1857. The finely executed bust of Handel was taken from the Roubilliac portrait owned by the Sacred Harmonic Society. The medals were distributed to the performers on Friday 4 September, at the Exeter Hall.

SY-1857 / 005   The Great Handel Festival
by Messrs Pinches   **Aes 42 mm**

Obverse Similar to obverse of SY-1857 /001, but the vertical inscription reads downwards, and it is signed in the field below the shoulder. The rim is plain.
Reverse Similar to reverse of SY-1857 /001.
Rim Plain obverse, beaded reverse.
Edge Named to a performer.

CRYSTAL PALACE.

Prospective Arrangements.

TWICE DAILY . . . The Wonderful Trained Wild Animals. Twelve African Lions and Three Bengal Tigers, Two Cheetahs, Two Panthers, Two Bears, Five Boarhounds, etc. etc.

The first instance in the world's history of Carnivorous Animals from various climates living, sleeping, playing, and performing together in the same cage.

Seats, Numbered, 2s.; Unnumbered, 6d. and 1s.

SATURDAY, JUNE 20TH . Military Concerts by the Band of Her Majesty's Coldstream Guards and the Crystal Palace Military Band. Illuminated Garden Fête.

TUESDAY, JUNE 23RD . MR. HARRY FURNISS in "THE HUMOURS OF PARLIAMENT; or, Life in the Best Club in London." Illustrated by numerous Original Scenes and Political Portraits displayed upon the Screen by the Oxyhydrogen light.

THURSDAY, JUNE 25TH . DRAMATIC PERFORMANCE: "Little Lord Fauntleroy." GREAT FIREWORK DISPLAY by C. T. Brock & Co. Naval Realistic Device representing the Battle of the Nile.

SATURDAY, JUNE 27TH . Military Concerts by the Band of Her Majesty's Coldstream Guards and the Crystal Palace Military Band. Illuminated Garden Fête.

TUESDAY, JUNE 30TH . Dramatic Performance: "The Doll's House."

THURSDAY, JULY 2ND . Annual Fête in Aid of Metropolitan and City Police Orphanage. Great Firework Display by C. T. Brock & Co.

SATURDAY, JULY 4TH . National Rose Society's Show. Illuminated Garden Fête and Grand Open-Air Ballet.

TUESDAY, JULY 7TH . Salvation Army Festival.

THURSDAY, JULY 9TH . Grand Archery Meeting. Great Firework Display by C. T. Brock & Co.

FRIDAY, JULY 10TH . Grand Archery Meeting.

SATURDAY, JULY 11TH . Probable Visit of Their Imperial Majesties the German Emperor and Empress. Review by the Emperor of Volunteer Fire Brigades. Special Firework Display. Open-Air Ballet.

WEDNESDAY, JULY 15TH Rose Fair and Grand Fête in aid of the Gardeners' Orphan Fund.

THURSDAY, JULY 16TH . Great Firework Display by C. T. Brock & Co.

SATURDAY, JULY 18TH . Tonic Sol-fa Jubilee Festival. Illuminated Garden Fête and Open-Air Ballet.

THURSDAY, JULY 23RD . Great Firework Display by C. T. Brock & Co.

SATURDAY, JULY 25TH . Church Sunday School Festival. Illuminated Garden Fête and Open-Air Ballet.

THURSDAY, JULY 30TH . Great Firework Display by C. T. Brock & Co.

DAILY—FREE CONCERTS AND POPULAR ENTERTAINMENTS, OPEN-AIR BALLET ON AND AFTER JULY 1, PICTURE GALLERY, MUSEUM, AND AQUARIUM.

Tenth Triennial Handel Festival Programme Announcements, June 1891.

RRR *unrecorded* PC

See note to SY-1857 /001.

SY-1857 / 010　The Great Handel Festival
by Messrs Pinches　　　　　　　Ae Wm 42 mm

Obverse　Similar to obverse of SY-1857 /005.
Reverse　Angel seated right, playing a lyre. *Signed* PINCHES LONDON
Rim　Plain.

RRR　*Brown 2598, Davis et al 134/257*　PC

Handel Festival & Choir, 1906.

Not dated, believed to be a musical award presented by the Sacred Harmonic Society.

SY-1857 / 015　The Great Handel Festival
by Messrs Pinches　　　　　　　　Aeg 42 mm

Obverse　Similar to reverse of SY-1857 /010.
Reverse　Laurel wreath.
Rim　Plain.

RRR　*unrecorded*　PC

Not dated, believed to be a musical award presented by the Sacred Harmonic Society.

SY-1857 / 020　Tonic Sol-Fa Association
by Messrs Pinches　　　　　　　　Ae 29 mm

Obverse　Tonic Sol-Fa Association monogram. *Inscription around the border:* CRYSTAL PALACE CHOIR SEPTEMBER 2ND 1857
Reverse　Tonic sol-fa notes on a scroll. *Inscription in the field:* FACILE TRUE INEXPENSIVE *Inscription around the border:* ❀ TONIC SOL-FA METHOD OF SINGING ❀
Rim　Plain.

RRR　*Davis et al 193/729*　CP PC

The Tonic Sol-Fa method of singing was invented by Sarah Ann Glover (1785–1867) a music teacher from Norwich. John Curwen improved and developed the system in 1841. The Tonic Sol-Fa Association was founded in 1857 and held regular festivals at the Palace. In the superb Hollywood musical *Sound of Music*, Maria taught the Von Trapp children how to sing using this method, by which the letters d, r, m, f, s, l, t (do, re, me, fa, so, la, ti or si) are used instead of notes.

SY-1857 / 025   Indian Mutiny
by Messrs Pinches   Ae Wm 63 mm

SY-1857 / 030   Foresters 3rd Visit
by Messrs Pinches   Wm 42 mm

Obverse   A forester's cap, bow and arrows, and a hunting horn above a *five line inscription*: THE ANCIENT ORDER OF / FORRESTERS / 3ᴿᴰ VISIT TO THE / CRYSTAL PALACE / AUG. 25. 1857. Thistle rose and shamrock each side.
Reverse   Similar to reverse of SY-1854 /070.
Rim   Plain.

RRR	*unrecorded*	PC

See note to SY-1854 /070.

SY-1858 / 001   Foundation of the Royal Dramatic College
by Messrs Pinches & W.J. Taylor   Wm 39 mm

Obverse   Draped bust of William Shakespeare facing, within centre arch of a gothic portico, flanked by two characters from his plays. *In exergue:* Royal arms. *Above:* ROYAL DRAMATIC COLLEGE *Below:* FOUNDED A.D. 1858 *Inscription around the border:* ALL THE WORLD'S A STAGE & ALL THE MEN & WOMEN MERELY PLAYERS
Reverse   Draped bust of William Shakespeare left within centre circle. *Inscriptions around radiating from the centre circle:* METROPOLITAN THEATRES / COVENT GARDEN / HER MAJESTY'S / DRURY LANE / HAYMARKET / ADELPHI / PRINCES'S / LYCEUM / OLYMPIC / ST JAMES'S / STRAND / SADLER'S WELLS / HOLBORN / MARYLEBONE / PRINCE OF WALES'S / ROYALTY / STANDARD / CITY OF LONDON / BRITANNIA / ASTLEY'S / HOLBORN AMPHITHEATRE / SURREY / VICTORIA / GARRICK / PAVILION
Rim   Plain.

RRR	*Brown* 2646	BG PC

Obverse   Laureate, winged figure of Justice standing right, one foot resting on a dead tiger, Indian captive kneeling behind; a cannon hidden among rocks. JUSTICE within rays to right. *In exergue: signed* PINCHES LONDON
Reverse   *Inscription within open wreath:* DURING THE / SEPOY MUTINIES / A.D. MDCCCLVII. *Inscription around the border:* DEDICATED TO THE BRAVE DEFENDERS OF OUR INDIAN EMPIRE
Rim   Plain.

Ae RR, Wm RR	*Brown* 2601 (ill.), *Eimer (I)* 1515	AM BM PC

More than 23,000 visitors attended the Fast Day held at the Palace on 7 October, where the medal was sold. At the service conducted by the Baptist Minister the Rev. C.H. Spurgeon, £475.16.11d was collected for the widows and orphans of H.M. Forces killed during the mutiny. The Crystal Palace Company contributed a further £200 towards the fund. White metal specimens are sometimes found in a circular brass case.

The Dramatic College was founded at Maybury near Woking, for the benefit of distressed actors and their families. It was proposed in 1858 at the Prince's Theatre by Dickens, Thackeray, Kean, Webster and others. Queen Victoria was its patron. The first stone was laid by Prince Albert on 1 June 1860. On 29 September 1862, the first seven beneficiaries moved in. A fund-raising fete was held annually at the Palace (see SY-1866 /015). At the 1867 fete, the Viceroy of Egypt donated £500 and the Sultan £1,000. Unfortunately such generous donations were very few and far between and by 1877, the money had run out and the college had to close. The building was sold in 1880 to become a centre for oriental studies.

SY-1859 / 001	Handel	Centenary
Commemoration		
by Messrs Pinches		Ae 17 mm

Obverse   Similar to obverse of SY-1859 /010.
Reverse   Similar to reverse of SY-1859 /010.
Rim   Plain.

RRR   *unrecorded*   PC

This tiny piece is a replica of SY-1859 /010. Possibly handed out to audiences.

SY-1859 / 005	Handel	Centenary
Commemoration		
by Messrs Pinches		Av Ar Ae 42 mm

Obverse   Similar to obverse of SY-1857 /001.
Reverse   A lyre dividing 1685 -1759. *Inscription around the border:* GEORGE FREDERICK HANDEL / BURIED IN WESTMINSTER ABBEY.
Rim   Beaded obverse, plain reverse.

Av RRR, Ar RRR, Ae R   *Brown* 2655, *Pinches* p.244 (ill.)   PC

In 1966, Messrs John Pinches Ltd struck 100 copies in 22ct gold and 1,000 copies in sterling silver from the original dies. John Harvey Pinches believes the dies were originally engraved by the first John Pinches for the 1857 Great Handel Festival.

SY-1859 / 010	Handel	Centenary
Commemoration		
by Messrs Pinches & W.J. Taylor		Ae 51 mm

Obverse   Draped bust of George Frederic Handel wearing cap left. *Inscription around the border:* GEORGE FREDERIC HANDEL *Signed* W. J. TAYLOR. LONDON
Reverse   *Inscription within a wreath of palm and laurel:* CENTENARY / COMMEMORATION / CRYSTAL PALACE / MDCCCLIX
Rim   Plain.
Edge   Inscribed with the name of a performer, a Judge, or a Steward.

N   *Brown* 2656, *Davis et al* 134/256, *Eimer (I)* 1527   AM BM BG BR FM ML PC

The festival took place from 20–24 June. The oratorios of *Messiah*, *Israel in Egypt*, the *Dettingen Te Deum*, and selections from *Belshazzar*, *Saul*, *Samson*, and *Judas Maccabaeus* were performed. The principal vocalists were the same as those in 1857; the chorus increased to 2,700 and the instrumentalists to 460. Receipts were in excess of £33,000, expenses about £18,000. The profit was shared 2 to 1 respectively between the Crystal Palace Company and the Sacred Harmonic Society. The medals were distributed in April 1860 to more than 3,100 performers, plus the Judges and Stewards.

Refreshments consumed at the Crystal Palace during this Festival were reported as being: 19,200 sandwiches, 14,000 pies, 240 fore-quarters of lamb, 120 balantine of lamb, 3509 chickens, 480 hams, 485 tongues, 150 galantines of chicken, 60 game pies, 3052 lobster salads, 3825 salmon mayonnaise, 300 score of lettuces, 40,000 penny buns, 25,000 twopenny buns, 32,249 ices, 400 jellies, 400 creams, 350 fruit tarts, 30,000 beverages, 9 tons of roast and boiled beef, 3500 quarts of tea, coffee and chocolate.

A comparison of attendances at the two Handel Festivals of 1857 and 1859 is interesting since it reflected the public appreciation of such monster musical meetings:-

1857 Performances	Numbers attending	1859 Performances	Numbers attending
Saturday: Rehearsal	8,344	Saturday: Rehearsal	19,680
Monday: 'Messiah'	11,129	Monday: 'Messiah'	17,109
Wednesday: 'Judas Maccabeus'	11,649	Wednesday: Selections	17,644
Friday: 'Israel'	17,292	Friday: 'Israel'	26,827
Total attendances	48,414	Total attendances	81,260

SY-1859 / 015   Tonic Sol-Fa Association
by Messrs Pinches & W.J. Taylor   Ae Wm 35 mm

Obverse *Three line inscription within a laurel wreath:* CRYSTAL PALACE / CHOIR / SEPT. 14TH 1859 *Inscription around the border:* TONIC SOL-FA ASSOCIATION • ❖ •
Reverse A female resting her left hand upon a pillar inscribed with tonic sol-fa notation, her right hand is pointing to a road leading uphill to a temple. *Signed* W.. J. TAYLOR. LONDON
Rim Plain.

RRR *Davis et al* 193/731 PC

See note to SY-1857 /020.

SY-1860 / 001   Royal Dramatic College
by Messrs Pinches & H. Brown   Ar Ae Wm 23 mm

Obverse Distant view of a building. *Inscription above:* FOUNDATION STONE LAID BY / THE PRINCE CONSORT / JUNE 1. 1860 *Signed* H. BROWN CRYSTAL PALACE
Reverse Bust of William Shakespeare plus two characters from his plays within three porticos. *Inscription below:* ROYAL DRAMATIC COLLEGE / FOUNDED A D 1858 *Inscription around the border:* ALL THE WORLD'S A STAGE & ALL THE MEN & WOMEN MERELY PLAYERS
Rim Plain.

Ae RRR, Wm RR *Brown* 2692, *Eimer (I)* 1534   BM PC

See note to SY-1858 /001.

SY-1860 / 005   Tonic Sol-Fa Association
by Messrs Pinches & W.J. Taylor   Wm 35 mm

Obverse *Three line inscription within a laurel wreath:* CRYSTAL PALACE / CHOIR / MAY 16TH. 1860 *Inscription around the border:* • TONIC SOL-FA ASSOCIATION • ❖
Reverse Similar to reverse of SY-1859 /015.
Rim Plain.

RRR *unrecorded* PC

See note to SY-1857 /020.

SY-1861 / 001   Tonic Sol-Fa Association
by Messrs Pinches & W.J. Taylor   Ae 32 mm

Obverse Four line inscription within a laurel wreath:
CRYSTAL PALACE / CHOIR / JULY 17TH / 1861
Reverse A female standing upon a plinth, holding in her left hand a scroll inscribed with tonic sol-fa notation, and in her right hand a palm frond. *Inscription around the border:* TONIC SOL-FA ASSOCIATION *Signed* W.J. TAYLOR LONDON
Rim Plain.

| RRR | *unrecorded* | PC |

Courtesy of Jim Allen. See note to SY-1857 /020.

SY-1861 / 005   Visit of Blondin
by ?   Ar Ae 15 mm

Obverse Draped bust of Charles Blondin facing. *Inscription around the border:* BLONDIN / HERO OF NIAGARA
Reverse Four line inscription within a border of rope: AT THE / CRYSTAL / PALACE / 1861
Rim Plain.

| RRR | *unrecorded* | PC |

Blondin with his rope, 1861. *Illustrated London News 1861.*

Charles Blondin (Jean Francois Gravelet, 1824–1897) tight-rope performer, made his first appearance at the Palace on a rope which stretched the whole length of the central transept. He later performed his daring feats on a rope two thousand feet in length, stretched across three enormous masts specially erected upon the terraces. His most popular act performed at the Crystal Palace was his fireworks display, which involved him pushing a barrow-load full of fireworks to the centre of the rope, and then lighting them. He died at Ealing in 1897.

SY-1863 / 001   Prince of Wales Marriage
by Messrs Pinches & H. Brown   Wm Wmg 42 mm
Av Ar Al Aeg Wm 53 mm

Obverse Conjoined bare heads of the Prince and Princess of Wales left. *Inscription around the border:* ALBERT EDWARD PRINCE OF WALES: BORN NOV. 9. 1841 + ALEXANDRA PRINCESS OF DENMARK BORN DEC.1. 1844 + *Signed* H. BROWN CRYSTAL / PALACE
Reverse Plumes above *inscription within a laurel wreath:* MARRIED / MARCH 10 / 1863
Rim Plain.

42 mm: Wm S, Wmg RR. 53mm: Av RRR, Ar RRR, Al RRR, Aeg RR, Wm S *Brown* 2759 AM BM PC

On 3 March 1863, the following advertisement appeared in *The Times*

> THE MARRIAGE MEDAL of His Royal Highness the Prince of WALES, two and one eighth inch in diameter. This medal has on its face an excellent likeness of the Prince and Princess, and on the reverse 'Married March 10, 1863,' encircled by flowers. In gold, from £10 to £25; silver 1 to 3 guineas; aluminium 12 /6d. The wedding medal, the Foresters' and Odd Fellows' wedding medal, one and five eighth inch in diameter, at lower prices. The marriage medal, in white metal sent in case for 20 postage stamps; any of the other medals in case for 16 stamps. H. BROWN, Medal Court, Crystal Palace, Sydenham.

The author has not yet seen a specimen of the gold and silver medals, nor the 'Foresters' and 'Odd Fellows' medals. In a later advertisement on 7 March, a miniature Princess Alexandra medal was offered for sale by Brown at 2/6d in silver, and at 3/- in aluminium. The author has not yet seen specimens of these two either.

SY-1863 / 005 Prince of Wales Marriage
by Messrs Pinches & W.J. Taylor Wm 31 mm

Obverse Conjoined bare heads of Prince and Princess of Wales right. *Inscription around the border:* H.R.H. PRINCE OF WALES H.R.H. PRINCESS OF WALES ✿ *Signed* W. J. TAYLOR
Reverse *Five line inscription within a floral wreath:* STRUCK / AT THE / CRYSTAL / PALACE / MEDAL PRESS *Signed* W.J. TAYLOR. MEDALLIST
Rim Plain.

RRR *unrecorded* PC

The medal is not dated, but there is no doubt it was struck to commemorate the marriage of the Prince of Wales.

SY-1864 / 001 Shakespeare Tercentenary
by Messrs Pinches & H. Brown Ae Aeg Wm 24 mm

Obverse Draped bust of William Shakespeare left *Inscription around the border:* WILLIAM SHAKESPEARE: BORN APRIL 23 1564: DIED APRIL 23 1616. ✿ *Signed* H. BROWN.
Reverse View of the birthplace. *Inscription around the border:* SHAKESPEARE'S BIRTHPLACE *Signed* H. BROWN
Rim Plain.

Ae R, Aeg RR, Wm R *Brown* 2807 PC

The showpiece of the commemorative fete held at the Palace on Saturday 23 April was a replica of Shakespeare's birthplace built in the centre transept. Included in the admission price of one shilling was a photograph of Shakespeare's house at Stratford-on-Avon, for visitors to compare with the replica. A monument was erected on the terraces and a court was given over entirely to exhibits, music and recitals.

SY-1864 / 005 Shakespeare Tercentenary
by Messrs Pinches & H. Brown   Ae 24 mm

Obverse Similar to obverse of SY-1864 /001.
Reverse View of the birthplace. *Inscription around border:*
SHAKESPEARE TERCENTENARY FESTIVAL *In exergue:*
1864 *Signed* H. BROWN
Rim Plain.

RR   *Brown* 2807A   PC

See note to SY-1864 /001.

SY-1864 / 010 Shakespeare Tercentenary
by Messrs Pinches & H. Brown   Ae Wm Wmg 42 mm

Obverse Draped bust of William Shakespeare left. *Inscription
on a raised border:* WILLIAM SHAKESPEARE: BORN
APRIL. 23. 1564: DIED APRIL 23. 1616 *Signed* H.
BROWN. CRYSTAL / PALACE
Reverse View of the birthplace. *In exergue:* BIRTHPLACE
OF / SHAKESPEARE *Inscription on a raised border:*
STRATFORD UPON AVON FESTIVAL 1864
Rim Plain.

Ae RR, Wm R, Wmg RR   *Brown* 2806   AM PC

See note to SY-1864 /001.

SY-1864 / 011 Shakespeare Tercentenary
by Messrs Pinches & H. Brown   Wm 42 mm

Obverse Similar to obverse of SY-1864 /010.
Reverse Similar to reverse of SY-1854 /070.
Rim Plain.

RRR   *unrecorded*   PC

Courtesy of C.E.

SY-1864 / 015 Shakespeare Tercentenary
by Messrs Pinches & H. Brown   Wm 42 mm

Obverse Similar to obverse of SY-1864 /010, but it has serif
script, and the border is not raised. *Signed* H. BROWN.
CRYSTAL PALACE
Reverse View of the birthplace (no chimney). *Inscription
around the border:* BIRTHPLACE OF SHAKESPEARE
STRATFORD UPON AVON *In exergue:* FESTIVAL 1864
Rim Plain.

RRR   *unrecorded*   PC

See note to SY-1864 /001.

SY-1864 / 020 Visit of General Garibaldi
by Messrs Pinches   Wm 42 mm

Obverse   Uniformed bust of General Garibaldi right. *Inscription around the border:* GIUSEPPE GARIBALDI BORN AT NICE 1807. *Signed* T.R. PINCHES F.
Reverse   Four line inscription in circle within a laurel wreath: WELCOME / TO / ENGLAND / 1864
Rim   Plain.

R	*Brown 2800*	PC

General Garibaldi (1807–1882), Italian patriot. Visited England in 1864 to further the cause of Italian unification. He attended a rally held at the Palace on Monday 18 April. This souvenir was sold there to commemorate the visit.

SY-1864 / 025   Visit of General Garibaldi
by Messrs Pinches   Wm 42 mm

Obverse   Similar to obverse of SY-1864 /020.
Reverse   Similar to reverse of SY-1854 /060.
Rim   Plain.

RRR	*unrecorded*	PC

Struck at the Palace and sold in a brass case. See note to SY-1864 /020.

SY-1864 / 030   Visit of General Garibaldi
by Messrs Pinches   Ae 42 mm

Obverse   Similar to obverse of SY-1864 /020.
Reverse   Inscription within closed wreath: ENGLAND / WELCOMES THE / LIBERATOR / OF ITALY *Inscription around:* TO COMMEMORATE THE VISIT OF GARIBALDI. APRIL 3ᴿᴰ 1864.
Rim   Plain.

RRR	*Brown 2799*

Description obtained from Brown, because the author has not seen a specimen. See note to SY-1864 /020.

SY-1866 / 001   Visitors to the Crystal Palace
by Messrs Pinches & W.J. Taylor   Wm 42 mm

Obverse   View of the Crystal Palace and terraces. *Inscription above:* CRYSTAL PALACE SYDENHAM *In exergue:* FIRST COLUMN ERECTED / AUG. 5. 1852 / OPENED JUNE 10. 1854 *Signed* W.J. TAYLOR LONDON
Reverse   *Inscription within linear circle:* STRUCK IN THE CRYSTAL PALACE / VISITORS / TO THE / 30 APRIL 1866 / 18,607,852 / BY W. J. TAYLOR Around the circle arranged in the form of a rose are ten tablets each with an inscription: *(1)* WIDTH / OF / BUILDING / 324 / FEET *(2)* LENGTH OF / NAVE / 1602 Fᵀ / HEIGHT / 104 Fᵀ *(3)* HEIGHT OF / CENTRE / TRANSEPT / 174 / FEET *(4)* IRON / USED IN / WATER / TOWERS / 1600 / TONS *(5)* WATER / TOWERS / 284 FT / ABOVE / CROSS OF / Sᵀ PAULS *(6)* PALACE / AND / GROUNDS / COVER / 200 / ACRES *(7)* HANDEL / ORCHESTRA / SEATS / 5000 / PERSONS *(8)* GLASS / USED IN / BUILDING / 25 / ACRES *(9)* IRON / USED IN / BUILDING / 9641 / TONS *(10)* LENGTH OF / HOT WATER / PIPES / 50 / MILES
Rim   Plain.

R	*Brown 2868, Eidlitz 775/84, Taylor 171l*	AM BM BR PC

SY-1866 / 005   Visitors to the Crystal Palace
by Messrs Pinches & W.J. Taylor   Wm 42 mm

Obverse   View of the Crystal Palace. *Inscription above:* CRYSTAL PALACE SYDENHAM BEING THE GREAT EXHIBITION OF 1851 REMOVED FROM HYDE PARK. *In exergue:* FIRST COLUMN ERECTED AUG 5. 1852 THE PALACE OF THE PEOPLE OPENED JUNE 10. 1854 *Signed* W. J. TAYLOR LONDON.
Reverse   Similar to reverse of SY-1866 /001.
Rim   Plain.

RRR	*Eidlitz 774/84, Taylor 171k*

Description obtained from Taylor, because the author has not seen a specimen.

SY-1866 / 010 Visitors to the Crystal Palace
by Messrs Pinches & W.J. Taylor   Wm 42 mm

Obverse View of the Crystal Palace and terraces. *Inscription above:* CRYSTAL PALACE SYDENHAM / THE / PALACE / OF THE PEOPLE. *In exergue:* DESIGNED BY SIR J. PAXTON / 1ˢᵗ COLUMN ERECTED AUG. 5. 1852 / OPENED / JUNE 10ᵀᴴ 1854 *Signed* W. J. TAYLOR LONDON
Reverse Similar to reverse of SY-1866 /001.
Rim Plain.

RRR *unrecorded* PC

SY-1866 / 015 Royal Dramatic College Fete
by Messrs Pinches & W.J. Taylor   Wm 38 mm

Obverse Draped bust of William Shakespeare left. *Inscription around the border:* WILLIAM SHAKSPEARE *Signed* W. J. TAYLOR. LONDON
Reverse Seven line inscription within a floral wreath: ROYAL / DRAMATIC / COLLEGE / FETE / CRYSTAL PALACE / JULY 7 & 9 / 1866
Rim Plain.

RRR *unrecorded* PC

On Saturday 7 July there were 17,000 people at the Palace and on Monday 9 July 28,000. The stalls and entertainments presided over by actors and actresses naturally attracted most attention, but apparently the bazaars, side shows, gypsy tent, knock-em downs and Aunt Sally were crowded throughout both days. See note to SY-1858 /001. An amusing letter regarding the 1864 fete can be found in *New Crystal Palace Matters* No. 1.

SY-1866 / 020 Christmastide
by ?   Wm 23 mm

Obverse Six line inscription within a wreath of oak: STRUCK / IN THE / CRYSTAL / PALACE / CHRISTMAS / 1866–67
Reverse Decorated Christmas tree. *Inscription around the border:* A HAPPY NEW YEAR
Rim Plain.

RRR *unrecorded* PC

Possibly handed out to audiences attending Christmas entertainments. The author has not seen a better specimen.

SY-1867 / 001 Restoration Fete
by Messrs Pinches & W.J. Taylor   Wm 42 mm

Obverse Similar to obverse of SY-1866 /010.
Reverse Phoenix rising from the flames. *Inscription above:* GRAND BENEFIT CONCERT / DEC. 30.1866 / TROPICAL END / PARTIALLY BURNT / RESTORATION FETE / 26. JUNE 1867 *Signed* W. J. TAYLOR LONDON

Rim Plain.

RRR	*Brown* 2879	BG PC

The Prince of Wales was present at the grand concert attended by an audience of 20,000, to raise the funds required to restore the north wing of the Palace, which was destroyed by fire on 30 December 1866. The financial situation of the Crystal Palace Company at that time prevented it from restoring the north transept, although sufficient repairs were undertaken to enable the north wing to be re-opened to the public on 15 February 1868. As a result the building was thereafter lop-sided.

SY-1867 / 005   Visit of Belgian Volunteers
by Messrs Pinches & W.J. Taylor   Wm 25 mm

Obverse Royal arms with supporters. *Signed* W. J. TAYLOR LONDON
Reverse *Ten line inscription:* VIVE LA BELGE L'UNION FAIT LA FORCE / TO / COMMEMORATE / THE VISIT / OF THE / BELGIAN / VOLUNTEERS / TO THE / CRYSTAL PALACE / 1867
Rim Plain.

RRR	*unrecorded*	BM

2,400 Belgian Civil Guards and Volunteers visited London from 10–22 July.

SY-1867 / 010   Reform Banquet
by Messrs Pinches & W.J. Taylor   Wm 38 mm

Obverse The British lion trampling on the dragon of Discord. *Inscription around the border:* FACTION DEFEATED THE PEOPLE TRIUMPHANT *In exergue:* REFORM BILL PASSED / AUG. 15. 1867
Reverse A triangle within ornate semi-circular border enclosing *inscription:* NO / CLASS / LEGISLATION *On the sides of the triangle:* LIBERTY IN RIGHT / EQUALITY IN LAW / FRATERNIY IN INTEREST *Above:* JUST MEASURES & HONEST MEN *Below:* REFORM BANQUET / CRYSTAL PALACE / SEPT. 30. 1867
Rim Plain.

RRR	*Brown* 2876, *Eimer (I)* 1593	BM PC

It took a further 61 years before universal adult suffrage was attained in Britain. Prior to the 20th century, the franchise was almost entirely confined to men, and in general, to those owning or holding property. The Reform Act of 1832 extended the franchise to men of the middle classes. The Reform Act of 1867 extended it to men of the urban working classes. The Reform Act of 1884 extended the vote to men of the rural working classes. The Reform Act of 1918 extended the vote to older women, and finally the Reform Act of 1928 extended the vote to younger women.

SY-1867 / 015   Robert Holt Token
by ?   Aeg 22 mm

Obverse Bare head of Queen Victoria left. *Inscription around the border:* H. M. G. M. QUEEN VICTORIA / 1867
Reverse View of the Crystal Palace the terraces and the north water tower. *Inscription above:* ROBERT HOLT *In exergue:* CRYSTAL / PALACE
Rim Beaded.

S	*Bell et al* 7750/CP13	PC

In 1987, shortly before he died, R.N.P. Hawkins sent a note to Siegfried Schwer to say he had discovered that Robert Holt had actually conducted his business of selling clocks, jewellery and leather goods in the Crystal Palace, and lived in a road close by. It is likely that he traded from the Clock Gallery in the Crystal Palace Arcade, which was described in a later Crystal Palace Programme as being the most attractive fancy fair in London. This is the earliest piece seen by the author which depicts a Brunel water tower. See also SY-ND /001.

If any further proof was needed that he was conducting a thriving business in the Crystal Palace, Robert Holt placed the following advertisement in the *Illustrated London News* in September 1861:

> LONDON CRYSTAL PALACE, 108 Oxford Street, — A large stock of Cabinet Papier-mache', Jewellery, and Fancy Goods Selling Off at 25 per cent to 50 per cent discount. At Mr. HOLT'S stands only.

SY-1867 / 020   Robert Holt Token
by ?   Aeg 22 mm

Obverse   Similar to obverse of SY-1867 /015, but has smaller script.
Reverse   Similar to reverse of SY-1867 /015.
Rim   Beaded.

RR   *unrecorded*   PC

Courtesy of John R.P. King.

SY-1868 / 001   Visit of the Duke of Edinburgh
by ?   Wm 31 mm

Obverse   Ten line inscription: CRYSTAL PALACE / JULY 4. 1868 / TO COMMEMORATE THE / MERCIFUL DELIVERANCE / OF H.R.H. THE DUKE OF / EDINBURGH / FROM ASSASSINATION / & HIS SAFE RETURN / TO / ENGLAND
Reverse   *Inscription within a floral wreath:* WELCOME / TO OUR / SAILOR / PRINCE
Rim   Beaded obverse, plain reverse.

RRR   *Brown* 2887   PC

During his visit to Australia in 1868, HRH Prince Alfred, second son of Queen Victoria, was shot in the back by an Irishman named O'Farrell at Port Jackson on 12 March. As the wound was only superficial, the Prince recovered very quickly, nevertheless, O'Farrell was convicted of attempted murder and executed. This medal was struck when the Prince visited the Palace with a number of his friends, after his safe return home.

SY-1869 / 001   Velocipede Exhibition
by Messrs Pinches & W.J. Taylor   Ae Aeg 42 mm

Obverse   View of the Crystal Palace and terraces. *Signed* W.J. TAYLOR LONDON.
Reverse   A laurel wreath. *Inscription around the border:* INTERNATIONAL VELOCIPEDE & LOCO-MACHINE EXHIBITION / 1869
Rim   Plain.

RRR   *unrecorded*   PC

The exhibition opened on 26 May. The velocipede was an early form of bicycle which became popular during the 1860s. It must have been hazardous to ride, because not only was it very heavy, but, since the pedals were mounted upon the front wheel, it proved extremely difficult to control on corners when the rider attempted to prevent it rubbing against the inside of his leg. Due to the poor state of the roads at that time, it was also a very uncomfortable ride, and it quickly became known as the 'boneshaker'.

The first National Cycle Show was held at the Palace in January 1890. Illustration courtesy of John Whitmore.

SY-1871 / 001   Anglo-Belgian Meeting
by Geerts   Ae 59 mm

SY-1871 / 010   National Temperance League Festival
by ?   Wm 38 mm

Obverse   Eight line inscription: OFFERT / PAR LA / SOCIETE LIBRE D'ABEONA / SOUS LE PATRONAGE / DE LA / DIRECTION / DU / PALAIS DE CRISTAL.
Inscription around the border: CONCOURS ANGLO-BELGE / LONDRES 1871
Reverse   Dove in flight holding a laurel wreath and ribbon.
Signed ED. GEERTS. F. BRUXELLES
Rim   Plain obverse, ornate reverse.

RRR   *unrecorded*   PC

Courtesy of Jim Allen.

Obverse   Nine line inscription: THE HOLDER OF THIS / MEDAL / WAS ONE OF THE / TEN THOUSAND SINGERS / WHO GAVE TWO CONCERTS / AT THE / CRYSTAL PALACE / ON TUESDAY AUG. 1. / 1871
Inscription around the border: UNITED KINGDOM BAND OF HOPE UNION CHOIR ✿
Reverse   A kneeling child in prayer. *Inscription above:* BE THOU FAITHFUL UNTO DEATH / LEAD US NOT INTO TEMPTATION *Inscription below:* TRAIN UP A CHILD IN THE WAY HE SHOULD GO / WINE IS A MOCKER
Rim   Plain.

RRR   **BR**   PC

The National Temperance League was formed in 1856. From 1862 it held an annual festival at the Palace and among the Temperance organisations attending were Band of Hope, Good Templars, Rechabites, Sons of the Phoenix, Sons of Temperance, and others. The Band of Hope was founded at Leeds in 1847 to promote Temperance principles among children. The United Kingdom Band of Hope Union was formed in 1855, and by the end of the century around 30,000 branches existed. The 10,000 singers referred to on the medal, were actually 5,000 singers who performed at two concerts.

SY-1871 / 005   Industrial Exhibition
by Messrs Pinches & W.J. Taylor   Ae 42 mm

Obverse   Head of Athena left. *Signed* W.J. TAYLOR. LONDON.
Reverse   Six line inscription in laurel wreath: Presented To / MISS / MATILDA CORNABY / FOR / Embroidery / CLASS IX *Inscription on raised border:* SYDENHAM INDUSTRIAL EXHIBITION / 1871 *Signed* W.J.T.
Rim   Plain.

RRR   *unrecorded*   PC

SY-1872 / 001 National Temperance League Festival
by ? Wm 38 mm

Obverse Ten line inscription upon a shield: THE HOLDER OF / THIS MEDAL / WAS ONE OF THE / TEN THOUSAND / SINGERS / WHO GAVE / TWO CONCERTS / AT THE / CRYSTAL PALACE / JULY 23. 1872 *Inscription around the border:* UNITED KINGDOM BAND OF HOPE UNION CHOIR ☆

Reverse Similar to reverse of SY-1871 /010.

Rim Plain.

RRR *unrecorded* PC

See *Crystal Palace Matters* No. 34 for an article about the Band of Hope meetings at the Palace; also note to SY-1871 /010.

The National Temperance League held its annual festival at the Palace on Tuesday 23 July. The number of persons admitted during the day was 62,280, many thousands of them came in excursion parties in special trains from distant parts of the country, some having arrived in London the previous day. Most of the adults were attired in gay scarves, worn partly as a collar, which denoted they were total abstainers. By a special arrangement with the directors of the Crystal Palace Company and the catering contractors no intoxicating drink was to be sold. The day's entertainment consisted mainly of sports, games and lectures, but the most imposing part was the grand choral concert performed by 5,000 children, all neatly dressed and decorated with a medal and the badges of their Order. A procession of all the Temperance Orders with their banners was marshalled at five o'clock, but it was rudely interrupted by thunderstorms and torrential rain, which drove the members into the palace for shelter.

SY-1873 / 001 Picture Gallery Prize
by Messrs Pinches, G.G. Adams & W.J. Taylor Ae 63 mm

Obverse Distant view of the Crystal Palace. Britannia attended by Plenty and Learning, Fame with trumpet overhead. *Inscription around the border:* ORNATUR PROPIIS INDUSTRIA DONIS *Signed* G.G. ADAMS. D:F:

Reverse Eight line inscription within a laurel wreath: AWARDED / BY THE / CRYSTAL PALACE Co. / FOR A PICTURE / BATTLE OF LA HOGUE / BY / A.C.A. BALLIN / 1873

Rim Plain.

RRR *Withers* 657 (see SY-1893/010 for ill.) PC

The Crystal Palace Picture Gallery was opened in June 1856. Artists who exhibited their pictures at the Gallery were eligible for one of the annual awards if the judges chose their work to be one of the best eight in either of the following three categories: History or Figure subjects in Oil; Landscapes, Sea-pieces, Animals and other subjects; Best Water Colour Drawings. There were eight awards in each category, i.e. 1 gold, 4 silver, 3 bronze. See SY-1893 /010 for an illustration of the 1893 Picture Gallery Prize List.

SY-1873 / 005 National Music Meeting
by ? Ar 31 mm

Obverse Ten line inscription: PRESENTED / BY / RICHARD FOTHERGILL M. P. / IN COMMEMORATION / OF THE VICTORY OF THE / SOUTH WALES CHORAL UNION / AT THE / CRYSTAL PALACE / JULY 10ᵀᴴ / 1873

Reverse Welsh harp within a wreath of laurel.

Rim Plain.

RRR *unrecorded* PC

The National Music Meetings were held at the Palace in 1872, 1873 and 1875. It did not take place in 1874 because the facilities were being used for the Handel festival. In class I which was contested by choral societies not exceeding 500 in number, the South Wales Choral Union won the Challenge Trophy in each of the first two years. Illustration courtesy of Jim Allen.

SY-1873 / 010	National Temperance League Festival
by ?	Wm 38 mm

Obverse Eleven line inscription: UNITED KINGDOM / BAND OF HOPE UNION CHOIR / THE HOLDER OF THIS MEDAL / WAS ONE OF THE / TEN THOUSAND / SINGERS / (ALL TOTAL ABSTAINERS) / WHO GAVE TWO CONCERTS / AT THE / CRYSTAL PALACE / JULY 22. 1873
Reverse Similar to reverse of SY-1871 /010.
Rim Scalloped obverse, plain reverse.

RRR	*unrecorded* PC

See note to SY-1871 /010.

SY-1874 / 001	National Temperance League Festival
by ?	Wm 38 mm

Obverse Eleven line inscription: THE HOLDER OF THIS / MEDAL / WAS A MEMBER OF / THE / Crystal Palace Choir / JULY 21. 1874 / THE CHOIR CONSISTED OF / 5000 VOICES / ALL PLEDGED ABSTAINERS / OF AT LEAST / ONE YEAR'S STANDING *Inscription around the border:* UNITED KINGDOM BAND OF HOPE UNION CHOIR ✿
Reverse Similar to reverse of SY-1871 /010.
Rim Plain.

RRR	*unrecorded* PC

See note to SY-1871 /010.

SY-1876 / 001	Picture Gallery Prize
by Messrs Pinches, G.G. Adams & W.J. Taylor	Ae 63 mm

Obverse Similar to obverse of SY-1873 /001.
Reverse Eight line inscription within a laurel wreath: AWARDED / BY THE / CRYSTAL PALACE Co. / FOR A PICTURE / 'ON THE COAST' / BY / W. LUKER /1876.
Rim Plain.

RRR	*Withers 657 (see SY-1893/010 for ill.)* PC

See note to SY-1873 /001.

SY-1879 / 001	First Good Templar Fete
by Messrs Pinches & W.J. Taylor	Wm 38 mm

Obverse View of the Crystal Palace, terraces and the south water tower. *Inscription above:* FIRST GOOD TEMPLAR FETE / HELD AT THE *In exergue:* CRYSTAL PALACE / JULY 13. 1879
Reverse Similar to reverse of SY-1854 /120.
Rim Plain.

RRR	*unrecorded (see SY-1881/005 for ill.)* PC

The Good Templars were founded in the United States of America as a Society of Teetotallers. The first English Lodge was formed at Birmingham in May 1868. The Grand Lodge of England was instituted on 25 July 1870. By 1874, there were more than 3,700 Lodges in the United Kingdom, with nearly a quarter of a million followers.

SY-1880 / 001	Band of Hope Union Fete
by ?	Wm 38 mm

Obverse Eight line inscription upon a shield: THE /

HOLDER OF THIS / MEDAL / WAS ONE OF THE / 15,000 / SINGERS / WHO GAVE / THREE CONCERTS
Inscription around the border: BAND OF HOPE UNION FETE AT THE CRYSTAL PALACE / • JULY 13, 1880 •
Reverse Similar to reverse of SY-1871 /010.
Rim Plain.

RRR *unrecorded* PC

See note to SY-1871 /010.

SY-1881 / 001 International Exhibition
by Messrs Pinches   Ae 63 mm

Obverse Four line inscription above a shield within a laurel wreath: CRYSTAL / PALACE / INTERNATIONAL / EXHIBITION / 1881
Reverse Similar to reverse of SY-1854 /065.
Rim Plain.

RR *Brown* 3107 AM PC

Possibly the International Woollen Exhibition, which was opened by the Duke of Connaught on 2 June.

SY-1881 / 005 Second Good Templar Fete
by Messrs Pinches & W.J. Taylor   Wm 38 mm

Obverse View of the Crystal Palace, terraces and south water tower. *Inscription above:* SECOND GOOD TEMPLAR FETE / HELD AT THE *In exergue:* CRYSTAL PALACE / JULY 12TH 1881
Reverse Similar to reverse of SY-1854 /120.
Rim Plain.

RRR *unrecorded* PC

See note to SY-1879 /001.

SY-1882 / 001 John Curwen
by Messrs Pinches   Ae 38 mm

Obverse Similar to obverse of SY-1891 /001.
Reverse *Inscription on wide border:* THE ASSOCIATION OF TONIC SOL-FA CHOIRS
Rim Plain.

RR *Brown* 3116 PC

Description obtained from Brown, because the author has not seen a specimen. See notes to SY-1857 /020 and SY-1891 /001.

SY-1882 / 005 National Temperance Jubilee Fete
by Messrs Pinches & W.J. Taylor Wm 39 mm

Obverse Draped bust of Joseph Livesey. *Inscription above:* JOSEPH LIVESEY *Inscription below:* 1882 / JUBILEE OF TOTAL ABSTINENCE *Signed* W.J. TAYLOR
Reverse Thirteen line inscription: THE PLEDGE SIGNED / SEPʀ 1ˢᵀ 1832 / BY / JOSEPH LIVESEY / AND SIX OTHER MEN / OF PRESTON. / 'WE AGREE TO ABSTAIN / FROM ALL LIQUORS / OF AN INTOXICATING QUALITY. / WHETHER ALE. POR TER. WINE / OR ARDENT SPIRITS. / EXCEPT AS / MEDICINES.' *Inscription around the border:* NATIONAL TEMPERANCE JUBILEE FETE / ✿ CRYSTAL PALACE SEPʀ 5ᵀᴴ 1882 ✿
Rim Plain.

RR	*Brown* 3140	BM PC

Joseph Livesey (1794–1884) published the *Preston Temperance Advocate*, the first news-sheet devoted entirely to temperance principles and matters.

SY-1882 / 010 National Temperance Jubilee Fete
by Messrs Pinches & W.J. Taylor Wm 39 mm

Obverse Similar to obverse of SY-1882 /005.
Reverse Eight line inscription upon a cartouche: THE / HOLDER OF THIS / TOOK PART IN / THE / CONCERTS / BY / 9,000 / VOICES *Inscription around the*

border: NATIONAL TEMPERANCE JUBILEE FETE / CRYSTAL PALACE / ✿ SEPʀ 5ᵀᴴ 1882 ✿
Rim Plain.

RR	*unrecorded*	PC

See note to SY-1882 /005.

SY-1882 / 015 National Temperance Jubilee Fete
by ? Wm 44 mm

Obverse Empty cartouche. *Inscription around the border:* NATIONAL TEMPERANCE JUBLILEE FETE / • CRYSTAL PALACE SEPᵀ 5ᵀᴴ 1882 •
Reverse Blank.
Rim Plain.

RRRR	*unrecorded*	PC

This would appear to be a trial strike. Note the extra L in JUBILEE.

SY-1883 / 001 National Temperance Fete
by ? Wm 38 mm

Obverse Seven line inscription within a quatrefoil: THE / GREAT / NATIONAL / TEMPERANCE FETE / CRYSTAL PALACE / JULY 10ᵀᴴ / 1883 *Inscription around the border:* THE HOLDER OF THIS MEDAL WAS ONE

OF THE BAND OF HOPE UNION CHOIR OF 15,000 SINGERS •

Reverse   Similar to reverse of SY-1871 /010.
Rim   Plain.

RR   *unrecorded*   PC

See note to SY-1871 /010.

SY-1884 / 001   School of Art Science & Literature
by Messrs Pinches   Ar 63 mm

Obverse   *Ten line inscription in beaded circle within a border of laurel:* CRYSTAL PALACE SCHOOL OF ART, SCIENCE AND LITERATURE / AWARDED / TO / Ada. C. Hay / FOR / WATER COLOUR PAINTING / EDWARD A. GOODALL R.W.S. / MASTER / July 1884. / • TWENTY FOURTH SESSION •

Reverse   Similar to reverse of SY-1854 /065.
Rim   Plain.

RRR   *unrecorded*   PC

The school was formed in 1860 and located in a building near the south water tower. Although it survived the great fire of 1936, it was burned down by vandals in 1950.

ANNOUNCEMENTS.

CRYSTAL PALACE COMPANY'S SCHOOL OF ART, SCIENCE, AND LITERATURE. — LADIES' DIVISION. — FIFTEENTH SESSION, 1874-75.

LECTURES ON SPECIAL SUBJECTS.

The Committee of Directors have made arrangements for the delivery of successive short series of LECTURES ON SPECIAL SUBJECTS by gentlemen of eminence in Art, Science, and Literature. These Lectures will be purely educational in character, and, as far as possible, complete in themselves, but will not in any way supplant the permanent private classes, to which they are designed to be accessory. They are intended to stimulate independent thought, and to lead the Student to a conception of some of the ulterior aims of the studies she pursues. They will be delivered in the largest Class Room of the School, generally on FRIDAYS, in the afternoon ; and the most moderate fee that is possible in each case will be fixed.

Ladies only will be admitted.

The FIRST COURSE will be of SIX LECTURES on

"THE INTERPRETATION OF NATURE AS IT RELATES TO MAN AND HIS EDUCATION."

BY THE

REV. CHARLES PRITCHARD, M.A., F.R.S., V.P.R.A.S., F.G.S., *Savilian Professor of Astronomy in the University of Oxford.*

SYLLABUS.

1. FRIDAY, Nov. 13.—The Universe external to the Earth.
2. FRIDAY, Nov. 20, The Gradual Formation of the Earth and the Advent of Man.
3. FRIDAY, Nov. 27, The Growth of Animal Life.
4. FRIDAY, Dec. 4, The Effect of the Physical Features of the Earth on Man.
5. FRIDAY, Dec. 11, Man in Contact with the Forces of Nature.
6. FRIDAY, Dec. 18, Summary of the Subject, and General Considerations.

Commence each day at half-past Three.

The subject matter of the Third, Fourth, and Fifth Lectures may possibly be somewhat modified ; but if so, due notice will be given.

FEES : For the Course—Students, 7s. 6d. ; Non-Students, 15s.

Tickets can be obtained only in the Office of the School in the Library next the Reading Room, Byzantine Court.

Special arrangements as to Fees will be made for Pupils from Schools, or other Educational Establishments, that are not in direct connection with the School of Art, Science, and Literature.

Cookery and Practical Domestic Economy (MISS MARY HOOPER). Wednesdays. A second section of this Class is being formed to meet at 3 p.m. The first lesson will be on November 11th.

Harmony (DR. JOHN STAINER, M.A.). Saturdays. An Advanced Class, to commence on Saturday next, November 13th, is now being formed. A few names can still be received.

By Order of the Committee,
F. K. J. SHENTON,
Superintendent Literary Department.

Crystal Palace Saturday Concert Programme Announcements, Nov. 1874

SY-1884 / 005 London International Exhibition
by Messrs Pinches & A. Fisch   Arg Aes Ae 63 mm

Obverse   Six line inscription within a wreath of palm and laurel: LONDON / INTERNATIONAL / EXHIBITION / CRYSTAL / PALACE / 1884 *Signed* A. FISCH
Reverse   Similar to reverse of SY-1854 /065.
Rim   Plain.
Edge   Inscribed with the name of the recipient.

Ae R, Aes RR, Arg RRR   *Brown* 3174   AM BR PC

The exhibition was opened by the Lord Mayor of London on 23 April.

SY-1884 / 010 Third Good Templar Fete
by Messrs Pinches & W.J. Taylor   Wm 38 mm

Obverse   View of the Crystal Palace, terraces and south water tower. *Inscription above:* THIRD GOOD TEMPLAR FETE / HELD AT THE *In exergue:* CRYSTAL PALACE / 8 JULY 1884
Reverse   Similar to reverse of SY-1854 /120.
Rim   Plain.

RRR   *unrecorded*   PC

See note to SY-1879 /001.

SY-1885 / 001 Fourth Good Templar Fete
by Messrs Pinches & W.J. Taylor   Wm 38 mm

Obverse   View of the Crystal Palace, terraces and south water tower. *Inscription above:* FOURTH GOOD TEMPLAR FETE / HELD AT THE *In exergue:* CRYSTAL PALACE / 14 JULY 1885
Reverse   Similar to reverse of SY-1854 /120.
Rim   Plain.

RRR   *unrecorded*   PC

See note to SY-1879 /001.

SY-1885 / 005   Visitors to the Crystal Palace
by Messrs Pinches & W.J. Taylor   Wm 42 mm

Obverse   Similar to obverse of SY-1866 /001.
Reverse   Similar to reverse of SY-1866 /001, but the inscription in the centre circle reads: VISITORS / TO THE / 25 JULY 1885 / 57,859,342
Rim   Plain.

RR   *Brown* 3193   BG PC

SY-1886 / 001   National Temperance Fete
by Messrs Pinches & W.J. Taylor   Wm 38 mm

Obverse   View of the Crystal Palace, terraces and south water tower. *Inscription above:* NATIONAL TEMPERANCE FETE / HELD AT THE *In exergue:* CRYSTAL PALACE / 13 JULY 1886
Reverse   Eight line inscription on a shield: THE HOLDER OF / THIS MEDAL / WAS ONE OF THE / FIFTEEN / THOUSAND / SINGERS / WHO GAVE THREE / CONCERTS *Inscription around the border:* UNITED KINGDOM BAND OF HOPE CHOIRS ❖
Rim   Plain.

RRR   *unrecorded*   PC

See note to SY-1871 /010.

SY-1887 / 001   Picture Gallery Prize
by Messrs Pinches, G.G. Adams & W.J. Taylor   Ae 63 mm

Obverse   Similar to obverse of SY-1873 /001.
Reverse   Eight line inscription within a laurel wreath: AWARDED / BY THE / CRYSTAL PALACE Co. / FOR A PICTURE / 'LITTLE FLORA' / BY / MRS. M. WELLS / 1887
Rim   Plain.

RRR   *Withers* 657 (see SY-1893/010 for ill.)   PC

See note to SY-1873 /001.

SY-1887 / 005   Tricycle World Record
by ?   Ae 35 mm

Obverse   Twin frames holding a winged wheel to left, London Arms with supporters to right. *Inscription above:* THE LONDON / WHEELERS / 1884.
Reverse   Inscribed: '150 Miles Tricycle Worlds Record made by A.L. Bower Crystal Palace 30 Sept 1887. Time 10 Hrs 18 M 29 5 /5 Secs.'
Rim   Plain.

RRRR   *unrecorded*   PC

See Lot 152, Bonham's sale, 12 September 1996.

SY-1887 / 010   National Cage Bird Show
by E. Tyler   Ar 38 mm

Obverse   View of Crystal Palace and Terraces. *Incuse inscription above:* CAGE BIRD SHOW / Feb 12 to 17. *In exergue:* CRYSTAL PALACE /1887. *Signed* E.TYLER
Reverse   Seven line inscription in laurel wreath: PRESENTED BY / J.F. HILLS' / FOR BIRDS SHEWN IN BEST / CONDITION BRITISH BIRD / CLASSES / WON BY / W.H. Booth

Rim Plain.

Lid of the case is inscribed E. TYLER / MEDALLIST / 42 EXMOUTH ST / LONDON W.C. This is the earliest Bird Show medal seen by the author.

SY-1888 / 001   Photographic Exhibition
by Messrs Pinches   Ae 42 mm

Obverse   Four line inscription between a ribbon and a laurel

spray: PHOTOGRAPHIC / EXHIBITION / CRYSTAL PALACE / 1888 *Inscription on ribbon:* LUX MIHI LAURUS
Reverse   Similar to reverse of SY-1854 /065.
Rim   Beaded obverse, plain reverse.
Edge   Usually inscribed with the name of the recipient.

SY-1888 / 005   First   National   Co-Operative Festival
by Messrs Pinches & W.J. Taylor   Wm 42 mm

Obverse   Similar to obverse of SY-1866 /001.
Reverse   *Ten line inscription:* 'UNION IS STRENGTH' / FIRST / NATIONAL / CO-OPERATIVE / ❀ FESTIVAL ❀ / HELD AT THE / CRYSTAL PALACE / AUGUST 18ᵀᴴ / 1888 / 'LABOUR & WAIT'
Rim   Plain.

Co-operative societies were formed to enable the working classes to purchase articles of daily consumption at lower prices. The first society was formed at Rochdale in 1844 with a capital of £28.

Writing in the June 1921 Colchester issue of the *Wheatsheaf*, Edward Owen Greening FRHS, claimed he inaugurated the co-operative festivals. Apparently it all started from the Co-operative Flower Show held at South Kensington in 1886. Within two years it had become so popular, it had to be moved to a venue large enough to incorporate the enormous increase in the number of exhibitors, and all the other features which were rapidly being added to the programme of events. By 1891, the Flower Show itself had grown to such gigantic proportions it almost filled the great nave from end to end, the entries numbered 4,500, and attendances exceeded 40,000. The festivals died out toward the end of the century, but the Flower Show was revived in 1921, and continued until the great fire of 1936.

ANNOUNCEMENTS.

THE

Great Flower Show of the Season

WILL TAKE PLACE

ON SATURDAY, THE 29TH OF MAY.

DRAMATIC PERFORMANCE
IN OPERA THEATRE.

PROMENADE CONCERT
BY
Crystal Palace Choir, United Bands of the Royal Artillery and
Coldstream Guards, and the Company's Orchestra.

*Admission: By Tickets purchased before the day, Five Shillings:
By Payment at the Doors, Seven Shillings and Sixpence.*

GUINEA SEASON TICKET FREE.

THE NEXT

GREAT FIREWORK DISPLAY

(By Messrs. C. T. Brock and Co.)

Including a great device in honour of the Arctic Expedition,

WILL TAKE PLACE ON

THURSDAY NEXT, MAY 27TH.

Admission One Shilling, or by Guinea Season Ticket.

SIXTH NATIONAL EXHIBITION
OF

SPORTING AND OTHER DOGS,

UNDER THE RULES AND MANAGEMENT OF THE KENNEL CLUB,

Tuesday, Wednesday, Thursday, and Friday,
June 1, 2, 3, and 4.

Admission One Shilling, or by Guinea Season Ticket.

Crystal Palace Saturday Concert Programme Announcements,
May 1875.

SY-1889 / 001   School of Art Science & Literature
by Messrs Pinches   Ae 42 mm

Obverse   Ten line inscription: To / E.C.R. Nelson /
STUDENT / CRYSTAL PALACE C^os / SCHOOL OF /

PRACTICAL ENGINEERING / FOR THE COURSE /
SATISFACTORILY COMPLETED / DEC^R 21ST / 1889.
Inscription around the border: CRYSTAL PALACE SCHOOL
OF ART SCIENCE AND LITERATURE ❖
Reverse   Similar to reverse of SY-1854 /065.
Rim   Plain.

RRR   *unrecorded*   PC

An article on the School of Practical Engineering can be found
in *New Crystal Palace Matters* No. 7.

SY-1889 / 005   Photographic Exhibition
by Messrs Pinches   Ae 42 mm

*Obverse   Four line inscription between a ribbon and a laurel
spray:* PHOTOGRAPHIC / EXHIBITION / CRYSTAL
PALACE / 1889 *Inscription on ribbon:* LUX MIHI LAURUS
Reverse   Similar to reverse of SY-1854 /065.
Rim   Beaded obverse, plain reverse.
Edge   HORACE W. GRIDLEY, SERIES — CL: A. SEC: 3.

RR   *unrecorded*   PC

SY-1889 / 010   National Co-Operative Festival & Home Industries Exhibition
by J.A. Restall   Ae 51 mm

Obverse   Four line inscription within a laurel wreath:
GERTRUDE BENNETT / FOR / PAINTING / AUG. 17.
1889. *Inscription around the border:* HOME INDUSTRIES
EXHIBITION / CRYSTAL PALACE
Reverse   Female seated before a wheel in a colonnade.
Inscription below: NATIONAL CO-OPERATIVE /
FESTIVAL *Signed* J. A. RESTALL / HUBERT
HERKOMER DEL. / 1888
Rim   Plain.

RRR   *unrecorded* (see SY-1890/010 for ill.)   PC

See note to SY-1888 /005; also article in *Crystal Palace Matters*, No. 22.

SY-1890 / 001　Picture Gallery Prize
by Messrs Pinches & G.G. Adams　　　Ae 63 mm

Obverse　Similar to obverse of SY-1873 /001.
Reverse　Eight line inscription in a laurel wreath:
AWARDED / BY THE / CRYSTAL PALACE Co. / FOR A
DRAWING ON THE THAMES / BY / ROBT. NIBBS /
1890.
Rim　Plain.

RRR　*Withers 657 (see SY-1893/010 for ill.)*　PC

R.H. Nibbs (1816–1893) London and Brighton painter of marines, landscapes and battles. Exhibited at the Royal Academy in 1841–1888. Also awarded a Picture Gallery prize in 1873, see A.H. Baldwin and Sons Ltd 1996 catalogue.

SY-1890 / 005　Kennel Club Open Championship
by J.A. Restall　　　Ar 38x29 mm

Obverse　Head of a pug. *Inscription around the border:* PUG
DOG CLUB *Signed* J. A. R.
Reverse　Five line inscription within a laurel wreath:
CRYSTAL PALACE / 1890 / Won by / MRS HARTLEY'S /
CONNIE NELSON
Rim　Plain.

RRR　*unrecorded*　PC

SY-1890 / 010　National Co-Operative Festival & Home Industries Exhibition
by J.A. Restall　　　Ae 51 mm

Obverse　Four line inscription within a laurel wreath: W.
Bennett / for / Fretwork /Aug. 16.1890. *Inscription around the
border:* HOME INDUSTRIES EXHIBITION / ❖ CRYSTAL
PALACE ❖
Reverse　Similar to reverse of SY-1889 /010.
Rim　Plain.

RRR　*unrecorded*　PC

See note to SY-1888 /005.

SY-1890 / 015　Photographic Exhibition
by Messrs Pinches　　　Ae 42 mm

Obverse　Similar to obverse of SY-1889 /005.
Reverse　Similar to reverse of SY-1854 /065.
Rim　Plain.
Edge　Inscribed R. FAULKNER, CLASS B. SEC. 1

RR　*unrecorded*　PC

Courtesy of C.E.

SY-1891 / 001   Tonic Sol-Fa Jubilee
by Messrs Pinches   Wm Wmg 39 mm

Obverse   Draped bust of John Curwen half right. *Inscription around the border:* JOHN CURWEN, FOUNDER OF THE TONIC SOL-FA METHOD. *Signed* J. PINCHES.
Reverse   Tonic sol-fa notation on a scroll, ornate design in the field. *Inscription around the border:* THE TONIC SOL-FA JUBILEE / + 1891 +
Rim   Plain.

Wm R, Wmg RR   *unrecorded*   PC

Tonic Sol-Fa Festivals were regularly held at the Palace. This festival was held on Saturday 18 July to celebrate the 50th Jubilee of the development of the Tonic Sol-Fa method. In the morning concert 5,000 juveniles gave an exhibition of singing by hand signs. The afternoon concert was performed by 4,000 provincial singers. In the evening 3,000 metropolitan singers performed. See note to SY-1857 /020.

SY-1891 / 005   The Crystal Palace Dog Show
by Messrs Pinches   Ae 51 mm

Obverse   Similar to obverse of SY-ND /025.
Reverse   Five line inscription: BREEDERS COMPETITION. / 1891 / IRISH WOLFHOUNDS. / WON BY / MR. G.E. Crisp.
Rim   Plain.

RRR   *unrecorded*   PC

The medal is unsigned.

SY-1892 / 001   Electrical Exhibition
by Messrs Pinches   Ae 63 mm

Obverse Four line inscription within a laurel wreath:
CRYSTAL / PALACE / ELECTRICAL / EXHIBITION
Incuse 1892 on shield below.
Reverse Similar to reverse of SY-1854 /065.
Rim Plain.
Edge *Inscribed:* HOOKHAM, TOWNLEY, & Co.

RRR *Brown* 3435 PC

The Exhibition opened on 9 January.

SY-1892 / 005   Electrical Exhibition
by Messrs Pinches   Av 42 mm

Obverse Similar to obverse of SY-1892 /001, but it has a
ribbon covering the ends of the wreath.
Reverse Similar to reverse of SY-1892 /001.
Rim Plain.
Edge *Inscribed:* J. WHITE

RRRR *Brown* 3435 PC

James White went into partnership with Lord Kelvin to form
a firm named Kelvin & James White Ltd and operated from a
factory in Glasgow. It later became part of Smith Industries.

SY-1892 / 010   Electrical Exhibition
by ?   Vulcanite 70 mm

Obverse Nineteen line inscription: FOR / THE
EXCELLENCE / OF AN EXHIBIT AT THE /
ELECTRICAL EXHIBITION / CRYSTAL PALACE 1892 /
THIS VULCANITE (EBONITE) / MEDAL OF THE
FIRST CLASS / HAS BEEN AWARDED TO: / The
Maguay Electric Light Syndicate, / lim, London W.C. / BY
THE HAMBURG INDIA RUBBER COMB Co /
HAMBURG. GERMANY / DR H. TRAUN
PROPRIETOR. / MANUFACTURERS OF VULCANITE /
INSULATING MATERIAL / LONDON WAREHOUSE: /
F. WINTER, 4A CRIPPLEGATE / BUILDINGS.
LONDON. E.C.
Reverse Aerial view of two factories. *Inscription above:*
HAMBURG *Inscription below:* HARBURG A / E On the left
side is a figure pushing a cart, on the right there is a winged
dog.

Rim Plain.

RRRR *unrecorded* PC

Courtesy of Jim Allen.

SY-1892 / 015   24th Annual Cat Show
by E. Tyler   Ar 38 mm

Obverse View of the Crystal Palace and terraces. *Inscription above:* 24th ANNUAL CAT SHOW / OCT 18 & 19. *In exergue:* CRYSTAL PALACE / 1892 *Signed* E. TYLER
Reverse *Seven line inscription in laurel wreath:* FOR / BEST TWO KITTENS / CLASS / 18 / WON BY / MR. E. HILL / No. 127
Rim Plain obverse beaded reverse.

RRR *unrecorded (see SY-1893/015 for ill.)* PC

See 1997 catalogue by A.H. Baldwin and Sons.

SY-1892 / 020   National Temperance Fete
by ?   Bracteate Tin 45 mm

Obverse A harp in the centre of an eight pointed star. *Inscription around:* NATIONAL TEMPERANCE CHORAL UNION
Reverse Blank
Rim Plain.

RRR *unrecorded (see SY-1893/020 for ill.)* PC

This uniface medal is attached to a plain beige ribbon inscribed: CRYSTAL PALACE / 1892. / CONTEST B / 2ND. PRIZE. / NOTTINGHAM / TABERNACLE / TEMPERANCE CHOIR

SY-1893 / 001   Photographic Exhibition
by Messrs Pinches   Ae 42 mm

Obverse Similar to obverse of SY-1888 /001, but the date on the shield is incuse.
Reverse Similar to reverse of SY-1854 /065
Rim Beaded obverse, plain reverse.
Edge Inscribed with the name of the recipient.

RR *unrecorded (see SY-1889/005 for ill.)* PC

SY-1893 / 005   Sports & Pastimes Exhibition
by Messrs Pinches   Ae 42 mm

Obverse *Seven line inscription:* SPORTS & PASTIMES EXHIBITION ❀ / AWARDED / TO / THRUPP / & MABERLY / CRYSTAL PALACE / 1893
Reverse Similar to reverse of SY-1854 /065.
Rim Plain.

RRR *unrecorded* PC

Thrupp and Maberly were Motorcar Traders of 425 Oxford St, London W1. In the 1903 Automobile Show Catalogue, they are listed as being on stand 187, which was located just outside the Medieval Court.

SY-1893 / 010   Picture Gallery Prize
by Messrs Pinches, G.G. Adams & W.J. Taylor Ae 63 mm

CRYSTAL PALACE PICTURE GALLERY.

COMPETITION FOR PRIZES, 1893.

The Medals offered to Artists by the Directors of the Crystal Palace Company were awarded on the 4th of May, as follows :—

TO ENGLISH ARTISTS.

FOR HISTORY OR FIGURE SUBJECTS IN OIL.

36	No.	1.	After the Charge	*John Charlton.*	Gold Medal.
221	,,	2.	The Children's Prayer	*Arthur Haker.*	Silver ,,
156	,,	3.	Zelica Supplanted	*F. Markham Skipworth.*	,, ,,
232	,,	4.	The Convalescent	*F. E. Sherrard.*	,, ,,
50	,,	5.	Old Dutchwoman	*Hugh Carter, R.I.*	,, ,,
51	,,	6.	Watching and Waiting	*Fred Morgan.*	Bronze ,,
20	,,	7.	Hope Deferred !...	*W. K. Stevens.*	,, ,,
62	,,	8.	The Apparition of St. Agnes	*F. Hamilton Jackson, R.B.A.*	,, ,,

FOR LANDSCAPES, SEA-PIECES, ANIMALS, AND OTHER SUBJECTS.

427	No.	1.	Royal Captives	*J. S. Noble.*	Gold Medal.
240	,,	2.	Sunset—Bighton Beach	*Edwin Hayes, R.I., R.H.A.*	Silver ,,
149	,,	3.	Corfe Castle	*Arnold Helcke.*	,, ,,
413	,,	4.	Far from Court—far from Care	*Davidson Knowles, R.B.A.*	,, ,,
220	,,	5.	Sheep Changing Pens	*W. Rupert Stevens.*	,, ,,
208	,,	6.	A Southerly Wind and a Cloudy Sky	*R. W. A. Rouse.*	Bronze ,,
189	,,	7.	Hit or Miss ?	*Phillip E. Stretton.*	,, ,,
44	,,	8.	A Devonshire Lane	*Harold Speed.*	,, ,,

FOR BEST WATER-COLOUR DRAWINGS, IRRESPECTIVE OF SUBJECT.

625	No.	1.	After the Ball	*Henry Sykes, R.B.A.*	Gold Medal.
626	,,	2.	On Tramp	*T. W. Couldery.*	Silver ,,
713	,,	3.	A Cornfield in Kent	*John R. Bromley, R.B.A.*	,, ,,
654	,,	4.	Trust	*A. M. Rossi.*	,, ,,
648	,,	5.	Peace and War	*B. W. Spiers.*	Bronze ,,
647	,,	6.	Island of Inchbuida Killin	*James MacCulloch, R.S.W.*	,, ,,
712	,,	7.	News from the Fleet	*Fred M. Evans.*	,, ,,
632	,,	8.	Chee Dale, Derbyshire	*Edward Hargitt, R.I.*	,, ,,

TO FOREIGN ARTISTS.

FOR HISTORY OR FIGURE SUBJECTS IN OIL.

148	No.	1.	Children Bathing in Brittany	*Max Fleischer.*	Gold Medal.
157	,,	2.	Arab Cobblers	*Hermann Linde.*	Silver ,,
74	,,	3.	Merry Travellers	*Adolf Lins.*	,, ,,
369	,,	4.	A Cloister Festival	*Adolf Homburg.*	,, ,,
292	,,	5.	Before the Roman Patron	*Leo von Fortunski.*	,, ,,
401	,,	6.	A Good Appetite	*Emma von Müller.*	Bronze ,,
83	,,	7.	An Organ Phantasy	*G. von Hoesslin.*	,, ,,
80	,,	8.	Returning to the Village—the End of the Day	*Georges Laugée.*	,, ,,

FOR LANDSCAPES, SEA-PIECES, ANIMALS, AND OTHER SUBJECTS.

379	No.	1.	The Harvest of the Alfalfa in France	*H. S. Bisbing.*	Gold Medal.
95	,,	2.	Shepherd's Hut—Bavarian Alps	*E. Meissner.*	Silver ,,
382	,,	3.	On the Landstrasse, near Munich	*Otto Ahrweiler.*	,, ,,
435	,,	4.	Crocodile Temple on the Nile	*Ernest Koëner.*	,, ,,
35	,,	5.	A Forest Shrine	*E. Weighberger.*	,, ,,
283	,,	6.	Landscape and Cattle	*Wilh. Frey.*	Bronze ,,
233	,,	7.	The Valley of the Durden	*Julien Dupré.*	,, ,,
414	,,	8.	The Mountain Lake—Evening	*Christian Mali.*	,, ,,

C. WENTWORTH WASS,
Superintendent of the Gallery.

Signed { J. B. BURGESS, R.A.
J. MACWHIRTER, R.A., H.R.S.A.
DAVID MURRAY, A.R.A.

Obverse Similar to obverse of SY-1873 /001.
Reverse *Eight line inscription within a laurel wreath:*
AWARDED / BY THE / CRYSTAL PALACE Co / FOR A
PICTURE / 'THE APPARITION' / BY / F.H. JACKSON /
1893
Rim Plain.

RRR *Withers* 657 PC

The medal, together with a list of the prize winners, was
presented in a leatherette case inscribed on the lid CRYSTAL
PALACE / PRIZE MEDAL / PICTURE GALLERY. See
opposite page for a list of the 1893 prize winners.

SY-1893 / 015   25th Annual Cat Show
by E. Tyler   Ar 38 mm

Obverse View of the Crystal Palace and terraces. *Inscription
above:* 25th ANNUAL CAT SHOW / Oct. 17 & 18 *In exergue:*
CRYSTAL PALACE / 1893 *Signed* E. TYLER
Reverse *Six line inscription in laurel wreath:* FOR / BEST
TWO KITTENS / CLASS / 16 / WON BY / MR. E. HILL
Rim Plain obverse, beaded reverse.

RRR *unrecorded* PC

An article on Crystal Palace Cat Shows can be found in *New
Crystal Palace Matters*, No. 3.

SY-1893 / 020   National Temperance Fete
by ?   Bracteate Tin 45 mm

Obverse Similar to obverse of SY-1892 /020.
Reverse Blank.
Rim Plain.

RRR *unrecorded* PC

This uniface medal is attached to a plain beige ribbon inscribed:
CRYSTAL PALACE / JULY 4 1893. / CONTEST B / 2ND.
PRIZE. / NOTTINGHAM / TABERNACLE /
TEMPERANCE CHOIR

SY-1894 / 001   National Cage Bird Show
by E. Tyler   Ar 38 mm

Obverse   View of the Crystal Palace and terraces. *Incuse inscription above:* CAGE BIRD SHOW / FEB^Y 3rd to 7th *In exergue:* CRYSTAL PALACE / 1894 *Signed* E. TYLER
Reverse   *Five line inscription within a laurel wreath:* MOST POINTS / Classes 1 to 23 / Won by / Messrs / Mackley Bro^s.
Rim   Plain.

RRR   *unrecorded*   PC

SY-1896 / 001   Church of England Temperance Society Fete
by Toye & Co   Ar Ae 36x30 mm

Obverse   C E T S amid crossed swords on a shield surmounted by a bishops mitre.
Reverse   *Four line inscription:* PRIZE MEDAL / CRYSTAL PALACE / FETE / 1896
Rim   Plain.

Ar RR, Ae R   *unrecorded*   PC

The Church of England Temperance Society was inaugurated by the Archbishop of Canterbury at Lambeth in February 1873. These fetes were held annually at the Palace until the commencement of World War I.

SY-1896 / 005   School of Art Science & Literature
by Messrs Pinches   Ar 63 mm

Obverse   *Ten line inscription in beaded circle within a border of laurel:* CRYSTAL PALACE SCHOOL OF ART, SCIENCE & LITERATURE / AWARDED / TO / Nina Rothney / FOR / PAINTING from the costumed figure / JOHN SCOTT R.I. / MASTER / July 25th 1896 / THIRTY SIXTH SESSION
Reverse   Similar to reverse of SY-1854 /065.
Rim   Plain.

RRR   *unrecorded* (see SY-1884/001 for ill.)   PC

SY-1897 / 001   Imperial Victorian Exhibition
by F. Bowcher for Spink & Son   Ae 51 mm

Obverse   Crowned laureate veiled bust of Queen Victoria left. *Inscription around the border:* VICTORIA D: G: BRITT: REGINA F: D: IND: IMP: / IN. COMMEMOR. AN. REG. SEXAGESIMI / MDCCCXCVII
Reverse   *Ten line inscription within a wreath of oak:* AWARDED / TO / FORMALIN / HYGEINIC Co. Ltd / BY / The Sanitary Record / AS A / DISTINCTIVE / MARK OF MERIT / 1897 *Inscription around the border:* IMPERIAL VICTORIAN EXHIBITION CRYSTAL PALACE SANITARY SECTION *Signed* SPINK & SON. LONDON
Rim   Plain.

RRRR   *unrecorded*   BM

SY-1897 / 005   National Cage Bird Show
by ?   Ae 44 mm

Obverse Bird perched on a branch. *Inscription around the border:* UNITED KINGDOM BELGIAN CANARY / ✣ ASSOCIATION ✣

Reverse *Three line inscription within a laurel wreath:* CRYSTAL PALACE /1897 / J. A. LEE

Rim Plain.

> RRR *unrecorded* PC

An article on Crystal Palace bird shows can be found in *New Crystal Palace Matters*, No. 8.

SY-1898 / 001   Visit of Salvation Army
by ?   Ae 32 mm

Obverse Draped bust of General William Booth facing. *Inscription around the border:* THE SALVATION ARMY / • THE WORLD FOR GOD •

Reverse *Ten line inscription:* TO COMMEMORATE / THE / PUBLIC WELCOME / ACCORDED TO / GENERAL BOOTH / ON HIS RETURN / FROM AMERICA / AT THE / CRYSTAL PALACE / 9 MAY 1898

Rim Plain.

> RRR *unrecorded* PC

William Booth (1829–1912) founded the Salvation Army in 1865 while engaged in mission work in the East End of London. The author has fond memories of great kindness being shown to him and other servicemen by members of this Elite Brigade in their canteens countrywide, which provided a warm welcome

and a cheap meal to many 'lost souls' during their off duty periods away from barracks in the 1940s.

SY-1898 / 005   National Cage Bird Show
by ?   Ae 44 mm

Obverse Similar to obverse of SY-1897 /005.

Reverse *Two line inscription within a laurel wreath:* CRYSTAL PALACE / 1898

Rim Plain.

> RRR *unrecorded* (see SY-1897/005 for ill.) PC

SY-1899 / 001   Kennel Club Open Championship
by H B   Ar 99x70 mm

Obverse *Eight line inscription:* KENNEL CLUB / LADIES BRANCH / ✩ WON AT ✩ / CRYSTAL PALACE 1899 / BY / MISS G. HOWORTH'S / GRIFFON BROXELLOIS 'MAMIE' / 1st LIMIT

Reverse Blank except for hallmark. *Signed* HB

Rim Plain.

> RRR *unrecorded* (see SY-1906/005 for ill.) PC

The Kennel Club was founded in 1873, it held its first show at the Palace in 1883. Description courtesy of Eric Price.

SY-1899 / 005   National Cage Bird Show
by ?   Ae 44 mm

Obverse Similar to obverse of SY-1897 /005.

Reverse *Three line inscription within a laurel wreath:* CRYSTAL PALACE / 1899 / F. Reddihough

Rim Plain.

> RRR *unrecorded* (see SY-1897/005 for ill.) PC

SY-1900 / 001   Church of England Temperance Society Fete
by Toye & Co   Ar Ae 36x30 mm

Obverse Similar to obverse of SY-1896 /001.

Reverse *Four line inscription:* PRIZE MEDAL / CRYSTAL PALACE / FETE / 1900

Rim Plain.

Ar R, Ae S *unrecorded (see SY-1896/001 for ill.)* PC

Courtesy of Ivor Bush. See note to SY-1896 /001.

SY-1900 / 005   Kennel Club Open Championship
by ?   Ar 39 mm

Obverse Head of a terrier within a wreath of shamrock.
Inscription around the border: IRISH • TERRIER • CLUB /
☆ FOUNDED • 1879 ☆
Reverse A crowned harp within sprays of shamrock above a
six line inscription: Won by / 'CHAMPION MUNSTER
GRIP' / with dog challenge cup / K. C. CRYSTAL
PALACE / 1900 / HARMONY
Rim Plain.

RRR *unrecorded* PC

Courtesy of Jim Allen.

SY-1901 / 001   School of Art Science & Literature
by Messrs Pinches   Ar 63 mm

Obverse Eleven line inscription in a beaded circle within a
border of laurel: CRYSTAL PALACE COMPANY'S
SCHOOL OF ART, SCIENCE AND LITERATURE. /
AWARDED TO / ANNIE MARSHALL / FOR /
MODELLING / etc. etc.
Reverse Similar to reverse of SY-1854 /065.
Rim Plain.

RRR *unrecorded (see SY-1884/001 for ill)* CP

The author was unable to examine the obverse in detail because
the medal is in a sealed display case at the Crystal Palace
Museum. See note to SY-1884 /001.

SY-1901 / 005   Naval & Military Exhibition
by ?   Wm Wmg 38 mm

Obverse Conjoined busts of King Edward VII and Queen
Alexandra in a medallion above view of Sydenham Crystal
Palace. *Inscription above:* NAVAL & MILITARY
EXHIBITION *In exergue:* CRYSTAL PALACE / 1901
Reverse Conjoined heads of Queen Victoria and Prince
Albert in a medallion above view of the Great Exhibition
building. *Inscription in three concentric lines:* JUBILEE OF
THE GREAT EXHIBITION / HYDE PARK 1851 /
SYDENHAM 1901
Rim Plain.

Wm N, Wmg R *Brown 3734, Eimer (I) 1858* BM BR CP PC

The exhibition was part of a Grand Patriotic Fete held at the
Palace on Saturday 21 September, in aid of the Soldiers and
Sailors Families Association. Medals were sold in a printed

paper packet (see above) which also contained a free admission ticket to the Palace. This entitled the holder to purchase a return rail ticket at single fare (minimum 3d), if presented at any London or suburban station of the London Brighton and South Coast Railway, or the South Eastern and Chatham Railway. Gilt specimens were also sold in a red printed card box bearing the same design as the above paper packet.

SY-1902 / 001   Coronation of King Edward VII
by H. Grueber   Al, Alg (shell) 38 mm

Obverse Conjoined crowned busts of King Edward VII and Queen Alexandra right. *Inscription around the border:* EDWARD. VII. ALEXANDRA. CROWNED / JUNE / 26TH / 1902 *Signed* H. GRUEBER. LONDON.
Reverse Kentish horse in a shield. BRYCE GRANT ESQ J. P. CHAIRMAN upon a ribbon above the following *six line inscription:* CELEBRATION / OF THE CORONATION OF / KING EDWARD VII /AT THE CRYSTAL PALACE. / TO THE SCHOOLCHILDREN OF / PENGE *Inscription around the border:* URBAN. DISTRICT. COUNCIL. OF. PENGE ★
Rim Beaded.

Al R, Alg RR   *unrecorded*   PC

Penge is one of an enormous number of local government authorities which presented schoolchildren with a souvenir medal to commemorate the Coronation. Due to the additional cost of engraving extra details on the medal, very few local authorities named the place where the celebration was held. How fortunate in this instance, that Penge U.D.C. thought the additional cost worthwhile. It would be interesting to know if any more of the surrounding local authorities held celebrations at the Palace without recording it on their medals.

The Coronation should have been held on 26 June, but as the King had to undergo an emergency operation on 24 June, the ceremony was postponed until 9 August. Most unofficial Coronation medals were struck and sold before the King's illness was announced, consequently a high proportion show the earlier date thereon.

SY-1902 / 005   Coronation of King Edward VII
by H. Grueber   Al 38 mm

Obverse Similar to obverse of SY-1902 /001, but dated AUG. 9TH. 1902.
Reverse Similar to reverse of SY-1902 /001, but the inscription on 5th and 6th lines reads: THE OLD FOLKS OF / PENGE.
Rim Beaded.

RRR   *unrecorded*   PC

Illustration courtesy of Howard and Frances Simmons. See note to SY-1902 /001.

SY-1902 / 010   Church of England Temperance Society Fete
by Toye & Co   Ar Ae 36x30 mm

Obverse Similar to obverse of SY-1896 /001.
Reverse *Four line inscription:* PRIZE MEDAL / CRYSTAL PALACE / FETE / 1902
Rim Plain.

Ar RR, Ae R   *unrecorded* (see SY-1896/001 for ill.)   PC

See note to SY-1896 /001.

SY-1902 / 015	**Motor Traders Show**
by Messrs Pinches	Ae 63 mm

Obverse *Five line inscription:* CRYSTAL PALACE & MOTOR TRADERS' SHOW, 1902. ❀ / BEST FINISHED CAR / FOREIGN MAKE / 10 H.P. / ' DECAUVILLE '
Reverse Similar to reverse of SY-1854 /065.
Rim Plain.
Edge *Inscribed:* MOTOR CAR Co.

RRRR	*unrecorded*	PC

The Crystal Palace and Motor Traders Co-operative Show was held from 14–22 February. It featured motor cars, motor trucks, and motor cycles etc. In the motor car section the Crystal Palace Company awarded only 20 medals spread across 15 categories. This medal was awarded to The Motor Car Company Ltd of 168 Shaftsbury Avenue, London WC 'For best finished car foreign make' for their exhibit of a 1902 model of a 10 H.P. Decauville, which was universally recognised as one of the best designed and constructed vehicles of the period.

This medal is one of only two awarded in this category. Courtesy of Eric Price.

SY-1902 / 020	**American Exhibition**
by Whitehead & Hoag	Aeg 29 mm

Obverse Britannia bestowing honours. *Inscription above:* AMERICAN EXHIBITION / CRYSTAL PALACE. LONDON. 1902. *Below:* a distant view of the Crystal Palace flanked by a lion and an eagle. *Signed* WHITEHEAD & HOAG Co. NEWARK N.J.
Reverse Ten line inscription: HIGHEST AWARD / TO / LUDWIG & Co. / FOR / THE LUDWIG PIANO / AND / PIANO PLAYER / NEW YORK / U. S. A. / PAN. AMERICAN EXPOSITION 1901.
Rim Beaded.

RRR	*unrecorded*	PC

Courtesy of Jim Allen.

SY-1902 / 025	**American Exhibition**
by Whitehead & Hoag	Aeg 29 mm

Obverse Similar to obverse of SY-1902 /020.
Reverse Blank.
Rim Beaded obverse.

RRR	*unrecorded*	PC

Courtesy of Jim Allen. Messrs Whitehead and Hoag are credited with being the first company to introduce button badges to Britain when, in 1897, they marketed their range of badges to commemorate the diamond jubilee of Queen Victoria.

SY-1903 / 001 Food Exhibition
by H.J.O. & Co — Ar 38 mm

Obverse   *Four line inscription on a raised centre within a wide border of laurel:* FOOD / EXHIBITION / Crystal Palace / 1903
Reverse   *Five line inscription:* Awarded / to / C.J. FARMER / FOR / BROWN BREAD
Rim   Plain.

RRR   *unrecorded*   PC

SY-1903 / 005 National Cage Bird Show
by J.A. Restall — Ar Ae 38 mm

Obverse   View of the Crystal Palace and terraces. In exergue CRYSTAL PALACE
Reverse   *Inscription in centre panel between ornate design:* AWARDED TO / J. F. BISHOP *Inscription around the border:* LONDON & PROVINCIAL / ❖ ORNITHOLOGICAL SOCIETY ❖
Rim   Plain obverse, beaded reverse.
Edge   1903 hallmark, *Signed* J. A. R.

Ar RRR, Ae RR   *unrecorded*   PC

SY-1903 / 010 School of Art Science & Literature
by Messrs Pinches — Ae 42 mm

Obverse   Similar to obverse of SY-1889 /001.
Reverse   Similar to reverse of SY-1889 /001, but to Jonathon Slade.
Rim   Plain.

RRR   *unrecorded*   PC

Courtesy of C.E.

SY-1903 / 015 Annual Cat Show
by Vaughton — Ar 39 mm

Obverse   Arms of National Cat Club. *Inscription above:* NATIONAL CAT CLUB *Inscription on ribbon:* BEAUTY LIVES BY KINDNESS.
Reverse   *Two line inscription above rose, shamrock & thistle:* C.P. SHOW / 1903
Rim   Plain.

RRR   *unrecorded*   PC

SY-1904 / 001 National Poultry Show
by Elkington — Ar Ae 51 mm

SY-1904 / 005 **National Cage Bird Show**
by J.A. Restall   Ar 38 mm

Obverse Seated female in a flowing robe studying a chick.
Inscription in the field: THE / UTILITY / POULTRY / CLUB
Signed ELKINGTON
Reverse *Six line inscription within a laurel wreath:* GREAT
NATIONAL / POULTRY SHOW / CRYSTAL PALACE /
1904 / J. WILCOCK. / FOWL HOUSE *Signed*
ELKINGTON
Rim Plain

Ar RRR, Ae RR *unrecorded* PC

The lid of the fitted case is inscribed: UTILITY / POULTRY
CLUB / MEDAL.

Obverse Similar to obverse of SY-1903 /005.
Reverse Laurel wreath. 1904 hallmark, *Signed* J. A. R.
Rim Plain.

RRR *unrecorded* PC

Courtesy of Jim Allen.

Largest Mandolin Band in the world, 1903.

Programme.

WEDNESDAY, JULY 20th, 1904.

Open To-day from 10.0 a.m. to 10.0 p.m. Admission 1s.

TO-DAY, and Daily till SATURDAY, July 23rd.

NATIONAL FIRE BRIGADE UNION'S

(Under the Patronage of HIS MAJESTY THE KING.)

ANNUAL CAMP COMPETITIONS AND REVIEW.

THURSDAY, JULY 21st.

GRAND REVIEW AND INSPECTION

TO-DAY (WEDNESDAY) and TO-MORROW (THURSDAY).

National Sweet Pea Society's Show.

INTERNATIONAL SPORTS AND GAMES EXHIBITION.

CLOSING AUGUST 31st, 1904.

All Day.	**SIR HIRAM MAXIM'S** ## CAPTIVE FLYING MACHINES THE SENSATION OF THE AGE! *Passenger Fare: Adults—SIXPENCE; Children—THREEPENCE.*
All Day.	**On the Great Lake** (bottom of Grounds). **BOATING and ROWING.** *Hire of Boats :* One Person, per hour, **1/-** ; Two Persons, **1/6** ; Three or more, **6d.** each. A Row round the Lake, each Person, **2d.** All description of Boats on hire
All Day.	**In South Nave.** **SEA TRIP THROUGH THE BAY OF NAPLES.** *The Greatest Novelty in the Entertainment World.* A Marvellous Travelling Illusion, in which the Visitor sails on Board a Felucca through this magnificent bay. Also Photo-Sculptural **Views of Pompeii "As It Was and As It Is."** Views taken on the spot by Signor Luzzati, giving a Representation of **The Eruption of Mount Vesuvius.** *Admission Threepence*
All Day.	**In South Nave.** **BILLIARD AND SMOKING ROOM** (Overlooking the Grounds).
All Day.	**In South Nave** (near High Level Entrance). **THE ELECTRIC STAIRWAY.** Price One Penny.
All Day.	**Near High Level Entrance.** **PIERROT'S RIFLE RANGE.** The Latest Animated and Self-Indicating Electric Targets
Daily	**In Gallery** (above High Level Entrance). **MINIATURE BILLIARDS. 50 Up for 3d.** 20 TABLES ! Erected by J. R. MALLY & Co., Goswell Road, London Tickets, 50 Up for 3d.

Crystal Palace Programme, July 1904.

Exhibitions & Attractions.

All Day FROM **10 a.m.**

SOUTH NAVE.

Natural History Tableaux and Jungle.—South-East Gallery.

The Crystal Palace Arcade.—CLOCK GALLERY. The most attractive Fancy Fair in London.

Camera Obscura.—SOUTH-EAST GALLERY. Admission 3d.

Royal Exhibition of Working Ants.—Clock Gallery. Six different Species of Living Ants always on view, with their Queens, Workers, Slaves, Domestics, Cows, &c. Curiosities of Ant Life. Admission 3d

Pompeian House.—South Transept.

The Palace Wild Sports Rifle Range.—BASEMENT FLOOR, facing Main Entrance from Grounds

Billiard and Smoking Room (overlooking the Grounds)

NORTH NAVE.

Egyptian, Greek, Roman, Alhambra, Byzantine, Mediæval, and Renaissance Courts.—Full of magnificent Replicas of the World's Priceless Art Treasures

Reading Room.—Open from 10 a.m till close of Palace. All the Morning and Evening Papers, as well as many of the Provincial, Scotch, Irish, and Foreign Newspapers, Magazines, and Reviews. Accommodation for Letter-writing, Postage Stamps, Paper, &c Latest Telegraphic Dispatches Day Tickets, 2d Annual Admission Tickets, 21s Six months, 12s 6d Three months, 7s 6d One month. 3s

Lending Library. Annual Subscription. 21s. Six months, 12s. 6d. Three months, 7s. 6d

Ethnological Tableaux.—North-East Gallery.

Monkey and Parrot House and Aquarium. ENTRANCE NEAR LIBRARY Specimens of Indian Fish, lent by the King Eighteen kinds of fresh water fish fed daily at 4 p.m.

WESTERN ANNEXE.

Crystal Palace Exhibition Printing Works (MESSRS GUY WHITTEM & Co.), adjoining High Level Main Entrance. Printing Machinery in operation from morning till night.

IN GROUNDS.

Crystal Palace Company's Gymnasium and School of Physical Culture, Boxing, Fencing, and Swimming—*Entrance from North Tower Gardens.*

The School is open for Classes Daily from 9 a.m. till 8 p.m. Saturdays, 9 till 1 and 3.30 till 5.

Separate Days for Ladies and Gentlemen.

Free Tickets of Admission to the Palace are provided for Pupils.

Special attention is given to Curative Exercises, Symmetrical Development, Deportment, Figure Culture, and Breathing Exercises.

Holiday Classes for Boys and Girls at special terms.

Heated Swimming Bath.

For Particulars apply to FRANK A. HANSARD, Director the Schools.

North Tower. ENTRANCE FROM NORTH NAVE.—Upwards of 200 feet above the Cross of St Paul's, and 700 feet above the level of the Thames. Picturesque panoramic prospect from Gallery, extending into eight counties.

Ascent by Lift, Adults, 6d.; Children, 3d.

Ascent by Stairs Adults 3d Children 1d

The Maze. Admission **3d.**

Switchback Railway. Return Fare, **3d.**

Swings, Roundabouts, ETC.

Cycle Track, Polo Ground, Lakes, Geological Islands, &c.

SY-1904 / 010   International Food Exhibition
by S. Kulle   Aeg 56 mm

Courtesy of A.H. Baldwin & Sons Ltd.

SY-1905 / 001   Colonial & Indian Exhibition
by Massonnet   Aeg 51 mm

Obverse   View of the centre transept and terraces. *In exergue:*
CRYSTAL PALACE / LONDON / 1904
Reverse   *Six line inscription in laurel wreath:*
INTERNATIONAL / FOOD / EXHIBITION / CRYSTAL
PALACE / LONDON / 1904 *Signed* S. Kulle
Rim   Plain.

RRR   *unrecorded*   PC

Courtesy of Melvyn Harrison.

SY-1904 / 015   Kennel Club Open Championship
by ?   Ar 39 mm

Obverse   Similar to obverse of SY-1900 /005.
Reverse   Similar to reverse of SY-1900 /005.
Rim   Plain.

RRR   *unrecorded*(see SY-1900 /005 for ill.)   PC

Obverse   Britannia with shield and trident receiving fruit
from a native boy. Ship, palms etc. in the background.
Inscription around the border: COLONIAL & INDIAN
EXHIBITION / ☆ CRYSTAL PALACE LONDON 1905 ☆
Reverse   *Three line inscription in centre circle:* OMNIA /
LABOR / VINCIT Roses, palm and ribbons around. *Signed*
MASSONNET ED.
Rim   Plain.

RRR   *unrecorded*   PC

SY-1905 / 005   Church of England Temperance Society Fete
by Toye & Co   Ar Ae 36x30 mm

Obverse   Similar to obverse of 1896 /001.
Reverse   *Four line inscription:* PRIZE MEDAL / CRYSTAL
PALACE / FETE / 1905
Rim   Plain.

| **Ar RR, Ae R** | *unrecorded* (see SY-1896/001 for ill.) | PC |

Courtesy of Ivor Bush. See note to SY-1896 /001.

SY-1905 / 010 Indoor Bowling Club
by ?   Enamelled badge 27 mm

Obverse Distant view of the Crystal Palace. *Inscription around the border:* CRYSTAL PALACE INDOOR BOWLING CLUB /. FOUNDED 1905.
Reverse Blank.
Rim Plain.

| **R** | *unrecorded* | CP PC |

At the turn of the century Dr W.G. Grace, the famous cricketer, resided at Sydenham and was a prominent bowls player in the area. With 35 other players he became a founder member of the Crystal Palace indoor bowls club, alleged to be the first indoor bowls club in the world. Until it moved down to the lower basement in 1909, the game was played on coconut matting in one of the galleries. In the Crystal Palace Museum there is a larger badge depicting a different view of the Palace.

SY-1905 / 015 British Bulldog Club
by ?   Ae 45 mm

Obverse Rose thistle and shamrock between shields of the home countries. *Inscription around the border:* THE. BRITISH. BULLDOG. CLUB. / ESTAB^D 1892.
Reverse Seven line inscription within palm wreath: AWARDED / FOR / MERIT / CRYSTAL PALACE / 1905 / Sally Lunn
Rim Plain.

| **RRR** | *unrecorded* | PC |

SY-1905 / 020 Death of John Pinches
by Messrs Pinches & G.W. De Saulles   Ae 32x25 mm

Obverse Draped bust of John Pinches right. *Inscription around the border:* JOHN PINCHES, BORN JAN. 1ST 1825, DIED APRIL 22ND 1905
Reverse Three line inscription: LABORARE / EST / ORARE
Rim Plain.

| **S** | Brown 3920 (ill.), Eimer (I) 1885 | PC |

John Pinches (1825–1905) one of a family of five brothers and a long serving prominent member of this distinguished firm of medallists. He was taught the art of steel engraving by his uncle, W.J. Taylor. Worked for William Wyon at the Royal Mint from 1846–1851, and then for Messrs Heaton in Birmingham, before joining the family firm in 1865. The number of medals produced on the Pinches Crystal Palace medal press was prodigious, and more than one hundred medals struck by the firm are recorded in this catalogue.

SY-1906 / 001 Church of England Temperance Society Fete
by Toye & Co   Ar Ae 36x30 mm

Obverse   Similar to obverse of SY-1896 /001, but the designs in the top corners are raised instead of incuse.
Reverse   Four line inscription: PRIZE MEDAL / CRYSTAL PALACE / FETE / 1906
Rim   Plain.

Ar RR, Ae R   *unrecorded* (see SY-1896/001 for ill.)   PC

See note to SY-1896 /001.

SY-1906 / 005 Kennel Club Open Championship
by HB   Ar 99x70 mm

Obverse   Eight line inscription: KENNEL CLUB / LADIES' BRANCH / ☆ WON AT ☆ / CRYSTAL PALACE — 1906 / BY / THE HON. MRS LYTTON'S / TOY SPANIEL (TRICOLOUR) / 'ROSE PETAL'
Reverse   Blank. Hallmark, *Signed* HB
Rim   Plain.

RRR   *unrecorded*   PC

The Lytton family seat is Knebworth House, Stevenage.

SY-1907 / 001 Balloon School Royal Engineers
by A. Fenwick   Ae Aeg Aes Wm 32 mm

Obverse   Conjoined crowned busts of King Edward VII and Queen Alexandra left. *Inscription around the border:* H. M. EDWARD. VII. KING. H. M. ALEXANDRA. QUEEN. / PROCLAIMED 1901 *Signed* AF
Reverse   'Nulle Secundus' in flight over London. *Inscription above:* BALLOON SCHOOL ROYAL ENGINEERS
Rim   Plain.

Wm S, Ae R, Aeg R, Aes R   *Brown* 3697, *Fearon (I)* 358.4   PC

This obverse design was used on a number of unofficial 1902 Coronation medals. The airship depicted on the medal was the first Army dirigible, and was named 'Nulle Secundus' by King Edward VII in May 1907. On 5 October 1907, on its maiden voyage, it ran into strong winds over London and had to make a forced landing at the Crystal Palace. Due to continuing bad weather it was unable to take off again and had to be deflated; it never flew again. Alan Warwick provides a more detailed account of the incident in *The Phoenix Suburb*.

SY-1907 / 005 International Exhibition of Artistique Furniture Home Decorations & Building Materials
by C. Massonnet   Aeg Aes 56 mm

Obverse Eight line inscription in centre circle:
INTERNATIONAL EXHIBITION / OF / ARTISTIQUE
FURNITURE / HOME DECORATIONS / AND /
BUILDING MATERIALS' / CRYSTAL PALACE /
LONDON 1907
Reverse Britannia with a lion at her feet. A lighthouse and
ships in the background. *In exergue:* LONDON. 1907
Rim Plain.

RRR	*unrecorded*	PC

SY-1907 / 010	**Kennel Club Open Championship**
by PHDW	Ar 99x70 mm

Obverse Eight line inscription: KENNEL CLUB / LADIES'
BRANCH / WON AT / CRYSTAL PALACE — 1907 / BY /
HON MRS LYTTON'S / BLENHEIM SPANIEL / 'CH
WINDFALL'
Reverse Blank. Hallmark, *signed* PHDW
Rim Plain.

RRR	*unrecorded* (see SY-1906/005 for ill.)	PC

See note to SY-1906 /005.

THE
PICTURE HOUSE
CRYSTAL PALACE
Now Showing :—
EVELYN BRENT, CLIVE BROOK, WILLIAM POWELL & DORIS KENYON
in
INTERFERENCE
also
SHIPS OF THE NIGHT
Featuring JOHANNA HEARNE & JACQUELINE LOGAN

Continuous Performance Daily 2.30 to 10.30
Prices (including tax) 6d., 9d., 1/3 and 1/10

THE KENNEL CLUB'S 68th OPEN CHAMPIONSHIP SHOW
OCTOBER 9th and 10th
THE PREMIER DOG SHOW OF THE WORLD
Over 2,000 dogs of 78 different varieties

THE CRYSTAL PALACE GRAND INTER-NATIONAL SHOW OF POULTRY, PIGEONS and RABBITS
NOVEMBER 20th, 21st, 22nd and 23rd

PHOTOCHROM CO. LTD., LONDON & TUNBRIDGE WELLS

Crystal Palace Brass Band Championship Programme
announcements.

SY-1907 / 015	**Jubilee of Tonic Sol-Fa Festivals**
by Messrs Pinches	Ae Wm 39 mm

Obverse Similar to obverse of SY-1891 /001.
Reverse Tonic sol-fa notation on a scroll, ornate design in
the field. *Inscription around the border:* THE JUBILEE OF
CRYSTAL PALACE FESTIVALS / + 1857–1907 +
Rim Plain.

Wm R, Ae RR	*unrecorded*	PC

See notes to SY-1857 /020 and SY-1891 /001.

SY-1907 / 020   National Cage Bird Show
by J.A. Restall   Ar Ae 38 mm

Obverse   Similar to obverse of SY-1903 /005.
Reverse   Similar to reverse of SY-1903 /005.
Rim   Plain obverse, beaded reverse.
Edge   1907 Hallmark, *Signed* J. A. R.

Ar RRR, Ae RR   *unrecorded* (see SY-1903/005 for ill.)   PC

SY-1907 / 025   Church of England Temperance Society Fete
by Toye & Co   Ar Ae 36x30 mm

Obverse   Similar to obverse of SY-1906 /001.
Reverse   Four line inscription: PRIZE MEDAL / CRYSTAL PALACE / FETE / 1907
Rim   Plain.

Ar RR, Ae R   *unrecorded* (see SY-1896/001 for ill.)   PC

Courtesy of Ivor Bush. See note to SY-1896 /001.

SY-1907 / 030   Kennel Club Open Championship
by Vaughton   Ae 51 mm

Obverse   Terrier standing on a plinth *inscribed:* THE DANDIE DINMONT TERRIER CLUB *Signed* VAUGHTON BIRM..
Reverse   Six line inscription within a floral wreath: CRYSTAL PALACE /1907 / PICKLE CUP / PEPPER BITCH / WON BY / MILVERTON DUCHESS *Signed* VAUGHTON BIRM
Rim   Plain.

RRR   *unrecorded*   PC

SY-1908 / 001   National Chrysanthemum Show
by Messrs Pinches   Ar 42 mm

Obverse   Eight line inscription: CRYSTAL PALACE. / NATIONAL / CHRYSANTHEMUM SOCIETY'S SHOW. / NOVEMBER 1908. / Awarded to / E. WILDMAN / FOR / 6 INCURVED BLOOMS
Reverse   Similar to reverse of SY-1854 /065.
Rim   Plain.

RRR   *unrecorded*   PC

SY-1909 / 001   50th Great National Cage Bird Show
by J.A. Restall   Ae 38 mm

Obverse   Similar to obverse of SY-1903 /005.
Reverse   Similar to reverse of SY-1903 /005.

Rim   Plain obverse, beaded reverse.

RR   *unrecorded*   **PC**

The medal is not dated, but inside the lid of the case is inscribed: The JUBILEE SHOW / 50ᵀᴴ GREAT NATIONAL / CAGE BIRD SHOW / CRYSTAL PALACE / 1909.

SY-1909 / 005   Kennel Club Open Championship
by Vaughton   Ae 51 mm

Obverse   Similar to obverse of SY-1907 /030.
Reverse   *Six line inscription within a floral wreath:*
CRYSTAL PALACE /1909 / BREEDERS / CHALLENGE CUP / MUSTARD DOG / GORDON PRINCE *Signed* VAUGHTON BIRM
Rim   Plain.

RRR   *unrecorded*   **PC**

SY-1909 / 010   Church of England Temperance Society Fete
by Toye & Co   Ar Ae 36x30 mm

Obverse   Similar to obverse of SY-1906 /001.
Reverse   *Four line inscription:* PRIZE MEDAL / CRYSTAL PALACE / FETE / 1909
Rim   Plain.

Ar RR, Ae R   *unrecorded (see SY-1896/001 for ill.)*   **PC**

See note to SY-1906 /001.

SY-1909 / 015   Universal Cookery & Food Exhibition
by ?   Ae 44 mm

Obverse   *Seven line inscription:* AWARDED / TO / C.D. PARISH / 2ᴺᴰ PRIZE FOR / HONEY / CRYSTAL PALACE / 1909
Reverse   County Arms above Beehive. *Inscription around the border:* SURREY BEEKEEPER'S ASSOCIATION.
Rim   Plain.

RRR   *unrecorded*   **PC**

The medal is in a fitted case inscribed: UNIVERSAL COOKERY & FOOD / EXHIBITION / LONDON 1909.

SY-1910 / 001   National   Brass   Band Championship
by D.G. Collins   Ae 32 mm

Obverse   *Four line inscription:* WON BY / F. SOWOOD / FODENS BAND / 1910 *Inscription around the border:* THE CRYSTAL PALACE / ★ BAND CHAMPIONSHIP ★ *Signed* D.G.C.

Reverse   The trophy. *Inscription around the border:* WINNERS OF THE THOUSAND GUINEA TROPHY ❀

Rim   Plain.

RRRR   *unrecorded*   PC

The Championships were held at the Palace from 1860 to 1863 but, as most of the competing bands came from the north of England, the high cost of travel forced the contest to revert back to the 'Belle Vue' at Manchester. However, in 1900, John Henry Iles, with the aid of Sir Arthur Sullivan, was successful in bringing the contest back to the Palace, where, apart from the interruption due to World War I, it was contested annually right up until the fateful fire of 1936. The winning band was presented with the 'Thousand Guinea Trophy' to hold for one year, a cash prize of £50, plus a musical instrument to the value of 25 guineas. Each bandsman, the bandmaster and the secretary, received a bronze medal. Members of the band winning the trophy for the second time received the same medal in silver, for a third win the medal was gold. An excellent coloured illustration of the magnificent 'Thousand Guinea Trophy' will be found in Harry Mortimer's splendid book *On Brass*. For details of the other medals awarded to F. Sowood see entries for 1930, 1933, 1936, 1937, 1938.

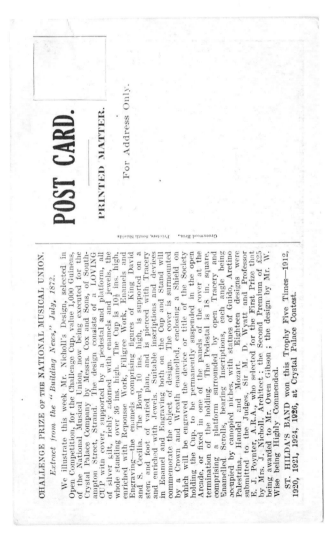

The Great Championship Contest
for the
CRYSTAL PALACE ONE THOUSAND GUINEA TROPHY

LAST YEAR'S WINNER
WINGATE'S TEMPERANCE

11.50 a.m.—In the Concert Hall

Grand Championship Brass Band Contest for the Crystal Palace One Thousand Guinea Challenge Trophy and the "Daily Telegraph" Challenge Cup, and other Prizes

Adjudicators:—H. GEEHL
J. BRIER
H. BENNETT

PRIZES

FIRST PRIZE.—The Championship of Great Britain and the Colonies, the winners of which will be the holders for the year (under special regulations) of the CRYSTAL PALACE NATIONAL CHALLENGE TROPHY, of the value of One Thousand Guineas, and a CASH PRIZE OF FIFTY POUNDS, and Messrs. BESSON & Co., LTD., 198 Euston Road, London, N.W. 1, sole manufacturers of the celebrated " Prototype " Band Instruments, will present one of their famous " New Standard " Tenor Slide Trombones, handsomely silver-plated and embellished, complete in attaché case, valued at TWENTY POUNDS (£20), and Messrs. WRIGHT & ROUND, 34 Erskine Street, Liverpool, will present one *Brass Band News* Gold Medal to the Resident Bandmaster, value FOUR GUINEAS.

Each Member of the Band, including the Bandmaster and Secretary, will also be presented with the CRYSTAL PALACE CHAMPIONSHIP BRONZE MEDAL, with Bar and Clasp.

Members of the Band winning the Trophy for the second time will be presented with the same medal IN SOLID SILVER ; and Members of the Band winning the Trophy for the third time will be presented with SOLID GOLD MEDALS.

SECOND PRIZE.—THE *DAILY TELEGRAPH* CHALLENGE CUP (subject to regulations), value Fifty Guineas, and a CASH PRIZE OF FORTY-FIVE POUNDS, and Messrs. BOOSEY & HAWKES, LTD., 295 Regent Street, London, W. 1, will present one Band Instrument, to be selected from their catalogue, to the value of TWENTY POUNDS.

THIRD PRIZE.—A CASH PRIZE OF FORTY POUNDS and THE UNIFORM CLOTHING & EQUIPMENT Co., LTD. 10/11 Clerkenwell Green, London, E.C. 1, will present one Bandmaster's Complete Suit, including Frockcoat Trousers and Cap, design to be selected by the winner, and also a Set of Gold-bronzed Music Stands, to the total value of SEVENTEEN GUINEAS.

FOURTH PRIZE.—A CASH PRIZE OF THIRTY-FIVE POUNDS, and THE ARMY & NAVY SUPPLY STORES 118/120 Praed Street, Paddington, London, W. 2, will present one Bandmaster's Complete Outfit, to the value of SIXTEEN GUINEAS.

FIFTH PRIZE.—A CASH PRIZE OF THIRTY POUNDS and Messrs. B. FELDMAN & Co., 125 Shaftesbury Avenue, London, W.C., will present one Boosey Bb Cornet " N.V.A. " Silbron Valves, triply-plated and engraved value FIFTEEN GUINEAS.

SIXTH PRIZE.—A CASH PRIZE OF TEN POUNDS and Messrs. CHAPPELL & Co., LTD., 50 New Bond Street, London, W. 1, will present one Triple Silver-plated and Engraved " Desideratum " Cornet No. 11, with Ab and Bb shanks, complete in high and low pitch, made by Messrs. Besson & Co., valued at FIFTEEN GUINEAS.

1. CHAMPIONSHIP CONTEST

TEST PIECE: "A DOWNLAND SUITE" ... *John Ireland*

SECTION I

No.	Draw	Conductor	Draw	Result	No.	Band	Conductor	Draw	Re.
1.	Baxendale's Works	J. A. Greenwood	23	4	13.	Irwell Springs	W. Halliwell	18	
2.	Bentley Colliery	W. Halliwell	3		14.	Luton	E. S. Carter	8	
3.	Black Dyke Mills	W. Halliwell	9	2	15.	Metropolitan Works	H. Heyes	22	
4.	Bradford City	H. Grace			16.	Middlesbrough Boro	J. Wilson	2	
5.	Brighouse and Rastrick	W. Halliwell	10		17.	Morris Motors	S. V. Wood	13	
6.	Carlisle St. Stephen's	W. Lowes	16	5	18.	Nelson Old	W. Halliwell	10	
7.	Crystal Palace	W. Reynolds	19		19.	Rothwell Temperance	N. Sidebottom	21	
8.	Eccles Borough	J. Dow	17		20.	St. Dennis	C. H. Baker	1	
9.	Foden's Motor Works	F. Mortimer			21.	Scottish C.W.S.	G. Hawkins	7	11
10.	Hanwell	J. C. Dyson	13		22.	Wigston's Temperance	C. Moore		
11.	Harton Colliery	W. Lowes			23.	Wingate's Temperance	H. Moss	15	
12.	Horden Colliery	J. Foster	14						

Admission to Concert Hall ... ... **TWO SHILLINGS**

NOTE.—The Director's Office is in front of the Concert Hall. At " THE BRITISH BANDSMAN " Stand, adjoining, can obtained the Conductor's parts of the Test Pieces——Price Two Shillings.

A MUSICAL EXHIBITION
By all the Leading Musical Instrument Manufacturers, etc.

WILL BE HELD IN THE SOUTH NAVE See List of Exhibitors. Pa

The Head Quarters of the National Brass Band Club will be in the Crystal Palace Club room and will be available members and friends. Mr. J. H. Kichenside, The Hon. Secretary, will be pleased to welcome them.

8

SY-1910 / 005 School Orchestras Annual Festival
by ?   Al 32 mm

Obverse Eight line inscription: NATIONAL UNION / OF / SCHOOL ORCHESTRAS' / ANNUAL FESTIVAL / CRYSTAL PALACE / JULY 16TH 1910 / INTERMEDIATE / ORCHESTRA
Reverse St Celia with musical instruments within sprays of palm and laurel.
Rim Plain.

S *unrecorded* PC

The medal is attached to a dated suspension bar by a red ribbon, and was worn by performers during the concert. 2,500 intermediate pupils performed at the afternoon concert.

SY-1910 / 010 School Orchestras Annual Festival
by ?   Al 32 mm

Obverse Similar to obverse of SY-1910 /005, but seventh line reads: ADVANCED
Reverse Similar to reverse of SY-1910 /005.
Rim Plain.

S *unrecorded* PC

The medal is attached to a dated suspension bar by a blue ribbon, and was worn by the performers during the concert. Two thousand advanced pupils performed at the evening concert.

The National Union of School Orchestras with Princess Christian as its patron, was founded to promote the study and practice of instrumental music in elementary schools in the London area; to provide scholarships and prizes for promising pupils, and to encourage evening classes, orchestral societies and local concerts. Twelve scholarships to the Guildhall School of Music were awarded annually to outstanding pupils, and two silver shields were offered for annual competition between

EAST LONDON INDUSTRIAL SCHOOL BAND.
WINNERS WOOD'S CHALLENGE CUP AT CRYSTAL PALACE, SEPTEMBER 26TH, 1908.

school orchestras, one for advanced pupils, the other for intermediate pupils. To stimulate interest a bi-monthly magazine entitled *The Young Musician and the School Orchestra* was introduced at a charge of one penny. It provided hints on 'one's' playing technique, news of competitions, articles on famous musicians, adverts, sheet music and 'do's and dont's' etc.

The first festival was held in 1905, when 700 boys and girls performed at the Crystal Palace. In 1906, 800 children performed in the Royal Albert Hall. From 1907–1909, the festival was held at the Alexandra Palace in North London, when the number of performers rose each year to reach 2,500 by 1909. By 1910, orchestras from more than 200 schools were wanting to participate, causing the number of performers to rise to around 4,500. Since there was no other building in the London area at that time capable of accommodating such a large number of performers, the festival reverted back to the Palace, and continued there until the commencement of World War I.

SY-1911 / 001   Coronation Fete
by ?   Wm 39 mm

Obverse Conjoined draped busts of King George V and Queen Mary left. *Inscription around the border:* • KING GEORGE V QUEEN MARY • ♣
Reverse City of London arms on a ribbon above a *six line inscription:* CROWNED 22ND JUNE 1911 / TO COMMEMORATE THE CORONATION / OF H. M. GEORGE. V / KING OF GREAT BRITAIN / AND / EMPEROR OF INDIA
Rim Beaded.

N *unrecorded* PC

In 1974 the author collected Coronation and Jubilee medals, and around that time he acquired this medal from a colleague, to whom it had been given on 30 June 1911, the last day in the week of Coronation festivities, when he was one of the 100,000 London schoolchildren who visited the Crystal Palace to greet their newly crowned King and Queen. This medal was given to City of London schoolchildren to commemorate the

Coronation, therefore the Crystal Palace is not mentioned thereon. However, the story surrounding it re-awakened the author's interest in the Crystal Palace which had laid dormant since that catastrophic night of 30 November 1936. With the medal is a tin box 137 x 58 mm, which contained a bar of chocolate, made by Rowntree & Co, and was given to each of the children attending the fete. The lid has the royal arms between coloured illustrations of the King and Queen and is inscribed: THE KING'S CORONATION FETE CRYSTAL PALACE 1911.

metal tin (reduced).

SY-1911 / 005   Festival of Empire Exhibition & Pageant of London
by Messrs Pinches   Ae 38 mm

Obverse Britannia holding a trident and an olive branch, flanked by a male holding a flaming torch, and a female holding a wheat sheaf, ships in background. *In exergue:* CRYSTAL PALACE / 1911 *Inscription around the border:* FESTIVAL OF EMPIRE IMPERIAL EXHIBITION AND PAGEANT OF LONDON •
Reverse Laurel wreath.
Rim Plain

RRR *unrecorded (see SY-1911/020 for ill.)* PC

On 12 May, King George and Queen Mary opened the festival which was organised to coincide with the Coronation. The

British exhibition was held within the Palace. Three-quarter size replicas of the parliament buildings of each of the other Commonwealth countries were erected in the grounds, built of wood and plaster, and housed their own national exhibits. The festival which included exhibitions, concerts, massed bands, side shows and fireworks was the biggest privately organised event ever held at the Palace. It was originally to have been held in 1910, but was postponed due to the death of King Edward VII. In the Crystal Palace Museum there is a Programme of the festival which did not take place, dated Thursday 9 June 1910. Aerial photographs from the early nineteen thirties show the Canadian parliament building still intact.

SY-1911 / 010 Festival of Empire Exhibition & Pageant of London
by Messrs Pinches & Elkington   Ae 38 mm

Obverse   Similar to obverse of SY-1911 /005.
Reverse   A border of wild roses around a blank centre.
Rim   Plain.

RRR   *Pinches 42/43*   PC

Believed to be a prize medal. See note to SY-1911 /005.

Aerial view of buildings at Festival of Empire, 1911. Valentines Series.

SY-1911 / 015 Festival of Empire Exhibition & Pageant of London
by Messrs Pinches & Elkington   Ar Ae 63 mm

Obverse   Similar to obverse of SY-1911 /005.
Reverse   A border of wild roses around a blank centre.
Rim   Plain.

RRR   *Pinches 42/43 (see SY-1911/010 for ill.)*   CP PC

Oxo & Lemco building at Festival of Empire, 1911. Reproduced by kind permission of Van den Bergh Foods and Unilever Historical Archives.

The silver version was in John Pinches' archive collection, and believed to be a trial strike. A bronze version in a fitted case by Elkington, is in the Crystal Palace Museum. See note to SY-1911 /005.

SY-1911 / 020 Festival of Empire Exhibition & Pageant of London
by Messrs Pinches & Elkington   Ar Arg 63 mm

Obverse   Similar to obverse of SY-1911 /005.
Reverse   *Three line inscription within a crowned laurel wreath:*
AWARDED TO / BOYD LTD. / LONDON.
Rim   Plain.

RRR   *Pinches 42/43 (obverse only)*   PC

A matched pair of silver gilt specimens in a red fitted case has been seen. See note to SY-1911 /005.

SY-1911 / 025   Festival of Empire Exhibition & Pageant of London
by Messrs Pinches, Elkington & A. Halliday Ae Al 38 mm

Obverse   Conjoined crowned busts of King George V and Queen Mary left. *Inscription around the border:* GEORGIUS. V. D. G. REX. ET. IMP. ET. MARIA. REGINA. *Signed* A. HALLIDAY in field, ELKINGTON on truncation.
Reverse   Similar to obverse of SY-1911 /005.
Rim   Plain.

RRR   *Brown 4087, Pinches 42/43*   PC

Obviously struck to commemorate both the Coronation and the Festival, bronze specimens were sold in a fitted case. The aluminium version has a red white and blue ribbon attached,

therefore, it may have been given to school-children attending the Festival. See note to SY-1911 /005.

SY-1911 / 030   Festival of Empire Exhibition & Pageant of London
by Messrs Pinches, Elkington & A. Halliday   Ae 63 mm

Obverse   Similar to obverse of SY-1911 /025.
Reverse   Similar to obverse of SY-1911 /005.
Rim   Plain.

RRR   *Brown 4087, Pinches 42/43*   PC

Sold in a leatherette case. See note to SY-1911 /005.

SY-1911 / 035   Festival of Empire Exhibition & Pageant of London
by A. Williamson   Coated board 64x54 mm

Obverse Dragon above Welsh harp. *Inscription around:* FESTIVAL OF EMPIRE / CRYSTAL PALACE / SEPT 1911 / COR. CYMRU.

Reverse *Nine line inscription:* A. WILLIAMSON, / Maker of all kinds of / Badges & Rosettes, / For / SHOWS, SPORTS, DANCES, & c. / NORTH MILL, / Ashton-under-Lyne, / LIST POST FREE, / Tel. 320.

Rim Plain.

RRR   *unrecorded*   PC

This badge would have been worn by a member of the Welsh contingent at their national pavilion. See note to SY-1911 /005.

SY-1911 / 040   Festival of Empire Exhibition & Pageant of London
by ?   Br 29x22 mm

Obverse Three line inscription: CRYSTAL / PALACE / 1911
Inscription around the border: FESTIVAL OF EMPIRE / • 1ST NATIONAL GYMNASTIC FESTIVAL •

Reverse Blank.

Rim Plain.

RR   *unrecorded*   BM CP PC

See note to SY-1911 /005.

SY-1911 / 045   School Orchestras Annual Festival
by ?   Al 31 mm

Obverse Eight line inscription: NATIONAL UNION / OF / SCHOOL ORCHESTRAS' / ANNUAL FESTIVAL / CRYSTAL PALACE / MAY 20TH 1911 / INTERMEDIATE / ORCHESTRA

Reverse Music stand and instruments within a laurel wreath.

Rim Plain.

S   *unrecorded*   PC

The medal is attached to a dated suspension bar by a red ribbon, and was worn by performers during the concert. Three and a half thousand intermediate pupils performed at the afternoon concert, watched by an audience exceeding 10,000. See note to SY-1910 /010.

SY-1911 / 050   School Orchestras Annual Festival
by ?   Al 31 mm

Obverse   Similar to obverse of SY-1911 /045, but seventh line reads: ADVANCED
Reverse   Similar to reverse of SY-1911 /045.
Rim   Plain.

S   *unrecorded*   PC

The medal is attached to a dated suspension bar by a blue ribbon, and was worn by performers during the concert. Two and a half thousand advanced pupils performed at the evening concert, watched by an audience exceeding 10,000. See note to SY-1910 /010.

SY-1911 / 055   National Cage Bird Show
by J.A. Restall   Ar 38 mm

Obverse   Similar to obverse of SY-1903 /005.
Reverse   Similar to reverse of SY-1903 /005.
Rim   Plain.
Edge   1911 hallmark, *Signed* J.A.R.

RR   *unrecorded* (see SY-1903/005 for ill.)   PC

SY-1911 / 060   Church of England Temperance Society Fete
by Toye & Co   Ar Ae 36x30 mm

Obverse   Similar to obverse of SY-1906 /001.
Reverse   *Four line inscription:* PRIZE MEDAL / CRYSTAL PALACE / FETE / 1911
Rim   Plain.

Ar RR, Ae R   *unrecorded* (see SY-1896/001 for ill.)   PC

Courtesy of Ivor Bush. See note to SY-1896 /001.

SY-1911 / 065   National Cage Bird Show
by ?   Ar Ae 32 mm

Obverse   London & Provincial Ornithological Society monogram in a laurel wreath.
Reverse   *Five line inscription in a laurel wreath:* 3ᴿᴰ PRIZE / CRYSTAL PALACE / FEBʸ 1911 / AUTON BROˢ / SPALDING
Rim   Plain.

Ar RRR, Ae RR   *unrecorded*   PC

SY-1911 / 070   Tug of War — Jones Challenge Shield
by ?   Ar 41 mm

Obverse   *Seven line inscription:* TUG OF WAR / FOR THE / JONES CHALLENGE SHIELD / 7TH YEAR WINNERS / COMMERCIAL UNION / CRYSTAL PALACE / 1ˢᵗ JUNE 1911.
Reverse   Adonis pulling on a rope.
Rim   Plain.
Edge   *Inscribed:* W. A. HORTON.

RRR   *unrecorded*   PC

Courtesy of Eric Price.

SY-1912 / 001   Gas Light & Coke Company Centenary Celebration
by Messrs Pinches   Ae Aes 35 mm

Obverse Seated female holding a torch and a shield bearing the company monogram.

Reverse Six line inscription within a border of palm: THE / GAS LIGHT / AND / COKE COMPANY / CENTENARY / 1812–1912

Rim Plain.

Aes RR, Ae S   *Pinches 44*   **PC**

The Gas Light & Coke Company, which at one time supplied gas to virtually the whole of the London area, held its centenary celebration fete at the Palace for 14,000 guests. This centenary medal, suspended from a plain blue ribbon, was worn by company staff, the same medal with a blue ribbon containing a white centre stripe was worn by stewards. A silver plated version without the suspension loop was presented to VIPs.

SY-1912 / 005   Church of England Temperance Society Fete
by Toye & Co   **Ar Ae 36x30 mm**

Obverse Similar to obverse of SY-1906 /001.
Reverse Four line inscription: PRIZE MEDAL / CRYSTAL PALACE / FETE / 1912 *Signed* TOYE & Co. LONDON
Rim Plain.

Ar RR, Ae R   *unrecorded (see SY-1896/001 for ill.)*   **PC**

See note to SY-1896 /001.

SY-1912 / 010   National Temperance Choral Union Jubilee Festival
by ?   **Ae Wm Al 38 mm**

Obverse View of the Crystal Palace in a cartouche.
Reverse Five line inscription: N. T. C. U. / JUBILEE / TEMPERANCE / FESTIVAL / 13ᵀᴴ JULY 1912
Rim Plain.

Ae RRR, Wm RR, Al RR   *unrecorded*   **PC**

Choral Union Concert Programme, July 1899.

SY-1912 / 015   School Orchestras Annual Festival
by ?   **Al 31 mm**

Obverse Eight line *Inscription:* NATIONAL UNION / OF / SCHOOL ORCHESTRAS' /ANNUAL FESTIVAL / CRYSTAL PALACE / JUNE 8ᵀᴴ 1912 / INTERMEDIATE / ORCHESTRA
Reverse Harp violin and open book within laurel wreath.
Rim Plain.

S   *unrecorded*   **PC**

The medal is attached to a dated bar by a red ribbon, and was worn by performers during the concert. Three and a half thousand intermediate pupils performed at the afternoon concert, watched by an audience exceeding 10,000. See note to SY-1910 /010.

SY-1912 / 020   School Orchestras Annual Festival
by ?   Al 31 mm

Obverse   Similar to obverse of SY-1912 /015, but seventh line reads: ADVANCED
Reverse   Similar to reverse of SY-1912 /015.
Rim   Plain.

S   *unrecorded*   PC

The medal is attached to a dated bar by a blue ribbon, and was worn by performers during the concert. Two and a half thousand advanced pupils performed at the evening concert, watched by an audience exceeding 10,000. See note to SY-1910 / 010.

SY-1912 / 025   Kennel Club Open Championship
by H.B.   Ar 99x70 mm

Obverse   Similar to obverse of SY-1906 /005, but to Mrs Lytton's Toy Spaniel 'Whirlwind'.
Reverse   Similar to reverse of SY-1906 /005.
Rim   Plain.

RRR   *unrecorded*   PC

Courtesy of C.E. See note to SY-1906/005.

SY-1913 / 001   National Cage Bird Show
by AC Co (possibly Alexander Clark Co)   Ar 39x24 mm

Obverse   Budgerigar on a perch within laurel sprays. *In exergue:* CAGE / BIRDS
Reverse   Five line inscription: FIRST / PRIZE / CRYSTAL / PALACE / 1913 *Signed* A C co.
Rim   Plain.

RR   *unrecorded*   PC

The exergue has a blue enamelled background.

SY-1913 / 005   Church of England Temperance Society Fete
by Toye & Co   Ar Ae 36x30 mm

Obverse   Similar to obverse of SY-1906 /001.
Reverse   Four line inscription: PRIZE MEDAL / CRYSTAL PALACE / FETE /1913 *Signed* TOYE & Co. LONDON
Rim   Plain.

Ar RR, Ae R   *unrecorded* (see SY-1896/001 for ill.)   PC

Courtesy of Ivor Bush. See note to SY-1896 /001.

SY-1913 / 010   School Orchestras Annual Festival
by ?   Al 31 mm

Obverse   Eight line inscription: NATIONAL UNION / OF / SCHOOL ORCHESTRAS' /ANNUAL FESTIVAL / CRYSTAL PALACE / JUNE 21ST 1913 / INTERMEDIATE / ORCHESTRA
Reverse   St Celia playing a harp within an oak wreath.
Rim   Plain.

S   *unrecorded*   PC

The medal is attached to a dated bar by a red ribbon, and was worn by performers during the concert. Three and a half thousand intermediate pupils performed at the afternoon concert, watched by an audience exceeding 10.000. See note to SY-1910 /010.

SY-1913 / 015   School Orchestras Annual Festival
by ?   Al 31 mm

Obverse Similar to obverse of SY-1913 /010, but seventh line reads: ADVANCED
Reverse Similar to reverse of SY-1913 /010.
Rim Plain.

S *unrecorded* PC

The medal is attached to a dated bar by a blue ribbon, and was worn by performers during the concert. Two thousand seven hundred advanced pupils performed at the evening concert, watched by an audience exceeding 10,000. See note to SY-1910 / 010.

SY-1913 / 020   National Gymnastic Display
by ?   Wm 34x27 mm

Obverse View of the Crystal Palace.
Reverse NATIONAL GYMNASTIC DISPLAY
Rim ?

RR *unrecorded*

Description obtained from Whitmore's catalogue November 1982, because the author has not seen a specimen.

SY-1914 / 001   The Crystal Palace Trustees
by Kenning & Son   Arg 28 mm

Obverse Distant view of the Crystal Palace and grounds in a circle of beads. *Inscription in a raised border:* THE CRYSTAL PALACE TRUSTEES ✤

Reverse Two line inscription: Mr. ALDERMAN / A. HUME NICHOLL *Signed* G. KENNING & SON / LONDON 1914 Hallmark.
Rim Scalloped.

RRRR *unrecorded* PC

In 1913, following the successful public appeal launched by the Lord Mayor of London, the Crystal Palace became the property of the nation. Local government authorities contributed nearly half of the sum raised by the appeal, thereby acquiring extensive rights of representation on the board of trustees, set up by the deed of trust to administer the Palace.

SY-1914 / 005   Church of England Temperance Society Fete
by Toye & Co   Ar Ae 36x30 mm

Obverse Similar to obverse of SY-1906 /001.
Reverse Four line inscription: PRIZE MEDAL / CRYSTAL PALACE / FETE / 1914 *Signed* TOYE & Co. LONDON
Rim Plain.

Ar RR, Ae R *unrecorded* (see SY-1896/001 for ill.) PC

Courtesy of Ivor Bush. See note to SY-1896 /001.

SY-1914 / 010   School Orchestras Annual Festival
by ?   Al 31 mm

Obverse *Eight line inscription:* NATIONAL UNION / OF / SCHOOL ORCHESTRAS' /ANNUAL FESTIVAL / CRYSTAL PALACE / JUNE 20TH 1914 / INTERMEDIATE / ORCHESTRA
Reverse Apollo with violin, lyre below, laurel spray to right.
Rim Plain.

S *unrecorded* PC

The medal is attached to a dated bar by a red white and blue ribbon, and was worn by performers during the concert. Three and a half thousand intermediate pupils performed at the afternoon concert, watched by an audience exceeding 10,000. See note to SY-1910 /010.

Following the outbreak of World War I the Admiralty requisitioned the Palace for use as a naval training depot, and would not permit the National Union of School Orchestras use of the concert facilities for the 1915 festival. As no other building could be found to house the 260 school orchestras then wishing to participate, it had to be abandoned. Considerable pressure was exerted to restore the festival in 1916, and it was agreed the best solution would be to divide the London area into seven parts i.e. East, North, North East, North West, South East, South West, and West. This enabled each division to promote its own festival at its chosen venue.

In the Crystal Palace Museum there is a Programme, for this, the 10th Annual Festival of the National Union of School Orchestras. The programme itself cost 2d, and showed the price of admission to the concert as 2/- , 1/- , 6d and 3d.

See note to SY-1910 /010.

SY-1914 / 015	School Orchestras Annual Festival
by ?	Al 31 mm

Obverse   Similar to obverse of SY-1914 /010, but seventh line reads: ADVANCED
Reverse   Similar to reverse of SY-1914 /010.
Rim   Plain.

S   *unrecorded*   **PC**

The medal is attached to a dated bar by a red white and blue ribbon, and was worn by performers during the concert. Three thousand advanced pupils performed at the evening concert, watched by an audience exceeding 10,000. See note to SY-1910 / 010.

SY-1922 / 001	Daily Mail Imperial Fruit Show
by Messrs Pinches	Ae 74 mm

Obverse   *Six line inscription within a border of fruit:* The / Daily Mail / IMPERIAL / FRUIT SHOW / CRYSTAL PALACE / OCTOBER. 27TH. — NOVEMBER 4TH. 1922
Reverse   Ceres in flowing robes holding a laden basket, standing behind a mound of fruit.
Rim   Plain.

RRR   *Pinches 35*   **PC**

Ex John Pinches archive collection. John Harvey Pinches notes that a smaller size version of the medal was produced in gold.

SY-1925 / 001   National Show of Bees & Honey
by W.J. Dingly   Ae 41 mm

Obverse   Distant view of Crystal Palace, a bee above.
Inscription around the border: THE NATIONAL SHOW OF
BEES & HONEY / CRYSTAL PALACE
Reverse   *Four line inscription within a laurel wreath:* 1925 /
CRYSTAL PALACE / CUP. / J.E. SWAFFIELD.
Rim   Plain.

RRR   *unrecorded* (see SY-1929/005 for ill.)   PC

More than one and a half tons of honey was exhibited during
the three days of the show, much of which was purchased by
the viewing public. See *New Crystal Palace Matters*, No. 1 for
an article on the National Show of Bees and Honey.

SY-1926 / 001   Grand International Show of Poultry Pigeons & Rabbits
by E.J. Fairbairns Ltd   Ar Ae 51 mm

Obverse   View of the Crystal Palace and terraces in a
cartouche. *Inscription above:* THE CRYSTAL PALACE /
GRAND INTERNATIONAL *Inscription below:* SHOW OF /
POULTRY PIGEONS & RABBITS
Reverse   *Four line inscription in a laurel wreath:*
AWARDED / TO / W. A. SLOCOCK / 1926
Rim   Plain.

Ar RRR, Ae RR   *unrecorded* (see SY-1929/001 for ill.)   PC

Courtesy of Jim Allen.

SY-1926 / 005   National Show of Bees & Honey
by W.J. Dingly   Ae 41 mm

Obverse   Similar to obverse of SY-1925 /001.
Reverse   *Four line inscription within a laurel wreath:* 1926 /
J.E. SWAFFIELD / CRYSTAL PALACE / CUP.
Rim   Plain.

RRR   *unrecorded* (see SY-1929/005 for ill.)   PC

See note to SY-1925 /001.

SY-1928 / 001   Grand International Show of Poultry Pigeons & Rabbits
by E.J. Fairbairns Ltd   Ar Ae 51 mm

Obverse   Similar to obverse of SY-1926 /001.
Reverse   *Five line inscription in a laurel wreath:* AWARDED /
TO / W. PRINCE-SMITH / ENGLISH OWL / 1928
Rim   Plain.

Ar RRR, Ae RR   *unrecorded* (see SY-1929/001 for ill.)   PC

The show was held from 20 to 22 November.

SY-1928 / 005   National Challenge Show of Cage Birds
by DGC   Ar Ae 45 mm

Obverse   View of the Crystal Palace and terraces in a
cartouche. *Inscription above:* CRYSTAL PALACE
NATIONAL / CHALLENGE / SHOW *Inscription below:*
OF / CAGE BIRDS / 1928
Reverse   *Three line inscription within a laurel wreath:*
AWARDED / TO / R. STEWART
Rim   Plain.

Ar RRR, Ae RR   *unrecorded*   PC

SY-1928 / 010   National Show of Bees & Honey
by W.J. Dingly   Ar 41 mm

Obverse   Similar to obverse of SY-1925 /001.
Reverse   *Four line inscription within a laurel wreath:* 1928 / TRADE CLASS / J. E. SWAFFIELD / 1ST PRIZE *Signed* W.J.D.
Rim   Plain.

RRR   *unrecorded (see SY-1929/005 for ill.)*   PC

See note to SY-1925 /001.

SY-1929 / 001   Grand International Show of Poultry Pigeons & Rabbits
by E.J. Fairbairns Ltd   Ar Ae 51 mm

Obverse   Similar to obverse of SY-1926 /001
Reverse   *Five line inscription in a laurel wreath:* AWARDED / TO / WHALEY & BRIGGS / INDIAN GAME BANTAM / 1929.
Rim   Plain.

Ar RRR, Ae RR   *unrecorded*   PC

The show was held at the Palace from 20 to 23 November.

SY-1929 / 005   National Show of Bees & Honey
by W.J. Dingly   Ar Ae 41 mm

Obverse   Similar to obverse of SY-1925 /001.
Reverse   *Four line inscription within a laurel wreath:* 1929 / TRADE CLASS / 1ST PRIZE / J.E. SWAFFIELD *Signed* W.J.D.
Rim   Plain.

RRR   *unrecorded*   PC

J.E. Swaffield was Secretary to the Gloucestershire Bee-Keepers Association. There is a bronze specimen on display in the Crystal Palace Museum. See note to SY-1925 /001

SY-1930 / 001   National   Brass   Band Championship
by D.G. Collins   Ar 32 mm

Obverse   Similar to obverse of SY-1910 /001, but stamped STERLING, *Signed* D.G.C.
Reverse   Similar to reverse of SY-1910 /001.
Rim   Plain.

RRRR   *unrecorded*   PC

This sterling silver medal is undated and uninscribed, but, as it was purchased with the bronze medals awarded to Fred Sowood, it is reasonable to assume this is the medal awarded to him when the band recorded its second win in 1930. See note to No.1910 /001.

SY-1930 / 005   Grand International Show of Poultry Pigeons & Rabbits
by T.H.E   Ar 39 mm

Obverse   A pigeon. *Incuse inscription around the border:* CRYSTAL PALACE SHOW / 1930
Reverse   *Two line inscription within a laurel wreath:* WON BY / G. H. LEECH *Signed* T.H.E.
Rim   Plain.

RRR   *unrecorded*   PC

Courtesy of Jim Allen.

SY-1930 / 010   Home & Garden Crafts & Industries Exhibition
by Birmingham Medal Co Ltd   Aeg 41 mm

Obverse   *Five line inscription above a view of the Crystal Palace within a trefoil:* HOME & GARDEN / CRAFTS / & / INDUSTRIES / EXHIBITION *Inscription around upon a raised border:* THE NATIONAL SHOW OF BEES & HONEY / • CRYSTAL PALACE •
Reverse   *Five line inscription within a laurel wreath:* 1930 / AWARDED / CAXTON WOOD. TURNERY. Co. / FOR / BEEHIVES. FRAMES. ETC.
Rim   Plain.

RRR   *unrecorded*   PC

The medal is not signed but the case is inscribed: BIRMINGHAM. / MEDAL Cº. Lᵀᴰ / BIRMINGHAM & LONDON. Honey shows were held annually at the Palace from 1923 to 1936. An article about the National Show of Bees and Honey can be found in *New Crystal Palace Matters* No. 1.

SY-1930 / 015   Grand International Show of Poultry Pigeons & Rabbits
by E.J. Fairbairns Ltd   Ae 51 mm

Obverse   Similar to obverse of SY-1929 /001.
Reverse   *Five line inscription in a laurel wreath:* AWARDED / TO / J. BEESLEY. / MODERN GAME BANTAM / 1930.
Rim   Plain.

RR   *unrecorded (see SY-1929/001 for ill.)*   PC

SY-1931 / 001   National Challenge Show of Cage Birds
by JC   Ar Ae 39 mm

Obverse   View of the Crystal Palace. *Inscription above:* THE NATIONAL SHOW / CRYSTAL PALACE *Inscription below:* CAGE BIRD / EXHIBITION
Reverse   *Five line inscription:* CLASS 166 / Cage 5 / 3ᴿᴰ / A. SCOTT / 1931 *Signed* J.C.
Rim   Plain.

Ar RRR, Ae RR   *unrecorded*   PC

SY-1931 / 005   National Challenge Show of Cage Birds
by D. George Collins Ltd   Ar Ae 45 mm

Obverse   Similar to obverse of SY-1928 /005
Reverse   *Three line inscription:* AWARDED / TO / B. CLEGG
Rim   Plain.

Ar RRR, Ae RR   *unrecorded* (see SY-1928 /005 for ill.)   PC

SY-1931 / 010   London Transport tag
by ?   Brass 39x33 mm

Obverse   *Four line inscription:* THE / CRYSTAL / PALACE / L.T.
Reverse   No. 342 above date 1931.
Rim   Plain.

RRR   *unrecorded*   PC

Possibly a tag worn by a conductor working on a London Transport bus or tram on a route to and from the Crystal Palace terminus.

SY-1932 / 001   National Challenge Show of Cage Birds
by JC   Ar Ae 29 mm & 39 mm

Obverse   Similar to obverse of SY-1931 /001.
Reverse   *Five line inscription:* CLASS 31 / CAGE 5 / THIRD / R. R. ROBERTS / 1932 *Signed* J. C.
Rim   Plain.

Ar RRR, Ae RR   *unrecorded*   PC

SY-1933 / 001   National Challenge Show of Cage Birds
by JC   Ar Ae 29 mm

Obverse   Similar to obverse of SY-1931 /001.
Reverse   *Five line inscription:* CLASS 191 / CAGE 7 / 4TH / D. CALDWELL / 1933 *Signed* J.C.
Rim   Plain.

Ar RRR, Ae RR   *unrecorded* (see SY-1931/001 for ill.)   PC

The show was held from 2–4 February.

SY-1933 / 005   National Challenge Show of Cage Birds
by JC for Vaughton   Ar enamelled 31x26 mm

Obverse   Canary on a perch. *Inscription around the border:* THE BORDER FANCY CANARY CLUB
Reverse   *Five line inscription:* WON BY / JOHN MARTIN / CRYSTAL PALACE / NATIONAL SHOW / 1933 *Signed* J. C.
Rim   Plain.

RRR   *unrecorded*   PC

This handsome enamelled piece depicts a yellow canary on a green perch against a black background.

SY-1933 / 010 National Brass Band Championship
by D.G. Collins — Ae 32 mm

Obverse *Four line inscription:* WON BY / FODENS / MOTOR WORKS. / F. SOWOOD. *Inscription around the border:* THE CRYSTAL PALACE / • BAND CHAMPIONSHIP • *Signed* D.G. C.
Reverse Similar to reverse of SY-1910 /001
Rim Plain.

RRRR *unrecorded* PC

The bronze medal awarded to Fred Sowood in 1910 has the date inscribed upon it, whereas, on his later medals, the date appears on a bronze suspension bar attached to the medal by a plain royal blue ribbon. During the 1930s, under their conductor Fred Mortimer, Fodens Motor Works Band dominated the championships by winning seven times between 1930 and 1938.

SY-1933 / 015 Grand International Show of Poultry Pigeons & Rabbits
by E.J. Fairbairns Ltd — Ar Ae 51 mm

Obverse Similar to obverse of SY-1926 /001.
Reverse *Five line inscription within a laurel wreath:* AWARDED / TO / W. F. HOLMES. / S. MODENA. / 1933
Rim Plain.

Ar RRR, Ae RR *unrecorded* (see SY-1929/001 for ill.) PC

SY-1934 / 001 National Show of Bees & Honey
by ? — Ae 43 mm

Obverse Two hives in a garden. *Inscription around the border:* BRITISH BEE — KEEPERS' ASSOCIATION / ❧ INSTITUTED 1874 ❧
Reverse *Three line inscription within a floral wreath:* CRYSTAL PALACE / MR TYRELL / 1934
Rim Plain.

RR *unrecorded* PC

Courtesy of John Reed. The medals cost the association: gold 65/- , silver 10/- , bronze 3/9d. Cases cost 1/3d, and are inscribed on the lid: BRITISH / BEE KEEPERS / ASSOCIATION.

SY-1935 / 001 National Challenge Show of Cage Birds
by The Alexander Clark Co Ltd — Ar 45 mm

Obverse   Similar to obverse of SY-1928 /005.
Reverse   *Four line inscription within a laurel wreath:* CLASS
223 / CAGE 6 / 3ᴿᴰ PRIZE / C.A. MOLES
Rim   Plain.

RRR   *unrecorded*   PC

SY-1936 / 001	National	Brass	Band
Championship			
by D.G. Collins			Ae 32 mm

Obverse   Similar to obverse of SY-1933 /010.
Reverse   Similar to reverse of SY-1933 /010.
Rim   Plain.

RRRR   *unrecorded (see SY-1933/010 for ill.)*   PC

See notes to SY-1910 /001, SY-1930 /001 and SY-1933 /010.

SY-1936 / 005	Grand	International	Show of
Poultry Pigeons & Rabbits			
by The Alexander Clark Co Ltd			Ar 51 mm

Obverse   Similar to obverse of SY-1926 /001.
Reverse   *Six line inscription within a laurel wreath:*
AWARDED / TO / E. P. MORTON / FOR BEST /
BANTAM / 1936. *Signed* A C C.L.
Rim   Plain.

RRR   *unrecorded (see SY-1929/001 for ill.)*   PC

SY-1937 / 001	National	Brass	Band
Championship			
by D.G. Collins			Ae 32 mm

Obverse   Similar to obverse of SY-1933 /010.
Reverse   Similar to reverse of SY-1933 /010.
Rim   Plain.

RRRR   *unrecorded (see SY-1933/010 for ill.)*   PC

Following the disastrous fire of 1936, the Brass Band
championship was transferred to the Alexandra Palace, where
it was held for the remaining two years prior to the
commencement of World War II. On both occasions, Fodens
Motor Works Band won the title, bringing the number of wins
under their conductor Fred Mortimer, to seven between 1930
and 1938. It is interesting to note that even though the venue
had changed, the medals had not, this was undoubtedly for
economic reasons, but pleasingly it provided two additional
medals for this catalogue. See notes to SY-1910 /001, SY-1930 /
001 and SY-1933 /010.

SY-1938 / 001	National	Brass	Band
Championship			
by D.G. Collins			Ae 32 mm

Obverse   Similar to obverse of SY-1933 /010.
Reverse   Similar to reverse of SY-1933 /010.
Rim   Plain.

RRRR   *unrecorded (see SY-1933/010 for ill.)*   PC

Fred Sowood was a horn player, he joined Fodens Motorworks
Band in 1909, and must have been a devoted and capable
musician to have retained his place in a works band all those
years. The author purchased six of his medals, five are bronze
and one silver, sadly the gold medal he earned in 1932 was not
with them, hopefully it has not been melted down. See notes to
SY-1910 /001, SY-1930 /001, SY-1933 /010 and SY-1937 /001.

SY-1938 / 005 National Challenge Show of Cage Birds
by The Alexander Clark Co Ltd — Ar 45 mm

Obverse Similar to obverse of SY-1928 /005.
Reverse *Four line inscription within a laurel wreath:* 2ND PRIZE / CLASS 115 / CAGE 7 / R. S. TODD. *Signed* A C C.L.
Rim Plain.

RRR *unrecorded* PC

Courtesy of Jim Allen. Following the fire in 1936, it appears the Crystal Palace Cage Bird show moved to the Royal Horticultural Hall, Westminster. In the *Postal History of the Crystal Palace*, Maurice Bristow mentions that in 1939 the 71st Crystal Palace Cage Bird show was held at the Royal Horticultural Hall, Westminster, and in an article on bird shows in issue No.8 of *New Crystal Palace Matters* there is a judges' card for the 1946 show also held there.

SY-1939 / 001 National Challenge Show of Cage Birds
by The Alexander Clark Co Ltd — Aeg 45 mm

Obverse Similar to obverse of SY-1928 /005.
Reverse Similar to reverse of SY-1938 /005.
Rim Plain.

RRR *unrecorded* PC

See note to SY-1938 /005.

SY-1940 / 001 National Challenge Show of Cage Birds
by The Alexander Clark Co Ltd — Ar 45 mm

Obverse Similar to obverse of SY-1928 /005.
Reverse Inscription in wreath.
Rim Plain.

R *unrecorded* CP

The author was unable to examine the reverse of this medal because it is in a sealed display case at the Crystal Palace Museum.
See note to SY-1938 /005.

SY-1984 / 001 Radio Rentals
by ? — Ae 39 mm

Obverse Bust of John Logie Baird right.
Reverse Hidden.
Rim Plain.

N *unrecorded* CP

The author was unable to examine the reverse of this medal because it is in a sealed display case at the Crystal Palace Museum.

An interesting article on John Logie Baird's work at the Palace appears in issue No. 6 of *New Crystal Palace Matters*.

SY-1987 / 001 National Cat Club Centenary Year
by ? — Enamelled Br 39 mm

Obverse 1887–1987 below Arms of the National Cat Club. Inscription around the border: ✳ NATIONAL CAT CLUB / CENTENARY YEAR ✳
Reverse Hidden.
Rim Plain.

N *unrecorded* CP

The inscriptions and the arms are red, blue, yellow and gold, on a white background. The author was unable to examine the reverse of the medal because it is in a sealed display case at the

Crystal Palace Museum. See article on Crystal Palace cat shows in *Crystal Palace Matters*, No.28, p.32.

Undated Pieces

SY-ND / 001   Crystal Palace Trustee Pass
by D.G. Collins   Ar 22 mm

Obverse   Three line inscription: CRYSTAL / TRUSTEE / PALACE
Reverse   Incuse inscription: 48 *Signed* DGC, plus a 1928 Birmingham Hallmark
Rim   Plain.

RRRR   *unrecorded*   CP

Unlike SY-1914 /001, this does not show the name of the trustee hereon. This was possibly for economic reasons to enable the pass to be re-issued when a trustee retired. No doubt there would have been a record kept in the Crystal Palace offices showing to whom the passes were issued.

SY-ND / 005   Robert Holt
by JM   Br 23 mm

Obverse   Bare head of Queen Victoria left. *Inscription around the border:* THE SOVEREIGN OF CIVILIZATION *Signed* J.M.
Reverse   Similar to reverse of SY-1867 /015.
Rim   Beaded.

RRR   *unrecorded*   PC

Similar to 'KEEP YOUR TEMPER' Whist counters by J. Moore, but not listed by Hawkins. See note to SY-1867 /015.

SY-ND / 010   Crystal Palace Stables
by Messrs Pinches   Wm 36 mm

Obverse   Four line inscription: CRYSTAL PALACE C^os. / PAID / 1/6 / ◆ STABLES ◆
Reverse   Blank *Signed* PINCHES & Co MAKERS CRYSTAL PALACE MEDAL PRESS
Rim   Toothed.

RRR   *unrecorded*   PC

Courtesy of Jim Allen. This interesting check refers to an important aspect of the Palace which has had precious little coverage.

SY-ND / 015   John Betjeman's Bygone Britain
by Messrs Pinches   Ar 39 mm

Obverse   View of the centre transept and terraces with people dressed in period costume.
Reverse   *Ten line inscription within an ornate border:* Bygone Britain / The Crystal Palace, London. / Built to house the Great Exhibition of 1851. / Designer: Sir Joseph Paxton. / Inspirer: H. R. H. Albert, Prince Consort. / Removed to Sydenham, South London, 1854. / 1600 feet long. / Destroyed by fire November 1936. / The Crystal Palace. London. / John Betjeman
Rim   Plain.

RR   *unrecorded*   PC

This is a modern piece from a cased set of 36 silver medals struck in the 1970s.

SY-ND / 020   Crystal Palace Refreshment Department
by Messrs Pinches   Ae 42 mm

Obverse   Three line inscription in circle: CRYSTAL / JT & WS / PALACE *Inscription around the border:* ✿ REFRESHMENT DEPARTMENT ✿
Reverse   *Inscription on scroll:* PASS TICKET, numbered above 350. *Signed* PINCHES LONDON
Rim   Toothed.

RRR   *unrecorded*   PC

Illustration courtesy of Simmons and Simmons. The identity of JT and WS has not yet been discovered. An interesting article on Crystal Palace catering appears in issue No. 2 of *New Crystal Palace Matters*.

SY-ND / 025   The Crystal Palace Dog Show
by Messrs Pinches   Ae 51 mm

Obverse   Three line inscription: THE CRYSTAL PALACE ✿ / DOG / SHOW
Reverse   Blank.

Rim   Plain.

RRR   *unrecorded*   PC

Ex John Pinches archive collection, thought to be a trial strike.

SY-ND / 030   Prize medal
by Messsrs Pinches, G.G. Adams & W.J. Taylor   Wm 63 mm

Obverse   Similar to reverse of SY-1854 /110, but the exergue is empty.
Reverse   Laurel wreath *Signed* W.J. TAYLOR. LONDON.
Rim   Plain.

RRR   *unrecorded*   PC

Similar to the Picture Gallery prize medals, but this is the first specimen seen by the author in this metal. Possibly a trial strike.

SY-ND / 035 Peter's Rifle Ground	
by ?	Wm 23 mm

Obverse   Conjoined heads of the Prince and Princess of Wales left. Inscription around the border: ALBERT EDWARD • ALEXANDRA •
Reverse   *Three line inscription:* PETERS RIFLE GROUND / PRIZE / • CRYSTAL PALACE •
Rim   Beaded obverse, plain reverse.

RRR	*unrecorded*	PC

No doubt it was struck in 1863 to commemorate the marriage of the Prince of Wales.

SY-ND / 040 Crystal Palace Company Check	
by ?	Wm 28 mm

Obverse   *Inscription around a blank centre:* CRYSTAL PALACE COMPANY ✤
Reverse   *Incuse inscription:* 381
Rim   Toothed.

RR	*unrecorded*	PC

It is not known what this check was used for.

SY-ND / 045 Crystal Palace Company Check	
by ?	Wm 35 mm

Obverse   *Incuse inscription in a beaded circle:* 458 *Inscription around the border:* CRYSTAL PALACE COMPANY ✿
Reverse   Blank.
Rim   Beaded.

RR	*unrecorded*	PC

Courtesy of Melvyn Harrison. It is not known what this check was used for.

Crystal Palace, c.1860

Imperial War Museum Exhibition, c. 1920. Reproduced by permission of Eric Price & Melvyn Harrison.

Aerial view, c.1930. Reproduced by permission of Eric Price & Melvyn Harrison.

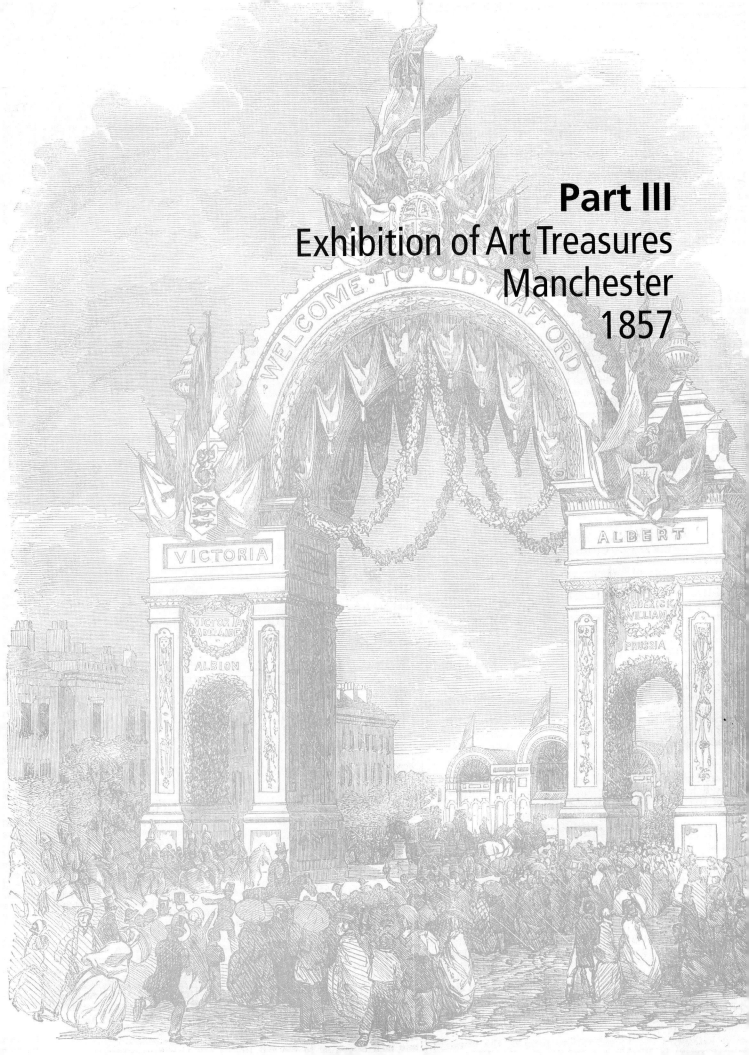

Part III
Exhibition of Art Treasures
Manchester
1857

Introduction

The Great Exhibition of 1851 was devoted almost entirely to works of industry, so there were very few objects of fine art on display apart from the statuary. The enormous thirst for knowledge created by the Great Exhibition, and its counterpart at Sydenham, led to a public clamouring for an exhibition devoted entirely to works of fine art. To satisfy this demand a group of public-minded businessmen decided in 1856 to promote an Art Loan Exhibition. This 'loan' aspect was necessary because, unlike most other countries, which had gathered their works of art into national museums and galleries, those in Great Britain were held mainly in the private collections of the wealthy.

There were many who doubted the possibility of raising the Guarantee Fund; whilst others thought that the owners of valuable works of art would not be so improvident as to send them into the tall chimneys district of Manchester. Surprisingly, the doubters were soon proven wrong, because a Guarantee Fund of £70,000 was easily raised, and to ensure the success of the Exhibition, the patronage of Queen Victoria and Prince Albert was obtained.

Eventually a site of about 30 acres, on land belonging to Sir Humphrey De Trafford, was chosen. This site ran alongside the London and North Western railway line; next to the Botanic Gardens at Old Trafford; about two miles west of Manchester city centre and, allegedly, was free from atmospheric impurities! The Committee had set their collective mind on a mini-Crystal Palace, and it adopted a design by Messrs C.D. Young & Co, of London and Leith. This plan, modified by Edward Salomons (architect to the Committee) was for a building 656 feet long by 200 feet wide, comprising a central nave with two side aisles and complete with arched glass roofs, and which, viewed from the front, resembled a smaller version of the three arched transepts of the Sydenham

Exterior View by Leighton Brothers. Contemporary print.

Royal procession passing the Infirmary. *Illustrated London News*, 1857.

Crystal Palace joined together. A formal ceremony of laying the foundation stone of the first pillar took place on 13 July 1856; the first column was raised on 14 August and on 20 February 1857 a public promenade was held in the completed structure.

It was planned that the exhibition would open on 1 May 1857, but, due to the overwhelming response received from the advertisement placed in the national press, (which had requested the loan of instructive works illustrating the ancient and modern schools of art), the organisers needed a further four days to prepare the magnificent display of paintings. In all, there were 1,115 oil paintings of 'the old school', 689 paintings by contemporary artists, 969 water colour drawings and engravings, and 388 portraits by British artists which were loaned by the National Gallery. In addition there were numerous collections of gold & silver plate, jewels, porcelain, furniture, armour, sculptures, bronzes, medals and coins etc. This 'Aladdin's Cave' formed what was probably the most important and splendid collection of art objects ever to be gathered together in any one place at any one time. Her Majesty the Queen provided twenty two pictures from Buckingham Palace plus seventeen from Windsor Castle. Many Dukes, Earls, Lords, and other wealthy possessors of the richest works of art, readily sent their treasures.

The opening of this exhibition of unique and valuable art treasures took place on 5 May 1857, and created intense excitement in Manchester and the surrounding manufacturing towns. Most of the mills and factories ceased production as tens of thousands of people thronged the streets to greet the arrival of Prince Albert for the opening ceremony. The welcoming crowds were ten times greater when, on 30 June, the Queen visited the Exhibition.

When the exhibition closed on 17 October, it had attracted more than 1,335,000 visitors, who had paid in excess of £100,000 for the privilege of reviewing the glittering array. Expenditure had amounted to £104,000, but the subsequent sale of the building ensured a surplus of more than £10,000.

The exhibits were not in competition with each other so no prize medals were awarded by the organisers. Fortunately, for us, there was a small number of unofficial commemorative medals struck by private firms. All known pieces have been recorded.

JOHN CASSELL'S
ART TREASURES EXHIBITION.

INTERIOR OF THE ART TREASURES EXHIBITION BUILDING AT MANCHESTER.

Medals

MA-001   The Inauguration
by T. Ottley   Oval Ae, Wm 51 x 41 mm

Obverse   Bare head of Prince Albert left. *Inscription around the border:* H. R. H. PRINCE ALBERT *signed* OTTLEY
Reverse   Distant view of the exhibition building. *Inscription above:* EXHIBITION OF ART TREASURES OF THE UNITED KINGDOM / AT MANCHESTER *In exergue:* H.R.H. PRINCE ALBERT / PRESIDED AT THE GRAND / INAUGURAL CEREMONY / 5ᵀᴴ MAY 1857
Signed OTTLEY BIRM
Rim   Beaded.

RRR   *Brown* 2604 (ill.)   PC

MA-005   The Inauguration
by Messrs Pinches   Brass case 45 & 67 mm

Lid   Arms of the City of Manchester. *Inscription above:* ART

191

TREASURES EXHIBITION *Inscription below:*
MANCHESTER / 1857
Base Seven line inscription: PINCHES & Co / DIE
SINKERS / SEAL ENGRAVERS / & c / 27 OXENDEN S^T /
LONDON / MEDALLISTS
Rim Plain.

R *Brown 2610 (note)* PC

Most of the white metal medals struck by Messrs Pinches to
commemorate this exhibition have been seen in one of these
brass cases.

MA-010   The Inauguration
by Messrs Pinches   Ae Wm 42 mm

Obverse   Diademed draped bust of Queen Victoria left.
Inscription around the border: VICTORIA REGINA *Signed*
PINCHES. LONDON
Reverse   View of the exhibition building. *Inscription above:*
EXHIBITION OF ART TREASURES *In exergue:* OPENED
AT MANCHESTER / BY HIS ROYAL HIGHNESS /
PRINCE ALBERT / MAY 5TH 1857
Rim   Plain.

RRR *Brown 2608, Taylor 173c*   BM PC

This obverse was used by Pinches in 1854 to commemorate the
opening of the Sydenham Crystal Palace, see SY-1854 /060; also
note to MA-005.

MA-015   The Inauguration
by Messrs Pinches   Ae Wm 42 mm

Obverse   Similar to reverse of MA-010.
Reverse   Three muses seated among symbols of art. *In
exergue:* MDCCCLVII *Signed* PINCHES LONDON
Rim   Plain.

Ae RR, Wm S   *Brown 2609, Taylor 173b*   BM BG FM PC

Bill Kennett has an unsigned white metal specimen. See note to
MA-005.

MA-020   The Inauguration
by Messrs Pinches   Ae Wm 42 mm

Obverse   Similar to reverse of MA-010, but has bushes in
front of the building.
Reverse   Similar to reverse of MA-015.
Rim   Plain.

Ae RR, Wm R   *unrecorded*   PC

See note to MA-005.

MA-025   The Inauguration
by Messrs Pinches   Ae Wm 42 mm

Obverse   Eight line inscription: EXHIBITION OF / ART TREASURES / OF THE / UNITED KINGDOM / OPENED AT MANCHESTER / BY HIS ROYAL HIGHNESS / PRINCE ALBERT / MAY 5TH 1857
Reverse   Similar to reverse of MA-015.
Rim   Plain.

Ae R, Wm S   *Brown* 2606   AM BM BG FM ML PC UM

See note to MA-005.

Obverse   Similar to obverse of MA-025, but with minor differences to last line.
Reverse   Similar to reverse of MA-015, but signed on exergue line.
Rim   Plain.

Ae R, Wm S   *Brown* 2606   AM BM BG FM ML PC UM

See note to MA-005.

MA-030   The Inauguration
by Messrs Pinches   Ae Wm 63 mm

MA-035   The Inauguration
by Messrs Pinches   Ae Wm 63 mm

The royal vsitors in the nave. Illustrated London News, 1857.

Obverse Centre is similar to reverse of MA-010. Around the border is a wreath entwined with four shields and a ribbon *inscribed:* MURRILLO, FLAXMAN, VANDYKE, RUBENS, CELLINI, RAPHAEL, M. ANGELO, TURNER.
Reverse Similar to reverse of MA-015, but *signed* PINCHES. F LONDON.
Rim Plain.

Ae RR, Wm R *Brown* 2605, *Eimer (I)* 1513, *Fearon (I)* 308.2, *Taylor* 173e   AM BM BG PC UM

See note to MA-005.

Description courtesy of Bill Kennett. The royal visit covered two days. The official ceremony was held on Tuesday 30 June and the royal party attended a private viewing on Wednesday 1 July.

MA-040   Royal Visit

by T. Ottley   Oval Wm 51 x 41 mm

Obverse Similar to reverse of MA-001.
Reverse *Fourteen line inscription:* IN COMMEMORATION / OF / HER MAJESTY THE QUEEN / & H. R. H. PRINCE ALBERT / ACCOMPANIED BY THE / PRINCESS ROYAL, THE PRINCE OF WALES, / THE PRINCESS ALICE, PRINCE ALFRED, / & HIS ROYAL HIGHNESS / PRINCE FREDERICK WILLIAM / OF PRUSSIA'S VISIT TO THE / EXHIBITION OF ART TREASURES / OF THE UNITED KINGDOM AT / MANCHESTER / JULY 1ˢᵗ 1857
Rim Beaded.

RRR *unrecorded* PC

MA-045   Royal Visit

by Messrs Pinches   Ae Wm 42 mm

Obverse Similar to obverse of MA-010.
Reverse View of the exhibition building. *Inscription above:* EXHIBITION OF ART TREASURES *In exergue:* TO

COMMEMORATE THE VISIT / OF HER MAJESTY /
JUNE 30ᵀᴴ 1857
Rim Plain.

Ae RR, Wm R	*Brown* 2607	AM PC

See notes to MA-005, MA-010 and MA-040.

MA-050 Royal Visit
by Messrs Pinches · Wm 42 mm

Obverse Similar to reverse of MA-045.
Reverse Similar to reverse of MA-010.
Rim Plain.

RR	*Brown* 2610

Description obtained from Brown, because the author has not
seen a specimen. See note to MA-005.

MA-055 Royal Visit
by Messrs Pinches · Wm 42 mm

Obverse Similar to reverse of MA-045.
Reverse Similar to reverse of MA-015.
Rim Plain.

RR	*unrecorded* PC

See note to MA-005.

'Land of the tall chimneys'. *Illustrated London News*, 1857.

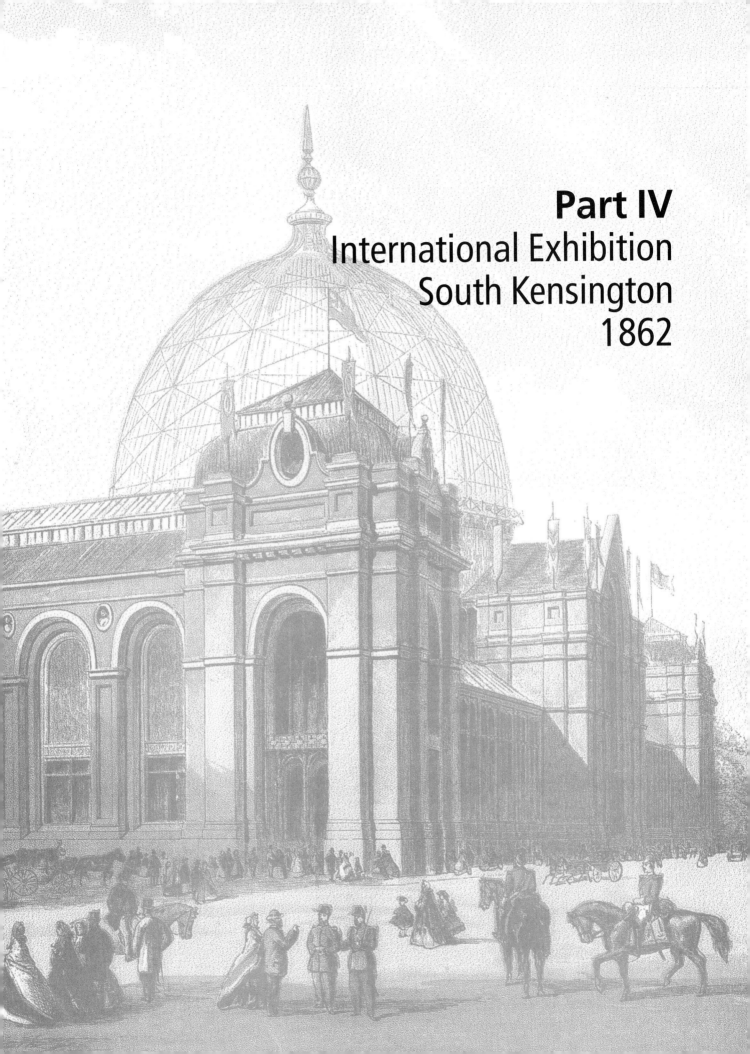

Part IV
International Exhibition
South Kensington
1862

Introduction

Following the closure of the Great Exhibition of 1851, the Royal Commissioners used £60,000 of the profits from the Exhibition to acquire the 86 acre Kensington Gore Estate, which was situated between Hyde Park and Cromwell Road. They proceeded to erect a series of buildings, which were to be used to develop Science and Art studies, and also to house the gifts donated by grateful exhibitors at the closure of the Great Exhibition. The South Kensington Museum, later named The Victoria and Albert Museum was, in 1857, the first National Museum to be opened on the site.

In 1858 the Society of Arts proposed that a second International Exhibition should be planned to take place in 1861 to mark the tenth anniversary of the Great Exhibition. The Commissioners granted the use of the land on the Kensington site rent free, contingent only on the Society undertaking to find the Exhibitors and raise the necessary financial guarantees. However, the uncertainty caused by the conflict in Italy leading to the creation of the present Italian State, led to the postponement of the Exhibition until 1862.

Captain Francis Fowke of the Royal Engineers, an inspector on the staff of the Department of Science and Art, and who had laid out the grounds on the Kensington site, was chosen by Henry Cole (who became the first Director of the South Kensington Museum) to design a building. His design, covering an area of 23 acres, was topped by two enormous glass domes, which promptly earned them the name 'Brompton Boilers'. Inevitably this choice attracted considerable resentment from many eminent architects of the day, including Sir Joseph Paxton (who denounced it as a beast), who felt that they had been denied the opportunity of submitting a design. Both Henry Cole and Captain Fowke came in for a great deal of public criticism later, when it was discovered that the building was very unstable, and that vast sums of money would have to be spent on rebuilding three quarters of it, if it were to be retained.

When the tender covering the design by Fowkes was sent out, Messrs Kelk & Lucas, who had been engaged upon various other works on the site, submitted the lowest tender at £610,000, but, this was more than double the cost which had been envisaged, and the scheme had to be drastically modified to bring it within the planned budget of £300,000, because at that particular point in time the Guarantee Fund had reached only £350,000. A contract was eventually negotiated with Messrs. Kelk & Lucas, contingent on the success of the Exhibition, whereby, £200,000 was to be paid out at the start, and a further £100,000 was to be paid after gate takings had reached £400,000.

To ease the anticipated congestion, a toll road was built from Bayswater to Kensington. A charge was made of threepence for each horse that passed and a hafpenny for each pedestrian. On the northern part of the site, and immediately behind the Exhibition building, the Royal Horticultural Society had laid out its gardens. These became an important added attraction because flower shows, fetes, promenade concerts, etc. were organised as a supplement to the Exhibition. Sadly they did not compensate for the enormous shadow cast upon the event by the premature death of Prince Albert[1], its most ardent supporter. This tragic event robbed the Exhibition of a Royal Inauguration Ceremony, and therefore it lacked the prestige and glamour bestowed on its predecessors.

The exhibition was eventually opened on 1 May 1862 by the Duke of Cambridge on behalf of Her Majesty. The building accommodated 25,000 exhibitors on 1,300,000 square feet of floor space. Compared to the Great Exhibition of 1851, the number of exhibitors and the floor area required were considerably enlarged because of the inclusion of a Fine Arts section. However, like the Great Exhibition, it closed on Sunday. The cost of admission was also almost as expensive i.e.

---

1. The Royal Horticultural Society gardens had absorbed a great deal of Prince Albert's time during the last few months of his life, and Queen Victoria was convinced that it was here that he had caught the fever which led to his death.

The opening. *Illustrated London News*, 1862.

a) Season tickets were priced at 3 guineas each, the holders also being privileged to attend the Grand Opening Ceremony. This price was halved in July. A combined ticket which allowed the Holder free admission to the Royal Horticultural Society gardens, and its entertainments, was available at 5 guineas.

b) Apparently the Commissioners did not want any visitors wandering about on the two days following the opening, because although the doors did not open until midday, the price of admission was still one guinea.

c) Daily admission from the fourth day was 5/- up until 17 May.

d) From 19 May, Monday to Friday daily admission prices were reduced to 2/6d, but the Saturday price remained at 5/- .

e) From June 2nd onwards the Monday to Thursday daily admission price was reduced to one shilling, with the Friday price remaining at 2/6d.

f) From June 15th the Saturday price was reduced to 2/6d.

g) The Prize Giving Ceremony was held on July 11th, the price of admission being £1.

h) The final fourteen days were devoted exclusively to the sale of Exhibitors goods, the price of admission being 2/6d.

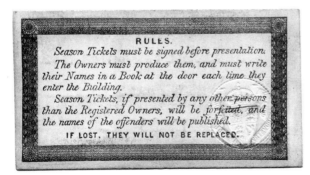

The 1851 Great Exhibition closed on 11 October and a comparison of the statistics of the two exhibitions at that date reveals:

	1862	1851
Number of visitors	5,305,913 [1]	6,039,195 [3]
Average number present each day	37,630	42,830
Highest number present at any time	67,552	93,224
Average daily admission receipts	£2,639	£3,007
Receipts in £	**1862**	**1851**
at the doors	293,070	
season tickets	79,000	
refreshments franchise fees	5,500	
refreshments share from sales	21,938	
catalogue advertisements	15,000	
catalogue sales	17,000	
waiting — rooms, umbrellas, etc.	4,941	
photographic contracts	2,350	
Gross receipts	438,799	506,100
Payments	488,799	292,794
Profit / (Deficit)	(50,000) [2]	213,306 [4]

1. Attendances from 13 October to the close should be added to this figure to arrive at the total number of visitors.
2. By the close of the Exhibition this deficit had been reduced to £11,000.
3. 24,791 in respect of the staff & the press etc., will need to be added to this number in order to reconcile with the figure shown in the 1851 chart.
4. This figure was reduced to £186,000 after the Commissioners made the following payments: £5,000 to Sir Joseph Paxton; £5,400 to Messrs Fox & Henderson; £5,000 for scientific advice and £9,000 to Foreign Commissioners.

By the close of the Exhibition the sale of 27,800 season tickets (5,773 at 5 guineas, 17,719 at 3 guineas, 26 at 50/-, 919 at 30/- and 3,363 at 10/- on the shilling days) realised £89,250; of which £8.672 was paid over to the Royal Horticultural Society as their share of the combined gate fees. Total attendances exceeded 6,200,000, but the overall income of £469,000 was insufficient to meet all of the costs, and a deficit of £11,000 was incurred. To balance the accounts, and prevent the necessity of calling upon the guarantors, Sir John Kelk generously donated that amount to the Royal Commissioners.

During August, the Commisioners found themselves involved in a number of petty law-suits. It appears that a determined season ticket holder summoned all the Commissioners to Brompton County Court on 6 August, to recover from them an umbrella which they detained on 10 July, in consequence of his refusal to pay the penny charged for its custody. This was followed by a walking stick incident when a man entered the picture gallery with a walking stick in his hand, on being asked to give it up he refused to do so and in consequence was seized and forcibly ejected. As a result he summoned the Commissioners for assault. Then on 10 August, yet another season ticket holder summoned them for alleged breach of contract for altering the admission charge on Saturdays from 5/- to 2/6d., claiming he was entitled to a refund of £4.15s plus costs in respect of his two season tickets which had been purchased at the higher price. In all three incidents the court found in favour of the Commissioners.

Arguably, the major success of the Exhibition was its ability to indicate the enormous progress in technology and industrial design which had been achieved since 1851.

Among the printed documents and forms that were in general use, Form No. 216 caught the attention of the author. It would appear that the Commissioners had learned a thing or two from the Great Exhibition, and decided to put them into practice in the following ways:

Instructions to Moneytakers

a) No change will be given.

b) No one is allowed through the turnstile without payment, or without handing over a day ticket.

c) Children are to be charged as adults.

d) Moneytakers are liable to make good any loss arising from bad money accepted.

e) Money must be dropped in box before the turnstile is moved.

f) Commissioners and Principal Officers will use Blue Ivory Passes.

g) Card passes will be used by all other staff, Jurors, Press, etc.

h) Between 6am and 8am moneytakers will be employed in various other capacities, but they will assemble at 9.15 am. to be inspected and allocated to their turnstiles.

The Government later purchased the site from the Commissioners and demolished the exhibition building (it was found to be unsafe) to make way for what is now the Natural History Museum; which was erected to house the natural history collections then held in the overcrowded British Museum. The building materials, including the domes, were purchased from the contractors and transported to Muswell Hill. Here they were intended for use in the construction of the Alexandra Palace, which was planned to be North London's serious rival to the Crystal Palace at Sydenham. Due, however, to the many problems experienced, including a catastrophic fire soon after it had opened, it was never able to achieve that position.

In retrospect, due to the wisdom and foresight of the Royal Commissioners, the Kensington site has become England's principal national cultural centre containing the Royal Albert Hall, the Victoria & Albert Museum, the Natural History Museum, the Science Museum and a number of other prominent academic institutions.

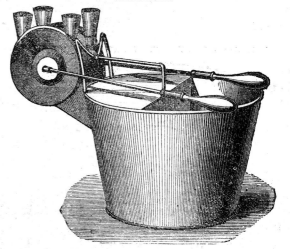

THE PATENT COW-MILKER IN THE INTERNATIONAL EXHIBITION.

WE seem quickly to be losing the poetry of rustic life. The mower is no longer required at the scythe, nor the reaper at the sickle; that bent figure at the barn-door swinging to the music of the flail is gone; the whistle of the ploughboy is gradually dying in the distance; and now we are called upon to dismiss the ruddy milk-maid. A machine has been invented for milking cows, and is now on exhibition in the United States' department of the International Exhibition. The teats of the cow just drop into four elastic tubes placed under them, in communication with an exhaust apparatus and a reservoir. The quick movement of two handles creates a vacuum, and the udder is instantaneously emptied of its contents in four continuous streams. While the operation is distressingly practical, it is very cleanly, and, we believe, agreeable to the cow. The milk is withdrawn at the rate of a gallon a minute. The patent of the "cow-milker" has been sold to Watkins and Keene, of Birmingham, for £5000, and a royalty to the original inventors; and it is stated that the firm have already received orders sufficient to cover the expenses of the patent, and that the machine is rapidly being adopted by all the great dairymen throughout the country. A prize medal and honourable mention have been awarded to the patent milking apparatus.

Extract from the *Illustrated London News*, 1862.

A. Official Medals

To commemorate this exhibition the Commissioners awarded only two styles of bronze medal. One, a 77 mm medal engraved by Leonard Charles Wyon and from a design by Daniel Maclise, apparently doubled as an award to Jurors and also as a prize medal to Exhibitors. Apart from the edge inscription, the only other distinguishing feature between the two medals is to be found in their cases; the Jurors medal has an inscription on the lid, whilst that of the Prize medal does not. The second style of medal, a 55 mm sized piece, is engraved by William Wyon on the obverse and by Leonard Charles Wyon on the reverse. This medal was awarded as a recognition For Services Rendered.

The prize medal was awarded for merit without distinction or degree, to Industrial Exhibitors within classes 1–36 only, and no Exhibitor was allowed more than one medal in any one class. An exhibitor accepting the office of juror could not be awarded a medal in the class or sub-class to which he had been appointed, either to himself individually or to a firm of which he was a partner.

In total there were 6,992 Prize medals awarded by the juries, but as only 1,640 of them were won by Exhibitors from the United Kingdom, perhaps all the complaints about the judging were justified.

Exhibiting firms with a number of partners were permitted to purchase duplicate medals directly from Leonard Charles Wyon at a cost of one guinea each and, just as in 1851, these were probably numerous. Unfortunately, yet again, a record showing the actual number of duplicate medals supplied has yet to be found. It is possible, that as in 1851, a cased set of the two official medals were presented to the Commissioners and other VIPs, but, if that is so, the author has yet to see one.

Once again the report of the Commissioners failed to disclose any details regarding the For Services medal; and apparently the number of these medals awarded was relatively small compared to those in 1851, because the author has seen only a handful in the past twenty five years, and surprisingly few have appeared on medal dealers' lists. A record of the number awarded has yet to be found. The Commissioners report did not explain why the Prize medal was also used as an award to Jurors, (probably for economic reasons) but, as in 1851, it is possible to find the number of medals awarded to Jurors by calculating the number of Jurors on each of the panels.

Leonard Charles Wyon used the minting facilities of Messrs Pinches again to produce these medals for the Commissioners, and was paid £6,409 for supplying them. Curiously, the prize medal is listed in the Royal Mint Museum Catalogue, even though it was not struck there.

A semi-official silver gilt cruciform shaped medal was commissioned by the International Entertainment Committee, (see SK-A020). No information has been found regarding this piece, which would appear to have been presented to members of the International Entertainment Committee only.

SK-A001   Prize medal — Jurors medal
by L.C. Wyon   Ae 77 mm

Obverse   Britannia seated with lion and shield, holding laurel wreath; group around exhibiting industrial products; *Signed* D. MACLISE R. A. DES. L.C. WYON FEC.

The Chairman of Juries delivering awards. *Illustrated London News*, 1862.

Reverse *Four line inscription within an oak wreath:* 1862 / LONDINI / HONORIS / CAUSA *Signed* L.C. WYON. F.
Rim Plain.
Edge Inscribed at the top with the name of the recipient and the class number.

> **S** *Brown* 2747, *Eimer (I)* 1553, *Fearon (I)* 313.4 AM BM BG ML PC

This version was awarded as a prize to exhibitors and is usually found in a fitted case with no inscription on the lid. The Commissioners report states that 6,992 Prize medals were awarded by the Juries, but that figure does not include the duplicate medals sold to members of firms with a number of partners. A silvered specimen from the collection of the second Duke of Cambridge has been seen. A certificate probably accompanied the medal when it was awarded, and if so, the author would be pleased to hear from a reader who has a specimen.

SK-A005 Prize medal — Jurors medal
by L.C. Wyon   Ae 77 mm

Obverse Similar to obverse of SK-A001, but signed in smaller script: D. MACLISE R. A. DES. LEONARD C. WYON FEC.
Reverse Similar to reverse of SK-A001, but *Signed* L. C. WYON. FEC.
Rim Plain.
Edge Similar to SK-A001.

> **R** *unrecorded* PC

All the specimens of this type seen by the author were awarded as prize medals. See note to SK-A001.

SK-A010 Prize medal — Jurors medal
by L.C. Wyon   Ae 77 mm

Obverse Similar to obverse of SK-A001, but *Signed* D. MACLISE R. A. DES. LEONARD C. WYON FEC.
Reverse Similar to reverse of SK-A001, but *Signed* LEONARD C. WYON
Rim Plain.
Edge Inscribed at the top with the name of the Juror and class number.

> **RRR** *unrecorded* PC

This version was awarded to Jurors, and is usually found in a fitted case with the lid inscribed: FROM / HER MAJESTY'S COMMISSIONERS / FOR THE / INTERNATIONAL EXHIBITION / 1862. The number of Jurors totalled 615, of which 287 were from overseas. Jurors received a letter from the Commissioners with their medal, but the official copy was missing from the file of official exhibition documents when they were examined by the author at the Victoria and Albert museum. The author would therefore be pleased to hear from any reader who has a specimen.

SK-A015 For Services medal
by W. Wyon & L.C. Wyon   Ae 55 mm

Obverse Diademed head of Queen Victoria left. *Inscription around the border:* HER MAJESTY QUEEN VICTORIA ❀ *Signed* W. WYON. R.A.
Reverse *Two line inscription within an oak wreath:* FOR / SERVICES *Inscription around the border:* INTERNATIONAL EXHIBITION. 1862 •
Rim Plain.
Edge Inscribed at the top with the name of the recipient.

RRR *Brown 2755A, Eimer (I) 1555* BM ML PC

William Wyon used this obverse to commemorate the visit of Queen Victoria to the Guildhall in 1837. It also formed the basis of Sir Henry Corbould's design of the penny black postage stamp in 1840. Leonard Charles Wyon possibly used the die as a tribute to his father who died just two weeks after the close of the Great Exhibition of 1851. A record has not been found of the number of medals presented, but it would appear to be considerably less than in 1851. A certificate probably accompanied the medal when it was awarded, and if so, the author would be pleased to hear from a reader who has a specimen.

SK-A020   International Entertainment Committee
by Sarl & Son   Arg 72x64 mm

Obverse   Britannia seated upon clouds above a terrestrial globe, surrounded by ten flags of various nations. *Two line inscription above London Arms:* EXHIBITION / 1862
Reverse   Five line inscription: THOMAS SCAMBLER OWDEN ESQ^RE / 1862. / Edw. Harrison Esq. Deputy / Chairman. / MEMBER OF THE INTERNATIONAL ENTERTAINMENT COMMITTEE
Rim   Plain.

RRRR *unrecorded* PC

A cruciform-shaped medal with a swivel mount attached to a plain blue ribbon. Housed in a fitted case inscribed on the inside lid SARL & SONS / GOLDSMITHS / 17 & 18 CORNHILL / LONDON. No information has been found regarding this medal, which appears to have been presented to members of the International Entertainment Committee only.

SK-A030   Pass To Works
by ?   Ivory 35 mm

Obverse   Seven line inscription: INTERNATIONAL EXHIBITION / PASS / TO WORKS ON / SATURDAYS / AFTER NOON / TILL. 1. FEB / MDCCCLXII
Reverse   Three line inscription: J. HAWORTH / AND / FRIEND
Rim   Plain.

RRR *Davis et al 186* PC

Since the Exhibition did not open until 1 May, this particular pass was possibly used by Inspectors and other Senior staff during preparatory works.

B. Unofficial Medals

Approximately sixty unofficial medals and tokens were produced to commemorate this second Universal Exhibition. While this is nowhere near the numbers produced for the Great Exhibition and Sydenham Crystal Palace, it is nevertheless a huge number if compared to any other exhibition or prestigious building before or since. As souvenirs, they were mostly made from white metal alloys costing only a few pence to produce, consequently most manufacturers failed to keep records of their output.

Like their 1851 counterparts, very little helpful information has been found about them other than they were struck by private firms as a commercial venture. Apparently Messrs Pinches and Messrs H. Uhlhorn, were both allowed to strike medals within the building for sale to the general public. No reference was found in the Commissioners' report of any income accruing from the sale of these particular unofficial medals, so perhaps a charge was not levied for the two franchises. But, if that was the case, it is difficult to understand why the report should mention that these two firms charged the following prices for the medals they struck and sold at the exhibition:

	Messrs Pinches 42 mm medals SK-B200 — B215	Messrs Uhlhorn 41 mm medals SK-B230 — B245
Bronze, in a leatherette case	3/6d	
White metal, in a leatherette case	1/-	
White metal, in a paper packet	6d	
Gilt bronze, in a circular card box		3/-
Silvered bronze, in a circular card box	2/-	

The author has not yet found a record of the number of medals sold by these two firms during the Exhibition.

SK-B001	
by Allen & Moore	Wm 39 mm

Obverse   Similar to obverse of Great Exhibition medal HP-B090.

Reverse   View of the exhibition building in a rectangular panel *inscribed:* WEST FRONT VIEW *Inscription above:* INTERNATIONAL / EXHIBITION / OPENED MAY 1ST 1862 *In exergue:* COVERS A SPACE OF 26 ACRES / 1200 FT LONG. 700 FT WIDE / DOMES 250 FT HIGH / COST £300'000

Rim   Plain.

R   *Brown* 2717   FM PC

SK-B005	
by Allen & Moore	Wm 39 mm

Obverse   Angel holding oval medallions with vis-à-vis heads of Napoleon III and Queen Victoria. Arms of France and Great Britain below. *Signed* ALLEN & MOORE BIRMINGHAM

Reverse   Similar to reverse of SK-B001.

Rim   Plain.

S   *Brown* 2718, *Taylor* 182j   AM BM BG FM ML PC UM

SK-B010	
by A. Bovy & M. Massonnet	Ar Ae Aes Aeg Wm 50 mm

Obverse   Laureate head of Queen Victoria left. *Inscription around the border:* VICTORIA QUEEN OF ENGLAND *Signed* A. BOVY.

Reverse   View of the exhibition building. *In exergue:* UNIVERSAL EXHIBITION / OF LONDON / 1862 *Signed* MASSONNET EDITOR

Rim   Plain.

Ar RR, Ae R, Aeg RR, Aes S, Wm S   *Eidlitz* 433/50, *Taylor* 182k ML PC

Silver, Bronze and Gilt specimens are usually found in a circular leatherette case. White metal specimens were sold in a circular card box, with the inside of the lid inscribed as above.

SK-B015
by A. Bovy & M. Massonnet   Aes Wm 50 mm

Obverse   Similar to obverse of SK-B010, but the design and the inscription is shadowed.
Reverse   Similar to reverse of SK-B010, but the design and the inscription is shadowed.
Rim   Plain.

S *unrecorded*   ML PC

This clever shadow effect has produced a very attractive variant. See note to SK-B010.

SK-B020
by A. Bovy & M. Massonnet   Ar Wm 50 mm

Obverse   Similar to obverse of SK-B010, but *inscribed:*
VICTORIA REINE D'ANGLETERRE
Reverse   Similar to reverse of SK-B010, but *inscribed:*
EXPOSITION UNIVERSELLE / DE LONDRES / 1862
Signed MASSONNET EDITEUR
Rim   Plain.

Ar RRR, Wm RR   *Eidlitz* 434, *Taylor* 182k   PC

There is also a shadowed variety of this version. See note to SK-B010.

SK-B025
by H. Brown & Messrs Pinches   Wm 42 mm

Obverse   View of the exhibition building. *Inscription above:*
INTERNATIONAL EXHIBITION / OPENED MAY 1 / CLOSED / NOVEMBER 1. 1862 *In exergue:* NUMBER OF VISITORS / 6,117,450 / SOUTH FRONT *Signed* H. BROWN CRYSTAL PALACE.
Reverse   View of Sydenham Crystal Palace. *Inscription above:* DESIGNED BY SIR JOSEPH PAXTON *In exergue:* THE FIRST COLUMN ERECTED / BY SAM^L LAING ESQ^{RE}

M.P. /AUGᵀ 5ᵀᴴ 1852 / OPENED JUNE 10ᵀᴴ 1854 *Signed*
T.R. PINCHES LONDON
Rim Plain.

RRR *Brown 2719* PC

Courtesy of Michael Gibbons. Brown 2719 records the number
of visitors as 6,177,450, whereas on the only specimen seen by
the author the number is recorded as 6,117,450. The reverse is
similar to the reverse of SY-1854 /060.

SK-B040
by G. Dowler   Wm 26 mm

Obverse View of the exhibition building. *Inscription above:*
THE EXHIBITION BUILDING / (WEST FRONT VIEW) /
OPENED MAY 1ˢᵀ / 1862 *In exergue:* LENGTH 1200 F:
WIDTH 700 F: / HEIGHT 100 F: / NAVE 85 F: WIDE: /
COST £300'000
Reverse Terrestrial globe with 1862 inscribed across the
equator, within a wreath divided by palm branches.
Inscription around: TO COMMEMORATE / THE
EXHIBITION / OF THE ARTS AND INDUSTRY / OF
ALL NATIONS
Rim Plain.

S *Brown 2731, Eidlitz 430/50, Taylor 182a* BM BG FM ML PC
UM

A silver-plated specimen of poor quality has been seen.

SK-B045
by G. Dowler   Wm 36 mm

Obverse Crowned draped bust of Queen Victoria left.
Inscription around the border: H.M.G. MAJESTY QUEEN
VICTORIA
Reverse View of the exhibition building. *Inscription above:*
THE EXHIBITION BUILDING / OPENED MAY 1ˢᵀ /
1862 *In exergue:* LENGTH 1200 F: / WIDTH 700 F: /
HEIGHT 100 F: / COST £300,000
Rim Plain.

RRR *Brown 2730*

Description obtained from Brown, because the author has not
seen a specimen.

SK-B050
by G. Dowler   Brass case 41 & 67 mm

Lid Draped bust of Prince Albert left. *Inscription around:*
HIS LATE R. H. THE PRINCE CONSORT. / BORN
AUGᵀ 26ᵀᴴ 1819. DIED DECᴿ 14ᵀᴴ 1861
Base Nine line inscription: PRINCE ALBERT / WAS THE /
ORIGINATOR / OF EXPOSITIONS / IN ENGLAND; /
PATRON OF THE ARTS, / AGRICULTURE, /
SCIENCES. / MANUFACTURES & c
Rim Beaded.

41 mm R, 67 mm RRR *Brown 2729* PC

SK-B055 was sold in the 41 mm case, SK-B105 was sold in the
67 mm case.

SK-B055
by G. Dowler — Wm 37 mm

Obverse View of the exhibition building. *Inscription above:* THE INTERNATIONAL EXHIBITION BUILDING. / (WEST FRONT VIEW) / OPENED MAY 1ST / 1862 *In exergue:* LENGTH 1200 F^T, WIDTH 700 F^T, / HEIGHT 100 F^T, NAVE 85 F^T WIDE, / HEIGHT OF DOMES 250 F^T, / DIAM^R AT BASE 160 F^T, / COST £300'000. *Signed* G. DOWLER BIRMM
Reverse Similar to reverse of SK-B040.
Rim Plain.

S *Brown* 2729, *Eidlitz* 429/50, *Taylor* 182b   AM BM BG FM ML PC UM

Sold in a circular brass case, see SK-B050.

SK-B060
by G. Dowler — Wm Wms 38 mm

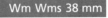

Obverse View of the exhibition building. *Inscription above:* THE INTERNATIONAL / EXHIBITION *In exergue:* AT KENSINGTON. / OPENED 1. MAY / 1862. / SOUTH FRONT VIEW *Signed* G. DOWLER
Reverse *Twelve line inscription:* THE INTERNATIONAL / EXHIBITION / 1862 / COVERS A SPACE OF / 26 ACRES, LENGTH 1200 F^T / WIDTH 700 F^T, HEIGHT 100 F^T / NAVE 85 F^T WIDE. / HEIGHT OF DOMES 250 F^T / AND 100 F^T DIAM: AT BASE / DESIGNED BY / CAPT. FOWKE R.E. / CONTRACTORS MESS^{RS} KELK & LUCAS

Rim Toothed.

Wm S, Wms R *Brown* 2728, *Eidlitz* 432/50, *Taylor* 182c   PC

SK-B065
by G. Dowler — Wm 42 mm

Obverse View of the exhibition building. *Inscription above:* THE INTERNATIONAL EXHIBITION BUILDING. / (WEST FRONT VIEW) / OPENED MAY 1ST / 1862 *In exergue:* COVERS A SPACE OF 26 ACRES / LENGTH 1200 F^T. WIDTH 700 F^T. / HEIGHT 100 F^T. NAVE 85 F^T. WIDE. / HEIGHT OF DOMES 250 F^T. / DIAM^R AT BASE 160 F^T. / COST £300'000
Reverse Similar to reverse of SK-B040.
Rim Plain.

RRR *Brown* 2727

Description obtained from Brown, because the author has not seen a specimen.

SK-B070
by G. Dowler — Wm 42 mm

Obverse Diademed head of Queen Victoria left. *Inscription around the border:* H.M.G.M. QUEEN VICTORIA
Reverse Similar to obverse of SK-B065 *Signed* G. DOWLER
Rim Plain.

RRR *unrecorded* PC

The two specimens seen by the author have an inverted reverse die.

SK-B075	
by G. Dowler	Wm 52 mm

SK-B080	
by G. Dowler	Wm 52 mm

Obverse Crowned Gothic bust of Queen Victoria left.
Inscription around the border: H.M.G. MAJESTY QUEEN VICTORIA
Reverse View of the exhibition building. *Inscription above:* THE BUILDING FOR THE INTERNATIONAL EXHIBITION / (SOUTH FRONT VIEW) / OPENED MAY 1ˢᵗ / 1862 *In exergue:* COVERS A SPACE OF 26 ACRES. LENGTH 1200 Fᵀ. / WIDTH 700 Fᵀ, HEIGHT 100 Fᵀ, NAVE 85 Fᵀ WIDE. / THE BUILDING IS OF BRICK. THE DOMES /ARE OF IRON & GLASS, HEIGHT 250 Fᵀ. /AND 160 Fᵀ DIAM: AT BASE. / (THE LARGEST DOMES EVER ERECTED) / COST £300'000. *Signed* G. DOWLER BIRMᴹ
Rim Beaded obverse, plain reverse.

RR	*Brown* 2724, *Taylor* 182d	BM PC

All specimens seen by the author have the axis of the reverse die pointing to 3 o'clock.

Obverse Diademed, draped bust of Queen Victoria left.
Inscription around the border: HER MOST GRACIOUS MAJESTY VICTORIA QUEEN OF GREAT BRITAIN •
Reverse Similar to reverse of SK-B075.
Rim Plain.

RRR	*Brown* 2720	PC

All specimens seen by the author have the axis of the reverse die pointing to 9 o'clock.

SK-B085
by G. Dowler — Wm 52 mm

Obverse Bare head of Prince Albert right. *Inscription around the border:* PRINCE ALBERT CONSORT OF QUEEN VICTORIA / BORN AUG^T 26 1819. DIED DEC^R 14 1861
Reverse Similar to reverse of SK-B075.
Rim Plain.

RR *Brown* 2726, *Taylor* 182e   BM PC UM

All specimens seen by the author have the axis of the reverse die pointing to 9 o'clock.

SK-B090
by G. Dowler — Wm 52 mm

Obverse Similar to reverse of SK-B075, but unsigned.
Reverse *Five line inscription within a laurel wreath:* EXHIBITION / OF THE / ARTS AND INDUSTRY / OF ALL / THE WORLD
Rim Plain.

RR *Brown* 2723, *Taylor* 182f   BM BG PC UM

SK-B095	
by G. Dowler	Wm 52 mm

Obverse Similar to reverse of SK-B075.
Reverse View of the Sydenham Crystal Palace. *Inscription above:* THE MIGHT OF INDUSTRY THE GLORY OF PEACE *In exergue:* THE CRYSTAL PALACE / SYDENHAM *Signed* DOWLER BIRM^M
Rim Plain.

R *Brown* 2725, *Eidlitz* 427 & 772/82, *Taylor* 182g BM BG BR PC UM

The reverse design is a modification of the one used by Dowler in 1853 to commemorate the erection of Sydenham Crystal Palace, see SY-1853 /001.

SK-B100	
by G. Dowler	Ae 61 mm

Obverse Diademed head of Queen Victoria left. *Inscription above:* VICTORIA QUEEN OF GREAT BRITAIN. D. G.
Reverse View of the exhibition building. *Inscription above:* THE BUILDING FOR THE INTERNATIONAL EXHIBITION / (WEST FRONT VIEW) / OPENED MAY

1ST / 1862 *In exergue:* COVERS A SPACE OF 26 ACRES. LENGTH 1200 F^T / WIDTH 700 F^T. HEIGHT 100 F^T. NAVE 85 F^T WIDE. / THE BUILDING IS OF BRICK. THE DOMES / ARE OF IRON AND GLASS, HEIGHT 250 F^T. / AND 160 F^T DIAM^R AT BASE. / (THE LARGEST DOMES EVER ERECTED) / COST £300'000. / DESIGNED BY CAP^N FOWKE R. E. CONTRACTORS MESS^RS KELK & LUCAS

RRR *Brown* 2722 AM

Description obtained from Brown, because the author has not seen a specimen.

SK-B105	
by G. Dowler	Wm 61 mm

Obverse Similar to reverse of SK-B100.
Reverse Similar to reverse of SK-B040.
Rim Plain.

Sold in a 68 mm circular brass case similar to SK-B050, but is signed G. DOWLER on the truncation.

Obverse Diademed, draped bust of Queen Victoria left. *Inscription around the border:* HER MOST GRACIOUS MAJESTY VICTORIA QUEEN OF GREAT BRITAIN ✿
Reverse View of the exhibition building. *Inscription above:* THE BUILDING FOR THE INTERNATIONAL EXHBITION / (SOUTH FRONT VIEW) / OPENED MAY 1ˢᵀ / 1862 *In exergue:* COVERS A SPACE OF 26 ACRES,

LENGTH 1200 Fᵀ / WIDTH 700 Fᵀ, HEIGHT 100 Fᵀ, NAVE 85 Fᵀ WIDE / THE BUILDING IS OF BRICK, THE DOMES / ARE OF IRON AND GLASS, HEIGHT 250 Fᵀ / AND 160 Fᵀ DIAM: AT BASE / (THE LARGEST DOMES EVER ERECTED) / COST £300,000 *Signed* G. DOWLER BIRM:
Rim Plain.

Obverse is similar to the obverse of SK-B080, but Queen Victoria is wearing a necklace.

Obverse Similar to reverse of SK-B110.
Reverse Britannia standing on a plinth holding a flag and an olive branch attended by Industry and Commerce. Eye of providence in cloud above. *Signed* DOWLER BIRM:
Rim Plain.

RRR	*Brown 2721, Eidlitz 422/50, Taylor 182i* PC UM

This reverse design was used by Dowler to commemorate the erection of the Sydenham Crystal Palace in 1853. See SY-1853 / 001.

Obverse Similar to reverse of SK-B110.
Reverse Similar to obverse of Sydenham Crystal Palace medal SY-1853 /001
Rim Plain.

RRR	*unrecorded* PC

Courtesy of Les Stevens. This reverse design was used by Dowler to commemorate the erection of the Sydenham Crystal Palace. See SY-1853 /001.

SK-B120	
by G. Dowler	Wm 75 mm

SK-B130	
by G.L.	Wm 69 mm

Obverse Bare head of Prince Albert in oval frame supported by Art and Science, Fame inscribing tablet below. *In exergue:* BORN 26TH AUG. 1819 / DIED 14TH DEC. 1861 *Signed* GL 'REGISTERED' 26TH APRIL 1862 LONDON

Reverse View of the exhibition building. *Inscription above:* In Memory of / HIS ROYAL HIGHNESS ALBERT / PRINCE CONSORT / FOUNDER OF THE EXHIBITION OF 1851 / & PROJECTOR OF THE EXHIBITION OF 1862.
Inscription below: THE INTERNATIONAL EXHIBITION BUILDING / (WEST FRONT VIEW) / OPENED MAY 1ST 1862. / Length 1200 ft. Width 700 ft. / Height 100 ft. Nave 85 ft. Wide / Height of Domes 250 ft. / Diamr. at Base 160 ft. / COST £300'000. *Signed* LONDON
Rim Plain.

RRRR	*Brown* 2749, *Taylor* 182l	BM PC

SK-B140
by J. Moore · Wm 52 mm

Obverse Crowned draped bust of Queen Victoria left. QUEEN OF GREAT BRITAIN On a wide border around: An ornate open wreath of roses, thistles and shamrocks entwined with oak leaves.
Reverse View of the exhibition building. *Inscription above:* INTERNATIONAL EXHIBITION, LONDON / (WEST FRONT VIEW) / OPENED 1 MAY 1862 *In exergue:* COVERS A SPACE OF 26 ACRES. / 1200 FT LONG. 700 FT WIDE. / NAVE 85 FT WIDE. / DOMES 250 FT HIGH / COST £300,000

RRR	*Brown* 2732

Description obtained from Brown, because the author has not seen a specimen.

SK-B150
by T. Ottley · Wm 42 mm

Obverse Crowned gothic bust of Queen Victoria left. *Inscription around the border:* H.M.G. MAJESTY QUEEN VICTORIA. *Signed* OTTLEY BIRM^M
Reverse Fame with a wreath, flying over the exhibition building. *Inscription above:* THE INTERNATIONAL EXHIBITION / IN THE 25TH YEAR OF THE REIGN OF / QUEEN VICTORIA. *In exergue:* OPENED 1ST MAY 1862. / DESIGNED BY / CAPTAIN FOWKE R. E. / ERECTED BY / MESSRS KELK AND LUCAS. *Signed* OTTLEY BIRM ^M
Rim Beaded obverse, plain reverse.

RRR	*Brown* 2738, *Taylor* 182n	BM BG PC

The axis of the reverse die points to 3 o'clock.

SK-B155
by T. Ottley · Wm 42 mm

Obverse Similar to reverse of SK-B150.
Reverse Britannia standing, holding laurel branch amid symbols of industry, art and transport. *Signed* OTTLEY BIRM^M
Rim Plain.

RR	*Brown* 2733, *Taylor* 182m	BM BG ML PC UM

SK-B160
by T. Ottley · Wm 51 mm

Obverse Conjoined draped busts of Princess Alice and Prince Louis of Hesse. *Inscription around the border:* H.R.H. PRINCESS ALICE AND H.G.D.H. PRINCE LOUIS OF HESSE. ✠

Reverse View of the exhibition building. *Inscription above:* THE INTERNATIONAL EXHIBITION OPENED 1ST MAY 1862 / IN THE 25TH YEAR OF THE REIGN OF / QUEEN VICTORIA. *In exergue:* END ELEVATION. / DIMENSIONS / LENGTH 383 YARDS. WIDTH 253 YARDS. / THE DOMES ARE 250 FT HIGH / & 157 FT DIAMETER AT THE BASE. / OCCUPIES 24 ACRES. & / COST £430,000. *Signed* OTTLEY BIRMM

Rim Plain.

RRR	*Brown* 2737	PC

The obverse commemorates the Marriage of Princess Alice to Prince Louis of Hesse-Darmstadt at Osborne House on July 1st. 1862.

Most unofficial medals were struck before the exhibition building was completed, therefore the cost is usually recorded as £300,000. This piece was struck some time after the exhibition was opened so it was able to record a more realistic cost. The reverse die axis points to 3 o'clock.

SK-B165
by T. Ottley   Wm 54 mm

Obverse Crowned Gothic bust of Queen Victoria left. *Inscription around the border:* H.M.G. MAJESTY QUEEN VICTORIA. *Signed* OTTLEY BIRMM

Reverse Fame with a wreath, flying over the exhibition building. *Inscription above:* THE INTERNATIONAL EXHIBITION OF / 1862. *In exergue:* OPENED 1ST MAY 1862 / DESIGNED BY / CAPTAIN FOWKE R. E. / ERECTED BY / MESSRS KELK AND LUCAS *Signed* OTTLEY BIRMM

Rim Beaded obverse, plain reverse.

R	*Brown* 2735, *Eidlitz* 424/50, *Taylor* 1820	BM BG FM ML PC UM

The medal was sold in a printed card box, see *Fearon (II)*, p.17.

SK-B170	
by T. Ottley	Wm 54 mm

Obverse   Similar to reverse of SK-B165.
Reverse   Britannia, supported by Peace and Plenty, to the right a Briton is beating the sword into a pruning hook. St Paul's Cathedral in the background. *Signed* OTTLEY. MEDALLIST BIRM^M
Rim   Plain.

RRR	*Brown* 2736	PC UM

Ottley used the reverse design in 1851 to commemorate the opening of the Crystal Palace, see HP-B270; also note to SK-B165.

SK-B175	
by T. Ottley	Wm 65 mm

Obverse   Diademed draped bust of Queen Victoria left. *Inscription around the border:* HER MOST GRACIOUS MAJESTY QUEEN VICTORIA. *Signed* OTTLEY BIRM^M
Reverse   Similar to reverse of SK-B150, but unsigned.
Rim   Plain.

RRR	*unrecorded*	PC

SK-B180	
by T. Ottley	Wm 65 mm

Obverse   Similar to obverse of SK-B175.
Reverse   Similar to reverse of SK-B165.
Rim   Plain.

RRR	*Brown* 2734	UM

Description obtained from Brown, because the author has not seen a specimen.

SK-B185
by T. Ottley
Wm 70 mm

Obverse   Similar to obverse of SK-B175.
Reverse   Similar to reverse of SK-B150.
Rim   Plain.

RRR	*unrecorded*	ML

SK-B190
by T. Ottley
Wm 74 mm

Obverse   Fame with a wreath, flying over the exhibition building. *Inscription above:* THE INTERNATIONAL EXHIBITION IN / THE 25TH YEAR OF THE REIGN OF / QUEEN VICTORIA. *In exergue:* OPENED 1ST MAY 1862. / DESIGNED BY / CAPTAIN FOWKE R.E. / ERECTED BY / MESSRS KELK AND LUCAS. *Signed* OTTLEY BIRM^{M}
Reverse   Four females seated upon clouds surrounding a terrestrial globe.
Rim   Plain.

RRR	*unrecorded*	PC

Ottley used the reverse design on three previous occasions to commemorate the opening of a Crystal Palace.

SK-B195
by T. Ottley | Wm 74 mm

Obverse Similar to obverse of SK-B190.
Reverse Similar to reverse of SK-B155.
Rim Plain.

RRR *Brown* 2733 BG PC UM

SK-B200
by Messrs Pinches | Ae Al Wm Wmg 42 mm

Obverse View of the exhibition building above a plinth
inscribed: WEST FRONT *Inscription above:*
INTERNATIONAL EXHIBITION *In exergue:* OPENED
MAY 1ST / MDCCCLXII
Reverse Britannia seated holding a union flag, Commerce
seated holding a flag *inscribed:* EUROPE / ASIA / AFRICA /
AMERICA / AUSTRALASIA *Signed* PINCHES LONDON
Rim Plain.

Ae S, Al R, Wm N, Wmg RR *Brown 2739, Eidlitz 428/50,
Fearon (I) 313.2, Taylor 182p* AM BM ML PC UM

White metal specimens were sold at 6d in a light grey paper
packet with a darker grey central design, see above. White metal
specimens in a leatherette case cost 1/- , bronze in a leatherette
case cost 3 /6d.

SK-B205
by Messrs Pinches   Wm 42 mm

Obverse   Similar to obverse of SK-B200.
Reverse   Similar to reverse of SK-B200, but the inscription on the flag is incuse.
Rim   Plain.

R   *Brown* 2742   PC

See notes to SK-B200 and SK-B210.

SK-B207
by Messrs Pinches   Aeg 21 mm

Obverse   Similar to obverse of SK-B200, but the plinth is not inscribed and there is a dome at the rear of the building.
Reverse   Similar to reverse of SK-B200, but unsigned.
Rim   Plain.

RRR   *unrecorded*   PC

The medal is suspended on a plain blue ribbon. It might have been given to schoolchildren attending the Exhibition, or even as a free handout to all visitors. The author was previously unaware that Pinches had struck a version in this metal and this size, fortunately it was discovered just in time to be squeezed in before going to press.

SK-B210
by Messrs Pinches   Ae Wm 42 mm

Obverse   Similar to obverse of SK-B200, but the plinth is not inscribed.
Reverse   Similar to reverse of SK-B200.
Rim   Plain.

Ae S, Wm N   *Brown* 2741, *Taylor* 182q   AM BM FM PC

Specimens sold in a leatherette case contained a leaflet written in copper plate script inscribed 'The obverse of the Medal represents the genius of Industry and Progress under the protection of Britannia's flag receiving the productions of the whole Globe as indicated on the Medal.' See note to SK-B200.

SK-B215
by Messrs Pinches   Wm 42 mm

Obverse   Similar to obverse of SK-B210.
Reverse   Similar to reverse of SK-B205.
Rim   Plain.

R   *Brown* 2740   BG FM PC UM

See notes to SK-B200 and SK-B210.

SK-B220
by Messrs Pinches — Ae Al Wm 51 mm

Obverse Similar to obverse of SK-B200.
Reverse Similar to reverse of SK-B200, but there are no grooves on the roll of cloth next to the knee of Commerce.
Rim Plain.

Ae RR, Al RR, Wm R *Brown* 2739, *Fearon (I)* 313.1, *Taylor* 182r AM BM PC UM

White metal specimens were sold in a cream coloured paper packet with a grey design in the centre similar to SK-B200.

SK-B230
by H. Uhlhorn, C. Schnitzspahn & J. Wiener — Ar Ae Aeg Aes 41 mm

Obverse Bare head of Prince Albert left. *Inscription around the border:* TO THE COMMEMORATION OF HIS LATE R. H. THE PRINCE CONSORT ALBERT *Signed* SCHNITZSPAHN F.
Reverse View of the exhibition building. *Inscription above:* INTERNATIONAL EXHIBITION 1862 *In exergue:* STAMPED IN THE BUILDING / BY H. UHLHORN / OF GREVENBROICH. / PRUSSIA. *Signed* J. WIENER
Rim Beaded obverse, plain reverse.

Ar R, Ae N, Aeg R, Aes N *Brown* 2743, *Eimer (I)* 1556, *Fearon (I)* 313.3, *Taylor* 182u AM BM BG FM PC UM

Gilt specimens in a circular card box cost 3 /- , silvered specimens in a circular card box cost 2 /- .

SK-B235
by H. Uhlhorn, C. Schnitzspahn & J. Wiener — Ar Ae Aeg Aes 41 mm

Obverse Similar to obverse of SK-B230.
Reverse Interior view of the exhibition building *Signed* J. WIENER. *In exergue:* INTERNATIONAL EXHIBITION / 1862. / STAMPED IN THE / BUILDING. *Down L /H side:* BY H. UHLHORN *Down R /H side:* OF GREVENBROICH / PRUSSIA

Rim Beaded obverse, plain reverse.

Ar R, Ae S, Aeg R, Aes S *Brown 2745, Eidlitz 435/50, Taylor 182s* BM PC

See note to SK-B230.

SK-B240
by H. Uhlhorn & J. Wiener Ar Ae Aeg Aes 41 mm

Obverse Similar to reverse of SK-B230.
Reverse Similar to reverse of SK-B235, but without the inscriptions.
Rim Plain.

Ar R, Ae R, Aeg R, Aes R *Brown 2746, Eidlitz 436/50, Taylor 182t* BM PC

See note to SK-B230.

SK-B245
by H. Uhlhorn & J. Wiener Ae 41 mm

Obverse Similar to reverse of SK-B230.
Reverse Similar to reverse of SK-B235.
Rim Plain.

R *Brown 2744* BM FM PC UM

The author has not seen a specimen in any other metal, even though Brown records specimens in various other metals. See note to SK-B230.

SK-B250
by J.S. & A.B. Wyon Ae 64 mm

Obverse Six plants arranged within a roseace. *Inscription around the border:* INTERNATIONAL EXHIBITION • LONDON 1862 / ✤ PRODUCTS OF QUEENSLAND ✤
Reverse Britannia handing a corn cob to Londinia attended by Industry and Commerce. *Inscription above:* PULCHRA TE PROLE PARENTEM *In exergue:* QUEENSLAND OFFERS / HER FIRST FRUITS / TO BRITAIN
Rim Plain.

RRR *Brown 2748* AM PC

SK-B260
by ?   Brg 22 mm

Obverse   Bare head of Queen Victoria left. *Inscription around the border:* VICTORIA REGINA
Reverse   View of the exhibition building. *Inscription above:* INTERNATIONAL EXHIBITION / OPENED 1 MAY 1862
In exergue: 1200 F. LONG. 700 F. WIDE. / DOMES 250 F. HIGH / COVERS A SPACE OF / 26 ACRES
Rim   Beaded.
Edge   Milled.

S   *Brown* 2752, *Taylor* 182v   BM PC

SK-B265
by ?   Brg 22 mm

Obverse   Similar to obverse of SK-B260.
Reverse   Similar to reverse of SK-B260.
Rim   Beaded.
Edge   Plain.

R   *Brown* 2752, *Taylor* 182v   BM PC

Similar to SK-B260, but it has a plain edge and is 0.2 mm larger.

SK-B270
by ?   Aeg Brg 22 mm

Obverse   Bare head of Queen Victoria left. *Inscription around the border:* H. M. G. M. QUEEN VICTORIA
Reverse   View of the exhibition building. *Inscription above:* THE EXHIBITION BUILDING / OPENED MAY 1 / 1862
In exergue: LENGTH 1200 F. WIDTH 700 F: / HEIGHT 100 F: / NAVE 85 F: WIDE. / COST £300'000.
Rim   Beaded.

Edge   Milled.

N   *Brown* 2754, *Eidlitz* 431/50, *Taylor* 182w   BM FM ML PC

SK-B275
by ?   Brg Brs 22 mm

Obverse   Similar to obverse of SK-B270, but has larger script.
Reverse   Similar to reverse of SK-B270, but has a stop after MAY 1.
Rim   Beaded.
Edge   Milled.

Brs RR, Brg N   *Batty* 405   PC

SK-B280
by ?   Br 22 mm

Obverse   Similar to obverse of SK-B260.
Reverse   Similar to reverse of SK-B270.
Rim   Beaded.

RR   *Brown* 2753

Description obtained from Brown, because the author has not seen a specimen.

SK-B285
by ?   Br (shell) 32 mm

Obverse   Bare head of Prince Albert right. *Inscription around the border:* PRINCE ALBERT CONSORT OF QUEEN

VICTORIA / BORN AUG^T 26 1819. MARRIED FEB^y 10 1840 / DIED DEC^R 14 1861
Reverse View of the exhibition building. *Inscription above:* INTERNATIONAL EXHIBITION / 1862 *In exergue:* LENGTH 1200 F^T WIDTH 85 F^T / HEIGHT OF DOMES 260 F^T / COST £300'000 / OPENED MAY 1ST
Rim Plain.

| RRR | *Brown* 2751 | PC |

This is the first medal seen by the author which records the height of the domes as 260 ft.

SK-B290	
by ? (possibly H. Smith)	Wm 38 mm

Obverse View of the exhibition building within a border of flowers. *Inscription above:* INTERNATIONAL / EXHIBITION *In exergue:* AT KENSINGTON /1862. / SOUTH FRONT VIEW *Signed* H.S. followed by either B or F
Reverse Twelve line inscription in a border of flowers: INTERNATIONAL EXHIBITION / AT / KENSINGTON / COVERING A SPACE OF / 26 ACRES / HEIGHT 260 F^T WIDTH 700 F^T / HEIGHT OF DOMES 250 F^T / 160 F^T DIAMETER / DESIGNED BY / CAPT. FOWKE / R. E. / CONTRACTORS MESS^RS KELK & LUCAS
Rim Plain.

| RRR | *Brown* 2750 | PC |

The nave looking east. *Illustrated London News*, 1862.

C. Trade Tokens

Compared to 1851, only a handful of tokens were issued by tradesmen and manufacturers to commemorate this second, but unfortunately not quite so prestigious or glamorous International Exhibition. Undoubtedly, the premature death of the Prince Consort cast its dismal shadow in this direction, making it appear improper to be too concerned with trade at a time of national mourning. The few pieces known to exist are listed by the name of the advertiser in alphabetical sequence.

SK-C010   R. Jeary, Norwich
by ?   Br 22 mm

Obverse   Similar to reverse of SK-B275.
Reverse   *Four line inscription:* R. JEARY / STATIONER / MARKET PLACE / NORWICH
Rim   Beaded.
Edge   Milled.

RR	*Bell et all* 4010	PC

SK-C020   W. Kibble, London
by T. Ottley   Wm 54 mm

Obverse   Similar to reverse of SK-B165.
Reverse   *Seven line inscription:* W. KIBBLE 22 GRACECHURCH S^T CITY. WATCH MAKER & JEWELLER. / GOLD WATCHES / £ 3..3..0. / SILVER WATCHES / £ 1..5..0. / WARRANTED FOR / TWO YEARS.
Rim   Plain.

RRRR *unrecorded* PC

This attractive token was sold in a printed card box with a green label on the front depicting the building and *inscribed* INTERNATIONAL EXHIBITION / OPENED 1st. MAY. / 1862.

SK-C030   M. Lyons, Birmingham
by ?   Ae Aeg Aes Br Brs 35 mm

Obverse   View of the exhibition building. *Inscription above:* INTERNATIONAL EXHIBITION / OF 1862. LONDON *In exergue:* COVERS 20 ACRES / OF LAND & HAS / A MILE OF WINDOWS
Reverse   *Eight line inscription:* M. LYONS / EXHIBITOR. / INVENTOR OF THE / BRIGHT MAGNETO / PLATING & / GILDING / 143 SUFFOLK ST. / BIRM^M
Rim   Plain.
Edge   Milled.

R *Davis 737* PC

M. Lyons also exhibited at the Great Exhibition, see HP-C260 and HP-C265.

SK-C035   M. Lyons, Birmingham
by ?   Ae 35 mm

Obverse   Similar to obverse of SK-C030, but the building is lower, and the dome smaller.
Reverse   Similar to reverse of SK-C030.
Rim   Plain.

RR *Davis 737* PC

See note to SK-C030.

SK-C040   Piesse & Lubin, London
by ?   Brg 22 mm

Obverse   Similar to reverse of SK-B260.
Reverse   *Six line inscription:* PIESSE & LUBIN / 2 / NEW BOND S^T / SWEET / SCENTS / LONDON
Rim   Beaded.
Edge   Milled.

R *Bell et all 2750* PC

This firm exhibited its perfumes and fragrances at the exhibition.

SK-C050   D. Uhlhorn, Cologne
           Br 21 mm

Obverse   Bare head of Prince Albert left. *Inscription around the border:* HIS LATE R. H. THE PRINCE CONSORT ALBERT
Reverse   *Six line inscription:* D. UHLHORN / COINING - / PRESS MAKER / GREVENBROICH / RHENISH - / PRUSSIA
Rim   Beaded.

RRR *unrecorded* PC

SK-C055   D. Uhlhorn, Cologne
Aeg 21 mm

Obverse   Bare head of Prince Albert left. *Inscription around the border:* HIS LATE R. H. THE PRINCE CONSORT ALBERT
Reverse   *Seven line inscription:* SECOND / EXHIBITION / OF THE / INDUSTRY / OF ALL / NATIONS / 1862 LONDON
Rim   Beaded.

RRR   *Brown* 2755

Description obtained from Brown, because the author has not seen a specimen.

SK-C060   D. Uhlhorn, Cologne
Ae 21 mm

Obverse   Seven line inscription: SECOND / EXHIBITION / OF THE / INDUSTRY / OF ALL / NATIONS / 1862 LONDON
Reverse   Six line inscription: D. UHLHORN / COINING - / PRESS MAKER / GREVENBROICH / RHENISH / PRUSSIA
Rim   Beaded.

RRR   *unrecorded*   PC

SK-C065   D. Uhlhorn, Cologne
Ae 21 mm

Obverse   Similar to obverse of SK-C060.
Reverse   *Six line inscription:* D. UHLHORN / COINING- / PRESSES MAKER / GREVENBROICH / NEAR COLOGNE / ON THE RHINE
Rim   Beaded.

RRR   *Bell* p.236 (ill.)   PC

The Majolica Fountain. *Illustrated London News*, 1862.

D. Associated Pieces

Recorded in this section are a number of associated pieces issued by other organisations and persons who were not necessarily involved with the Exhibition. The entries are listed by medallist in alphabetical sequence.

SK-D001   Parksine Exhibition
by J. Moore   'Parksine' 42 mm

Obverse   Bare head of Prince Albert right. *Inscription around the border:* PRINCE ALBERT, CONSORT OF QUEEN VICTORIA. *Signed* J. MOORE BIRM^M
Reverse   *Six line inscription in a floral wreath:* PARKSINE / EXHIBITION / MEDAL, AWARDED / 1862. / A. PARKES BIRM^M / PATENTEE.
Rim   Patterned obverse, plain reverse.

RRR   *Brown* 2732A   PC

'Parksine', an electric insulator and a precursor of celluloid, was invented by Alexander Parkes of Birmingham. It was shown by him at the 1862 Exhibition where he was awarded a Prize medal for its invention. The reverse die is inverted.

SK-D010   School of Military Engineering: Fowke Memorial medal
by G. Morgan   Ae 58 mm

Obverse   Uniformed bust of Francis Fowke left. *Inscription around the border:* FRANCIS FOWKE *Signed* G. MORGAN
Reverse   *Five line inscription in a border of laurel:* MEMORIAL MEDAL / ESTABLISHED BY THE OFFICERS / OF ROYAL ENGINEERS AS AN / ARCHITECTURAL PRIZE IN THE / CORPS.
Rim   Plain.
Edge   Inscribed with the name of the recipient.

R   *Brown* 2940, *Eimer (I)* 1581, *Eimer (II)* 250 (ill.)   BM PC RM

Francis Fowke (1823–65), Architect and a Captain in the Royal Engineers, was appointed by Sir Henry Cole to design the building for the 1862 Exhibition at South Kensington. He was also largely responsible for the design of the Royal Albert Hall. In 1872 the medal was established as an architectural prize by the School of Military Engineering at Chatham.

Obverse   Bare head of Prince Albert left. *Inscription around the border:* ALBERT PRINCE CONSORT, BORN AUGUST 26 1819, DIED DECEMBER 14 1861. *Signed* CHARLES WIENER FEC:

Reverse   *Inscription within a wreath of oak:* FOUNDER / OF THE / INTERNATIONAL / EXHIBITIONS / OF 1851 AND 1862.

Rim   Plain.

R   *Brown* 2710, *Eimer (I)* 1552   AM BM BG ML PC

In order to get the 1862 Exhibition project up and running, Prince Albert agreed to personally guarantee £10,000 if the Society of Arts was able to raise a further £240,000 from other sources. The fund eventually reached £450,000, but there was still a small deficit which was covered by Sir John Kelk.

Obverse   Similar to obverse of SK-D020.

Reverse   *Five line inscription in a wreath of oak:* FOUNDER / OF THE / INTERNATIONAL / EXHIBITIONS / OF 1851 AND 1862. *Inscription around the border:* INAUGURATION OF THE MEMORIAL OF THE EXHIBITION 1851. / JUNE 10ᵀᴴ 1863.

Rim   Plain.

R   *Brown* 2790   AM BM PC

On 10 June 1863, the Prince of Wales uncovered the Memorial of the Great Exhibition of 1851 in the gardens of the Royal Horticultural Society, facing the northern front of the 1862 Exhibition building. The memorial is 42ft high and 18ft across the base. At the angles and below the feet of the statues representing the four continents are bronze reliefs representing the medals awarded at the Exhibition. There are four tablets on the base: the southern tablet records the names of the Commissioners and the Executive Committee; the eastern tablet records the names of the Exhibiting Countries; the western tablet records various statistics of the Great Exhibition; the northern tablet dedicates the memorial itself. The statue of Prince Albert is 10ft high and dressed in the robes of the Great Master of the Bath. The cost of the memorial was £7,500. The memorial was moved in 1899 to Albert Court, facing the southern aspect of the Royal Albert Hall. At the time of writing, the statue has been removed for renovation while the south walk is being re-developed.

From the Horticultural Gardens. *Illustrated London News*, 1862.

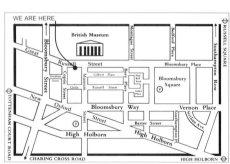

Index

Get your *free* copy of
The Phoenix

The Phoenix, the only monthly coin, bank-note and antiquities newspaper in the UK!

- 24 tabloid-sized pages
- Hundreds of items on offer
- British and World Coins
- British and World Banknotes
- Greek & Roman Coins
- Greek, Roman and Egyptian antiquities
- Medallions
- Special offers and discounts
- Hundreds of photographs in every issue

Coincraft is a family firm which has dealt in coins for over 40 years. At Coincraft we believe in old fashioned values; such as the collector is always right, even when occasionally he or she is wrong!

ORDER WITH CONFIDENCE!

Our guarantee to you

All items listed in *The Phoenix* are guaranteed authentic. If for any reason you are dissatisfied with anything ordered from *The Phoenix*, simply return it to us in undamaged condition within 45 days for a full no-questions-asked refund.

We have total confidence in the goods we sell. We want YOU to have total confidence in us!

Please send me a complimentary copy of *The Phoenix* – your monthly catalogue of British and World Coins, British and World Banknotes, ancient coins, medallions, tokens and antiquities.

NAME ....

ADDRESS ....

....

....

....

POSTCODE .... COUNTRY ....

CCP000601

Get your *free* copy of The Phoenix

The Phoenix,

the only monthly

coin, banknote

and antiquities

newspaper in

the UK!

- 24 tabloid-sized pages
- Hundreds of items on offer
- British and World Coins
- British and World Banknotes
- Greek and Roman Coins
- Greek, Roman and Egyptian antiquities
- Medallions and Tokens
- Special offers and discounts
- Hundreds of photographs in every issue

Coincraft is a family firm which has dealt in coins for over 40 years. At Coincraft we believe in old fashioned values; such as the collector is always right, even when occasionally he or she is wrong!

By Air Mail
Par Avion

Please
place
stamp
here

The Phoenix

c/o Coincraft

44 & 45 Great Russell Street

London WC1B 3LU

UK

The Crystal Palace Foundation

is a registered charity and is staffed by volunteers. Since its establishment in 1979, the Foundation has achieved the status of being
the leading authority on the Crystal Palace. The Foundation's aims
are to promote the memory of the Palace and to enhance the public
amenities of the former Palace site at Sydenham.

*The Foundation's main activities
are:*

- Supporting the
  Crystal Palace Museum

- Promoting education
  and research

- Publishing works
  concerned with the Palace

- Organizing exhibitions,
  talks and other events

- Restoring & conserving
  original features within
  Crystal Palace Park

Membership of the Foundation is open to all.

For membership details please send an SAE to:
The Membership Secretary, The Crystal Palace Foundation,
c/o The Crystal Palace Museum, Anerley Hill, London, SE19 2BA

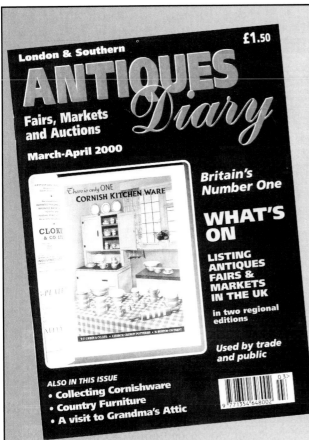

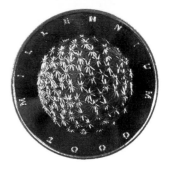

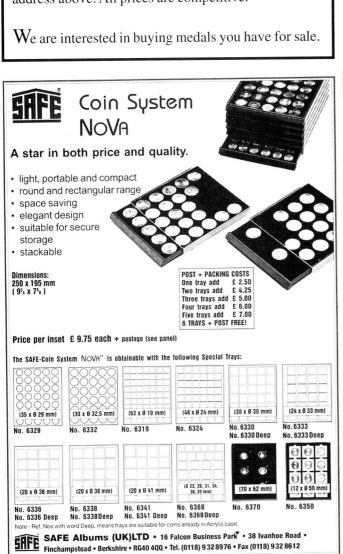

Price Guide

The values shown are a guide to the price a collector can expect to pay when buying from a dealer, and refer to specimens in Extremely Fine condition. This means the piece must show little actual wear except on the highest points of the design and should be free from nicks, scuffs, scratches and any other defects. Accordingly, a specimen in uncirculated condition in its original case or packet will attract an additional premium, as will those awarded to VIPs. Also, due to the passage of time, it is often extremely difficult, and in some cases nigh impossible, to find the certificates and other types of paperwork, such as descriptive leaflets, which were sometimes presented with these pieces. The presence of any of this paperwork will automatically attract an additional premium.

Medals were made to be looked at, whereas smaller tokens such as Unofficial Farthings were made to be used, consequently most of them did sustain some degree of wear and therefore they are less often found in Extremely Fine condition.

Seldom do any of the hundreds of different prize medals which were awarded at the Sydenham Crystal Palace tend to reach the marketplace. Consistently throughout the 1990s, whenever the odd specimen did appear for sale, supply and demand ensured the price moved upward substantially.

Prior to the 1990s, Prize medals of the 1851 Great Exhibition and the 1862 Kensington Exhibition were generally regarded in the same category as most other exhibition medals and could be purchased for what are nowadays regarded as ridiculously low prices. However, since then, there has been an upsurge of interest in these pieces, accompanied by a much more realistic appreciation of their important historical significance and social interest, which has tended to push their values up to previously unknown levels.

Demands from unexpected sources can sometimes influence the value of a particular specimen. A case in point is the two Prize medals mentioned in the last paragraph. Most of these medals were awarded to businesses, therefore, if by chance, one of them happens to be named to a company whose historical records have been destroyed, it could very well provide the only tangible evidence that the company actually existed, or possibly, that it participated in a certain line of business etc, etc. This could make such a specimen very desirable and much more sought-after in commercial quarters than in the numismatic market place, thereby attracting a sizeable premium over and above its numismatic value, even if that medal is named to what would otherwise be a quite ordinary company. Other instances of demand from unexpected sources are also known.

Understandably none of these variable factors can be specifically catered for in this price guide which aims simply to provide an approximate value at the time of publication. As mentioned earlier the rarity rating refers to a specimen in Extremely Fine condition and it should not be used to describe a specimen which is in an inferior state.

The author enlisted the aid of many leading numismatic dealers when compiling this guide, and he is very grateful indeed for the valuable advice they so generously offered. An unpriced item means the author has not seen a specimen for sale.

1851 Great Exhibition

A. Official Medals

Cat.No.	Description		Rarity	Size mm	Metal	Value £
HP-A001	Council medal	unawarded	RRRR	89	Ae	350
		awarded	RRRR	89	Ae	500
HP-A005		stop instead of colon, unawarded	RRRR	89	Ae	350
		awarded	RRRR	89	Ae	500
HP-A010	Prize medal	unawarded	R	77	Ae	80
		awarded	R	77	Ae	150
HP-A015		unawarded	R	77	Ae	80
		awarded	R	77	Ae	150
HP-A020		hem of Europa's gown missing, unawarded	RRR	77	Ae	120
		awarded	RRR	77	Ae	175
HP-A025		signature around lower rim, unawarded	R	77	Ae	80
		awarded	R	77	Ae	150
HP-A030		presentation piece in glazed frame, unsigned	RRRR	77	Pewter	250
		signed	RRRR	77	Ae	250
		presentation piece not glazed	RRRR	77	Ae	200
HP-A034		test — trial pieces, if original	RRRR	77	Ar	500
			RRRR	77	Pewter	250
HP-A037		electrotypes double sided	RRR	77	Ar	200
			R	77	Ae	75
HP-A040	Jurors medal	unawarded	RRR	64	Ae	150
		awarded	RRR	64	Ae	250
		test — trial pieces	RRRR	64	Pewter	250
HP-A050	For Services medal	unawarded	S	48	Ae	30
		awarded	S	48	Ae	50
HP-A055	Exhibitors Medal	unawarded	N	45	Ae	20
		awarded	N	45	Ae	40
HP-A060	Presentation case	of 5 official medals	RRRR		Ae	2000

B. Unofficial Medals
by Allen & Moore

Cat.No.	Description		Rarity	Size mm	Metal	Value £
HP-B001	Albert R	Crystal Palace	RRR	23	Br	25
HP-B005	Crystal Palace	9 line legend	S	23	Brg	10
HP-B010	brass medal box	empty	RRR	28	Br	30
		containing 4 medals from set A (HP-A015–035)	RRR	26	Wm	150
		containing 4 medals from set B (HP-A040–065)	RRR	27	Wm	200
HP-B015	Victoria Gothic bust L	Crystal Palace dimensions in border	RR	26	Wm	25
HP-B020	Albert bust L		RR	26	Wm	25
HP-B025	Victoria & Albert busts L		RRR	26	Wm	25
HP-B030	Prince of Wales on anchor		RR	26	Wm	25
HP-B035	Royal Children in 3 ovals		RR	26	Wm	25
HP-B040	Victoria Gothic bust L	Crystal Palace, no border dimensions	RRR	27	Wm	30
HP-B045	Albert bust L		RRR	27	Wm	30

Cat.No.	Description		Rarity	Size mm	Metal	Value £
HP-B050	Victoria & Albert busts L		RRR	27	Wm	30
HP-B055	Prince of Wales on anchor		RRR	27	Wm	30
HP-B060	Royal Children in 3 ovals		RRR	27	Wm	30
HP-B065	Crystal Palace no border dimensions	11 line legend	RRR	27	Wm	25
HP-B070	Crystal Palace no trees	11 line legend	S	27	Wm	10
HP-B075		AND missing from line 6	R	27	Wm	15
HP-B080		11 line legend	RRR	30	Wm	-
HP-B085	Crystal Palace with trees	13 line legend	RR	31	Wm	25
HP-B090	Victoria Gothic bust L	Crystal Palace V & A in exergue	R	39	Wm	20
HP-B095	Crystal Palace Victoria & Albert in exergue	16 line legend	RR	39	Wm	25
HP-B100		Interior view	R	39	Wm	20
			RRR	39	Ae	60
HP-B105	Crystal Palace, French text	Interior view	RR	39	Wm	25
HP-B110		19 lines, French text	RRR	39	Wm	40
HP-B115	Victoria & Albert in exergue	16 line legend	R	45	Wm	25
HP-B120	Victoria & Albert busts L in wreath	Crystal Palace	S	52	Wm	20
HP-B125	Victoria Gothic bust L in wreath		R	52	Wm	30
HP-B130	Albert head R, toothed border		R	52	Wm	30
HP-B135	Albert head R, ornate border		R	52	Wm	30
HP-B140			RR	64	Wm	50
HP-B145		glazed frame	RRR	89	Aeg	300
		glazed frame	RRR	89	Wms	300
		broken glazed frame	RRR	89	Aeg	250
			RRR	89	Wms	250
HP-B150	similar to HP-B145		RRRR	112	Aeg	-

by J. Davis

Cat.No.	Description		Rarity	Size mm	Metal	Value £
HP-B160	Albert head R	Crystal Palace	RR	44	Wm	30
HP-B165	Victoria & Albert heads L		RR	49	Wm	40

by G. Dee

Cat.No.	Description		Rarity	Size mm	Metal	Value £
HP-B170	Albert head L	Crystal Palace	RRR	29	Wm	35

by H (R. Heaton & Sons)

Cat.No.	Description		Rarity	Size mm	Metal	Value £
HP-B180	Victoria head L	Exhibition Palace	RR	22	Ae	25

by HB (R. Heaton & Sons)

Cat.No.	Description		Rarity	Size mm	Metal	Value £
HP-B190	Exhibition Palace unsigned	Exhibition Palace signed	RR	22	Ae	30
HP-B195	Exhibition Palace signed	Blank	RRR	22	Ae	40

by R. Heaton & Sons

Cat.No.	Description		Rarity	Size mm	Metal	Value £
HP-B200	Crystal Palace	9 line legend	N	31	Wm	12
HP-B205		Blank	RRR	31	Ae	40
HP-B210		10 line legend	RRR	31	Wm	40
HP-B215		9 line legend	S	34	Wm	15
HP-B220		11 line legend	R	38	Wm	18

by J. Hinks

Cat.No.	Description		Rarity	Size mm	Metal	Value £
HP-B230	Albert head R	Crystal Palace	RRR	39	Wm	30
HP-B235			RRR	45	Wm	35
			RRR	45	Ae	50

by L.C. Lauer

Cat.No.	Description		Rarity	Size mm	Metal	Value £
HP-B240	Victoria & Albert heads L	Crystal Palace	RRR	22	Wm	30
HP-B245		German text	RRR	22	Ae	40

by Neveux

Cat.No.	Description		Rarity	Size mm	Metal	Value £
HP-B250	5 line legend	Ceres	RRRR	34	Ae	100

by T. Ottley

Cat.No.	Description		Rarity	Size mm	Metal	Value £
HP-B260	Albert head L	Crystal Palace	RR	54	Wm	30
HP-B265	Albert head R		RR	54	Wm	30
HP-B270	Crystal Palace	4 figures on foreshore	RRR	54	Wm	40
HP-B275	Albert head L	Crystal Palace	R	74	Wm	60
HP-B280		Crystal Palace 4 line legend above	RR	74	Wm	75
HP-B285	Victoria & Albert vis-a-vis above Crystal Palace in card box	Britannia	RR	74	Wm	75
			RRR	74	Wm	90
			RRR	74	Ae	120
HP-B290	Crystal Palace	4 Angels around globe	RRR	74	Wm	75
			RRR	74	Ae	120
HP-B295	Victoria & Albert vis-a-vis above Crystal Palace		RRR	74	Wm	75
			RRR	74	Ae	120
HP-B300	Albert head L	Britannia	RRR	74	Ae	120
HP-B305	4 Angels around globe	Britannia	RRR	74	Ae	120

by T. Pope

Cat.No.	Description		Rarity	Size mm	Metal	Value £
HP-B310	Victoria head L no legend	Crystal Palace	R	22	Br	20
			R	22	Ae	20
HP-B320	Victoria head L, 1852 below truncation		RR	22	Ae	30

by J. Taylor

Cat.No.	Description		Rarity	Size mm	Metal	Value £
HP-B330	Albert head L in 4 circles	Crystal Palace	RRR	39	Wm	50

by W.J. Taylor

Cat.No.	Description		Rarity	Size mm	Metal	Value £
HP-B340	Albert head L in paper packet	Royal Arms	N	38	Wm	8
			RR	38	Wm	30
			S	38	Ae	15

by J. Wiener

Cat.No.	Description		Rarity	Size mm	Metal	Value £
HP-B350	7 line legend	Yacht between buildings	RRRR	37	Ae	100

by ?

Cat.No.	Description		Rarity	Size mm	Metal	Value £
HP-B360	Victoria head L	Crystal Palace	RRR	20	Brg	30
HP-B365			RRR	23	Aeg	30
			RRR	23	Brg	30
HP-B370	Crystal Palace	9 line legend	RRR	27	Wm	-
HP-B375	Crystal Palace	9 line legend	RRR	26	Br	40
					Wm	40
HP-B380	Albert head R	Crystal Palace	RRR	26	Wm	35
HP-B385	Crystal Palace	9 line legend	RRR	27	Br	30
HP-B390	Victoria head L	Crystal Palace	RRR	28	Ae	30

Cat.No.	Description		Rarity	Size mm	Metal	Value £
					Aeg	30
					Br	30
HP-B395	Vic diadem head L	Crystal Palace	RRR	30	Wm	30
HP-B400	Interior view	10 line legend	RRR	31	Wm	30
HP-B405	Victoria head L	Crystal Palace	RRR	35	Aeg	35

C. Trade Tokens
Exhibition Palace

Cat.No.	Name	Location	Rarity	Size mm	Metal	Value £
HP-C001	J. Lee	Devonport	R	24	Ae	30
HP-C005	J. Pease	Plymouth	RRR	24	Ae	50
HP-C010	B. Hadley	Hay-on-Wye	RRR	22	Ae	60
HP-C015	W. Taylor	Ledbury	RR	22	Ae	40
HP-C020	Bowen	Kington	RRR	22	Ae	55
HP-C025	Callant's	Bridgnorth	S	22	Ae	20
HP-C030	R. Cooper	Oldham	N	22	Ae	18
HP-C035	J & E Harding,	Ludlow	RR	22	Ae	40
HP-C040	W. Manley's	Leighton Buzzard	S	22	Ae	25
HP-C045	Parry's	Wrexham	RRR	22	Ae	50
HP-C050	T. Pope & Co.	Birmingham	RR	22	Ae	35
HP-C055	W. Roberts	Lynn	S	22	Ae	30
HP-C060	W. Taylor	Ledbury	R	22	Ae	30
HP-C065	T. Underwood	Birmingham	RR	22	Ae	45
HP-C070	J.W. White	Ross	RR	22	Ae	40
HP-C075	W. Coker	Lynn	RRR	22	Wm	60
HP-C080	J. Robey	Newcastle	S	22	Ae	22
HP-C085	H. Baldwin's	Bath	R	22	Ae	30
HP-C090	J. Casson	Woolwich	N	22	Ae	15
HP-C095	R. Cockerill	London	RR	22	Ae	40
HP-C100	V. Drayson	Gravesend	R	22	Ae	30
HP-C105	A. Light	Brompton	R	22	Ae	30
HP-C110	T. Pope & Co	Birmingham	N	22	Ae	15
HP-C115	J. Robey	Newcastle	S	22	Ae	20
HP-C120	J. Blackwell	Birmingham	R	22	Ae	30
HP-C125	J. Casson	Woolwich	R	22	Ae	30
					Aes	30
HP-C130	J. Casson	Woolwich	S	22	Ae	18
HP-C135	Bond & Co	Devonport	R	22	Ae	30
HP-C140	J. Bellamy	Gloucester	R	22	Ae	30
HP-C145	T. Cordeux	Bristol	R	22	Ae	30
HP-C150	J. Healey	Bolton	R	22	Ae	30
HP-C155	Scarr Brothers	Limerick	RR	22	Ae	40
HP-C160	J. Schlesinger	London	S	22	Ae	20
HP-C165	D. Gowans & Co	New Orleans	RRR	22	Aes	50
HP-C170	E & D Kinsey	Cincinnati	RRR	22	Aes	50

The Crystal Palace

Cat.No.	Name	Location	Rarity	Size mm	Metal	Value £
HP-C175	J. Knight	Bath	RR	22	Br	50
HP-C180	W. McCoombe	Bath	RR	22	Br	50
HP-C185	T.F. Andrews	Wolverhampton	RRR	30	Ae	50
HP-C190	Baker's	Birmingham	R	30	Ae	30
HP-C195	Edwards Flint & Co	London	RR	30	Wm	40
HP-C200	Everett's	London	R	30	Wm	30
HP-C205	Hamilton & Chapin	Springfield	RRR	30	Wm	50
HP-C210	Macartney	Belfast	RR	30	Wm	50
HP-C215	J.G. McGee & Co	Belfast	RRR	30	Wm	50
HP-C220	Henry Moss	Lincoln	RRR	30	Wm	50
HP-C225	Murray Greene & Lloyd	Belfast	RR	30	Wm	40
HP-C230	Phillips	Nottingham	R	30	Ae	25
			RRR	30	Wm	50
HP-C235	Ed Smith	Newark	RRR	30	Ae	50
HP-C240	T. Wood	London	RRR	30	Ae	50
HP-C245	Hunt & Co	Cheltenham	RRR	28	Ae	40
HP-C250	T. Probert	Newcastle	RRR	28	Ae	40
HP-C255	C.G. Bowers	Macclesfield	RRR	28	Ae	50

Others

Cat.No.	Name	Location	Rarity	Size mm	Metal	Value £
HP-C260	M. Lyons	Birmingham	S	34	Br	25
HP-C265	M. Lyons	Birmingham	R	34	Ae	30
HP-C270	Edmund Leach	Rochdale	RRR	26	Ae	40

Cat.No.	Name	Location	Rarity	Size mm	Metal	Value £
HP-C275	J. Rigg	Liverpool	RRR	28	Br	50
HP-C280	T. May	Wavertree	RRR	32	Br	50
HP-C285	H. Owen	Liverpool	RRR	32	Br	50
HP-C290	Aranzabe Labayen	Matanzas	RRR	32	Br	50
HP-C295	S. Jacobs	Melbourne	RRR	32	Br	50
HP-C300	Tilly Haynes	Springfield	RRR	27	Ae	50
			RRR	27	Wm	50
HP-C305	Allan ,Son & Co	London	RR	39	Wm	35
HP-C310	E. Grove, Outfitter	Lambeth	RRRR	39	Wm	75
HP-C315	Corr-Vander Maeren	Brussells	RR	51	Wm	40
HP-C320	Price's Hope Dining Rooms	London	RRRR	51	Wm	75
HP-C325	Brewster & Co	East Dereham	R	22	Ae	30
HP-C330	W.J. Taylor	London	RRR	26	Wm	40
HP-C335	W.J. Taylor	London	RRR	22	Ae	50
HP-C340	D. Uhlhorn	Cologne	RRR	37	Ae	120
			RRR	37	Aeg	150
			RRR	37	Aes	150
HP-C345	F.C. Key & Sons	Philadelphia	RRR	18	Wm	50

D. Associated Pieces

Cat.No.	Description		Rarity	Size mm	Metal	Value £
HP-D001	Presentation Medal — Albert head L	St George	RRRR	56	Av	2500
HP-D005	City of London Entertainment — Victoria head L	legend	RRRR	36	Ar	300
HP-D010	Canadian Prize by B. Wyon — Arms	wreath	RRR	37	Ae	75
					Aes	75
HP-D015	Londinia, Crystal Palace, St Paul's etc.	Wreath	RRR	63	Ae	80
HP-D018		People on beach	RRR	59	Aeg	50
HP-D020	Crystal Palace	Munich Crystal Palace 1855	RRR	22	Ae	40
HP-D025		JETON in wreath	RRR	22	Ae	40
HP-D030		SPIEL — PFENNIG in wreath	RRR	22	Aeg	40
HP-D035	Aucher Brothers advertising piece		RRR	48	Aeg	50
HP-D040	1854 Melbourne Ex. — Kangaroo	Seated female	RR	29	Ae	25
HP-D045	1854 Melbourne Ex. — Kangaroo	Seated female	RR	29	Ae	25
HP-D050	1880 Melbourne Ex — Albert bust R	Exhibition building	RR	22	Ae	15
HP-D055	Chance's Smethwick Schools — Bust R	legend	RR	55	Ae	50
HP-D060	John Green Waller — Bust R	legend	RR	52x43	Ae	40
HP-D065	Londinia, Crystal Palace etc.	Fame etc. plus cruciform	RRR	59	Aeg	75
HP-D070			RRR	59	Aeg	75
HP-D075	Crystal Palace	Man & boy vewing Festival buildings	R	39	Ae	30
			RR	39	Ar	75
			RRR	39	Av	250
HP-D080		Festival of Britain symbol	R	70	Soap	20
HP-D085	Crystal Palace and Festival of Britain symbol	Blank	RR	130	Pottery	30
HP-D090	Printing plate: Victoria & Albert heads, trident & dolphins		RRRR	53	Br	-

1852 First Column erected

Cat.No.	Description		Rarity	Size mm	Metal	Value £
SY-1852/001	The Age weekly newspaper-Crystal Palace	Legend	RR	45	Wm	30

1853 Crystal Palace erected

Cat.No.	Description		Rarity	Size mm	Metal	Value £
SY-1853/001	Crystal Palace	Britannia on plinth	RRR	74	Wm	75

1854 Crystal Palace Opened
by Allen & Moore

Cat.No.	Description		Rarity	Size mm	Metal	Value £
SY-1854/005	Victoria & Albert busts L	Crystal Palace	RR	27	Wm	20
SY-1854/010	Victoria Gothic bust L		RRR	39	Ae	75
SY-1854/015	Victoria & Albert heads vis-à-vis		RRR	39	Wm	40
SY-1854/020	Paxton bust L in frame		RR	51	Wm	40
SY-1854/025			RRR	51	Wm	60

by T. Ottley

Cat.No.	Description		Rarity	Size mm	Metal	Value £
SY-1854/045	Crystal Palace	5 line legend in wreath	RRR	54	Wm	50
SY-1854/050		Britannia	RRR	74	Wm	75
SY-1854/055		4 females on clouds	RRR	74	Wm	75

by Pinches

Cat.No.	Description		Rarity	Size mm	Metal	Value £
SY-1854/060	Vic diademed bust L	Crystal Palace	RRR	42	Wm	40
SY-1854/065	Crystal Palace	Britannia opening doors	RRR	42	Wm	40
			RRR	42	Ae	75
SY-1854/070		Arms of Ancient Order of Foresters	RR	42	Wm	25
SY-1854/075	Brass case	empty	S	42	Br	10
		empty	R	63	Br	20
SY-1854/080	Crystal Palace	Britannia opening exhibition	N	42	Wm	10
	in brass case		R	42	Wm	20
	in plain leather case		S	42	Wm	15
SY-1854/085			S	42	Ae	15
	in plain leather case		S	42	Ae	20
	in leather case gilt embossed		RR	42	Ae	40
SY-1854/090			S	63	Wm	30
	in brass case		R	63	Wm	50
			S	63	Ae	45
	in plain leather case		R	63	Ae	55

Cat.No.	Description		Rarity	Size mm	Metal	Value £
	in leather case gilt embossed		RR	63	Ae	75
SY-1854/095	3 Medals in red Morocco case, lid gilt embossed	(see SY-1854/090, /110 & /135)	RRR	63	Ae	350
			RRR	63	Wm	250
SY-1854/100	2 White metal medals in leather case 155mmx 82mm	(see SY-1854/090 & /130)	RRR	63	Wm	150
SY-1854/105	Names of the Directors of the C.P.C.	Britannia	RRR	63	Ae	120
SY-1854/110	Vic & Albert heads L	Britannia & Fame etc	S	63	Wm	40
			R	63	Wm	50
	in leather case		RR	63	Wm	60
	in brass case		R	63	Ae	50
	in plain leather case		RR	63	Ae	60
	in leather case gilt embossed		RRR	63	Ae	75
SY-1854/115	Crystal Palace	6 line legend in wreath	RRR	42	Wm	50
SY-1854/120	Crystal Palace	Good Templars insignia	RRR	42	Wm	—
SY-1854/125	Paxton head L	Crystal Palace	RR	42	Wm	25
			RR	42	Ae	35
SY-1854/130		6 line legend	RRR	63	Wm	75
SY-1854/135		Crystal Palace	RR	63	Ae	50
	in plain leather case		RR	63	Ae	60
	in leather case gilt embossed		RRR	63	Ae	75
SY-1854/140		Blank — uniface trial strike	RRRR	63	Ae	175
SY-1854/145	Victoria diademed head L	Crystal Palace	RRR	30	Wm	—

Grand Military Fete

Cat.No.	Description		Rarity	Size mm	Metal	Value £
SY-1854/150	Crystal Palace	Arms of Foresters	RRR	42	Wm	30
SY-1854/155	Crystal Palace	French Flag — Visit of French Guides	R	42	Wm	25
			RR	42	Ae	45
SY-1854/160	5 line legend in wreath	Trophy of flags	RR	42	Wm	30

Crimean War

Cat.No.	Description		Rarity	Size mm	Metal	Value £
SY-1854/165	Battle of Alma	List of Regiments	S	42	Wm	15
	In brass case		R	42	Wm	25
			R	42	Ae	35
			RRR	42	Ar	80
SY-1854/170	Battle of Balaclava	List of Regiments	S	42	Wm	15
	In brass case		R	42	Wm	25
			R	42	Ae	35
			RRR	42	Ar	80
SY-1854/175	Battle of Inkermann	List of Regiments	S	42	Wm	15
	In brass case		R	42	Wm	25
			R	42	Ae	35
			RRR	42	Ar	80
SY-1854/180	4 line legend in wreath	Troops on fortifications	RRR	35	Wm	30

1855

Cat.No.	Description		Rarity	Size mm	Metal	Value £
SY-1855/001	Vic & Napoleon III heads vis-à-vis	Crossed flags	N	42	Wm	10
			S	42	Ae	30
SY-1855/005	Funerary plinth	Raglan's HQ at Sebastopol	R	42	Wm	25
			RR	42	Ae	40
SY-1855/010	Crystal Palace	Arms of Ancient Order of Foresters	RR	42	Wm	25

1856

Cat.No.	Description		Rarity	Size mm	Metal	Value £
SY-1856/001	Date in wreath	Dove above altar	R	42	Wm	20
SY-1856/005	Florence Nightingale reading book	Oval badge in wreath	RR	42	Wm	30
			RRR	42	Ae	60
SY-1856/010	no floral sprays		RRR	42	Wm	40
SY-1856/015	Dual Arms, Wine Duties Festival	10 line legend	RRR	51	Wm	50

1857

Cat.No.	Description		Rarity	Size mm	Metal	Value £
SY-1857/001	Handel bust, name upward	Lyre	S	42	Ae	16
SY-1857/005	downward		RRR	42	Aes	30
SY-1857/010		Angel with lyre	RRR	42	Wm	30
			RRR	42	Ae	50
SY-1857/015	Angel with Lyre	Wreath	RRR	42	Aeg	40
SY-1857/020	Tonic Sol-fa Association monogram	Scroll	RRR	29	Ae	40
SY-1857/025	Justice standing by rocks	Legend: Sepoy Mutinies	RR	63	Wm	40
			RR	63	Ae	80
			RR	63	Ar	200
SY-1857/030	Bow & cap above legend	Arms of Foresters	RRR	42	Wm	35

1858

Cat.No.	Description		Rarity	Size mm	Metal	Value £
SY-1858/001	Shakespeare bust in arch	Shakespeare bust in circle	RRR	39	Wm	30

1859

Cat.No.	Description		Rarity	Size mm	Metal	Value £
SY-1859/001	Handel bust L	legend in wreath	RRR	17	Ae	25
SY-1859/005		Lyre	R	42	Ae	25
		1966 restrikes	RRR	42	Ar	—
			RRR	42	Av	—
SY-1859/010		legend in wreath	N	51	Ae	30
SY-1859/015	Crystal Palace Choir	Female withTonic sol-fa notes	RRR	35	Wm	25
			RRR	35	Ae	40

1860

Cat.No.	Description		Rarity	Size mm	Metal	Value £
SY-1860/001	Distant view of college	Shakespeare bust in arch	RR	23	Wm	10
			RRR	23	Ae	20
SY-1860/005	Crystal Palace Choir	Female withTonic Sol-fa notes	RRR	35	Wm	25

1861

Cat.No.	Description		Rarity	Size mm	Metal	Value £
SY-1861/001	Crystal Palace Choir	Female withTonic Sol-fa notes	RRR	32	Ae	30
SY-1861/005	Blondin bust	legend	RRR	15	Ae	25
			RRR	15	Ar	30

1863

Cat.No.	Description		Rarity	Size mm	Metal	Value £
SY-1863/001	Prince & Princess of Wales heads L	legend in wreath	S	42	Wm	10
			RR	42	Wmg	20
			S	53	Wm	20
			RR	53	Aeg	25
			RRR	53	Al	50
			RRR	53	Ar	—
			RRR	53	Av	—
SY-1863/005			RRR	31	Wm	35

1864

Cat.No.	Description		Rarity	Size mm	Metal	Value £
SY-1864/001	Shakespeare bust L	Birthplace	R	24	Wm	8
			R	24	Ae	10
			RR	24	Aeg	12
SY-1864/005			RR	24	Ae	12
SY-1864/010			R	42	Wm	20

Cat.No.	Description		Rarity	Size mm	Metal	Value £
			RR	42	Wmg	25
			RR	42	Ae	30
SY-1864/011		Arms of Ancient Order of Foresters	RRR	42	Wm	35
SY-1864/015		Birthplace (no chimney)	RRR	42	Wm	35
SY-1864/020	Garibaldi bust R	legend in wreath	R	42	Wm	15
SY-1864/025		Crystal Palace	RR	42	Wm	35
SY-1864/030		legend in wreath	RRR	42	Ae	40

1866

Cat.No.	Description		Rarity	Size mm	Metal	Value £
SY-1866/001	Crystal Palace	10 panels	R	42	Wm	20
SY-1866/005	being Gt Ex removed		RRR	42	Wm	30
SY-1866/010	Palace of the People		RRR	42	Wm	25
SY-1866/015	Shakespeare bust L	legend in wreath	RRR	38	Wm	35
SY-1866/020	Christmastide		RRR	23	Wm	15

1867

Cat.No.	Description		Rarity	Size mm	Metal	Value £
SY-1867/001	Crystal Palace	Phoenix rising from flames	RRR	42	Wm	35
SY-1867/005	Royal Arms	Visit of Belgian Volunteers	RRR	25	Wm	40
SY-1867/010	Lion & dragon	Reform Banquet	RRR	38	Wm	40
SY-1867/015	Vic head L	Crystal Palace, Robert Holt	S	22	Aeg	20
SY-1867/020		smaller script	RR	22	Aeg	30

1868

Cat.No.	Description		Rarity	Size mm	Metal	Value £
SY-1868/001	10 lines Visit of Duke of Edinburgh	legend in wreath	RRR	31	Wm	30

1869

Cat.No.	Description		Rarity	Size mm	Metal	Value £
SY-1869/001	Crystal Palace	Velocipede Exhibition	RRR	42	Ae	50
			RRR	42	Aeg	60

1871

Cat.No.	Description		Rarity	Size mm	Metal	Value £
SY-1871/001	Anglo-Belgian Meeting	Dove with ribbon	RRR	59	Ae	65
SY-1871/005	Athena head L	Sydenham Industrial Exhibition	RRR	42	Ae	35
SY-1871/010	Ten thousand singers	Child praying	RRR	38	Wm	20

1872

Cat.No.	Description		Rarity	Size mm	Metal	Value £
SY-1872/001	Ten thousand singers	Child praying	RRR	38	Wm	20

1873

Cat.No.	Description		Rarity	Size mm	Metal	Value £
SY-1873/001	Britannia & Fame etc	Picture Gallery Prize	RRR	63	Ae	75
	cased		RRR	63	Ae	90
	with list of prizewinners, cased		RRRR	63	Ae	120
SY-1873/005	National Music Meeting	Harp in wreath	RRR	31	Ar	40
SY-1873/010	Ten thousand singers	Child praying	RRR	38	Wm	20

1874

Cat.No.	Description		Rarity	Size mm	Metal	Value £
SY-1874/001	Five thousand voices	Child praying	RRR	38	Wm	20

1876

Cat.No.	Description		Rarity	Size mm	Metal	Value £
SY-1876/001	Britannia & Fame etc. cased	Picture Gallery Prize	RRR	63	Ae	75
			RRR	63	Ae	90
	with list of Prizewinners, cased		RRRR	63	Ae	120

1879

Cat.No.	Description		Rarity	Size mm	Metal	Value £
SY-1879/001	Crystal Palace	Good Templars insignia	RRR	38	Wm	30

1880

Cat.No.	Description		Rarity	Size mm	Metal	Value £
SY-1880/001	Fifteen thousand singers	Child praying-	RRR	38	Wm	25

1881

Cat.No.	Description		Rarity	Size mm	Metal	Value £
SY-1881/001	4 line legend in wreath	Britannia opens doors	RR	63	Ae	50
SY-1881/005	Crystal Palace	Good Templars insignia	RRR	38	Wm	30

1882

Cat.No.	Description		Rarity	Size mm	Metal	Value £
SY-1882/001	John Curwen bust	Tonic Sol-fa Association choirs	RR	38	Ae	30
SY-1882/005	Joseph Livesey bust	Temperance Jubilee Fete	RR	39	Wm	20
SY-1882/010			RR	39	Wm	20
SY-1882/015	Temperance Jubilee Fete in cartouche	Uniface trial	RRRR	44	Wm	50

1883

Cat.No.	Description		Rarity	Size mm	Metal	Value £
SY-1883/001	Fifteen thousand singers	Child praying	RR	38	Wm	20

1884

Cat.No.	Description		Rarity	Size mm	Metal	Value £
SY-1884/001	School of Art Science & Literature	Britannia	RRR	63	Ar	220
SY-1884/005	London International Exhibition		R	63	Ae	60
			RR	63	Aes	80
			RRR	63	Aeg	100
SY-1884/010	Crystal Palace	Good Templars insignia	RRR	38	Wm	30

1885

Cat.No.	Description		Rarity	Size mm	Metal	Value £
SY-1885/001	Crystal Palace	Good Templars insignia	RRR	38	Wm	30
SY-1885/005	Crystal Palace	10 Panels	RR	42	Wm	30

1886

Cat.No.	Description		Rarity	Size mm	Metal	Value £
SY-1886/001	Crystal Palace	legend in shield	RRR	38	Wm	30

1887

Cat.No.	Description		Rarity	Size mm	Metal	Value £
SY-1887/001	Britannia & Fame etc	Picture Gallery Prize	RRR	63	Ae	75

Cat.No.	Description		Rarity	Size mm	Metal	Value £
	cased		RRR	63	Ae	90
	cased with list of prizewinners		RRRR	63	Ae	120
SY-1887/005	London Wheelers	Tricycle World record	RRRR	35	Ae	150
SY-1887/010	Crystal Palace Cage Bird Show	legend in wreath	RRR	38	Ar	75

1888

Cat.No.	Description		Rarity	Size mm	Metal	Value £
SY-1888/001	Photographic Exhibition	Britannia opens doors	RR	42	Ae	30
SY-1888/005	Crystal Palace	First Co-operative Festival	RRR	42	Wm	30

1889

Cat.No.	Description		Rarity	Size mm	Metal	Value £
SY-1889/001	School of Practical Engineering	Britannia opens doors	RRR	42	Ae	60
SY-1889/005	Photographic Exhibition /		RR	42	Ae	30
SY-1899/010	Legend in wreath	National Co-operative Festival	RRR	51	Ae	50

1890

Cat.No.	Description		Rarity	Size mm	Metal	Value £
SY-1890/001	Britannia & Fame etc.	Picture Gallery Prize	RRR	63	Ae	75
	cased		RRR	63	Ae	90
	cased with list of prizewinners		RRRR	63	Ae	120
SY-1890/005	Pug Dog Club	Legend in wreath	RRR	38x29	Ar	60
SY-1890/010	Legend in wreath	National Co-operative Festival	RRR	51	Ae	50
SY-1890/015	Photographic Exhibition	Brittania opens doors	RR	42	Ae	30
			RRR	42	Ar	65

1891

Cat.No.	Description		Rarity	Size mm	Metal	Value £
SY-1891/001	John Curwen bust	Tonic Sol-fa Jubilee	R	39	Wm	12
			RR	39	Wmg	15
SY-1891/005	Crystal Palace Dog Show	Legend in wreath	RRR	51	Ae	50

1892

Cat.No.	Description		Rarity	Size mm	Metal	Value £
SY-1892/001	Electrical Exhibition	Britannia opens doors	RRR	63	Ae	60
SY-1892/005			RRRR	42	Av	370
SY-1892/010		Two Factories	RRRR	70	Vulcanite	100
SY-1892/015	Crystal Palace 24th Cat Show	Legend in wreath	RRR	38	Ar	90
SY-1892/020	National Temperance Choral Union	Blank	RRR	45	Tin	30

1893

Cat.No.	Description		Rarity	Size mm	Metal	Value £
SY-1893/001	Photographic Exhibition	Britannia opens doors	RR	42	Ae	30
SY-1893/005	Sports & Pastimes Exhibition		RRR	42	Ae	40
SY-1893/010	Britannia & Fame etc.	Picture Gallery Prize	RRR	63	Ae	75
	cased		RRR	63	Ae	90
	cased with list of prizewinners		RRRR	63	Ae	120
SY-1893/015	Crystal Palace 25th Cat Show	Legend in wreath	RRR	38	Ar	90
SY-1893/020	National Temperance Choral Union	Blank	RRR	45	Tin	30

1894

Cat.No.	Description		Rarity	Size mm	Metal	Value £
SY-1894/001	Crystal Palace Cage Bird Show	Legend in wreath	RRR	38	Ar	75

1896

Cat.No.	Description		Rarity	Size mm	Metal	Value £
SY-1896/001	Shield shaped C of E Temperance Fete	Legend	R	36x30	Ae	15
			RR	36x30	Ar	30
SY-1896/005	School of Art Science & Literature	Britannia	RRR	63	Ar	220

1897

Cat.No.	Description		Rarity	Size mm	Metal	Value £
SY-1897/001	Victoria crowned bust L	Imperial Victorian Exhibition	RRRR	51	Ae	100
SY-1897/005	Belgian Canary on perch	Legend in wreath	RRR	44	Ae	40

1898

Cat.No.	Description		Rarity	Size mm	Metal	Value £
SY-1898/001	General Booth bust	Salvation Army Visit	RRR	32	Ae	40
SY-1898/005	Belgian Canary on perch	Legend in wreath	RRR	44	Ae	40

1899

Cat.No.	Description		Rarity	Size mm	Metal	Value £
SY-1899/001	Shield shaped Kennel Club Ladies Branch	Blank	RRR	99x70	Ar	100
SY-1899/005	Belgian Canary on perch	Legend in wreath	RRR	44	Ae	40

1900

Cat.No.	Description		Rarity	Size mm	Metal	Value £
SY-1900/001	Shield shaped C of E Temperance Fete	Legend	R	36x30	Ae	15
			RR	36x20	Ar	30
SY-1900/005	Irish Terrier	Harp & legend	RRR	39	Ar	75

1901

Cat.No.	Description		Rarity	Size mm	Metal	Value £
SY-1901/001	School of Art Science & Literature	Britannia	RRR	63	Ar	220
SY-1901/005	Naval & Military Exhibition in paper packet with ticket	Jubilee of Gt Exhibition	N	38	Wm	10
			RR	38	Wm	25
			R	38	Wmg	15
	in paper packet with ticket		RR	38	Wmg	30
	in red card box with ticket		RR	38	Wmg	35

1902

Cat.No.	Description		Rarity	Size mm	Metal	Value £
SY-1902/001	Edward & Alexandra busts R	Penge Arms, to children	R	38	Al	15
			RR	38	Alg	25
SY-1902/005	to Penge Old Folk		RRR	38	Al	25
SY-1902/010	Shield shaped C of E Temperance Fete	Legend	R	36x30	Ae	15
			RR	36x30	Ar	30
SY-1902/015	Motor Traders Show	Britannia opens doors	RRRR	63	Ae	75
SY-1902/020	Crystal Palace American Exhibition	Legend	RRR	29	Aeg	30
SY-1902/025		Blank	RRR	29	Aeg	25

1903

Cat.No.	Description		Rarity	Size mm	Metal	Value £
SY-1903/001	Food Exhibition	Legend	RRR	38	Ar	35
SY-1903/005	Crystal Palace	L & POS Cage Bird Show	RR	38	Ae	30
			RRR	38	Ar	60
SY-1903/010	School of Art Science & Literature	Britannia	RRR	42	Ae	50
SY-1903/015	Cat Club Arms	Legend, rose etc	RRR	39	Ar	90

1904

Cat.No.	Description		Rarity	Size mm	Metal	Value £
SY-1904/001	Female studying chick Utility Poultry Club	Legend	RR	51	Ae	40
			RRR	51	Ar	70
SY-1904/005	Crystal Palace	Legend Cage Bird Show	RRR	38	Ar	60
SY-1904/010	Crystal Palace	International Food Exhibition	RRR	56	Aeg	50
SY-1904/015	Irish Terrier head	harp & legend	RRR	39	Ar	80

1905

Cat.No.	Description		Rarity	Size mm	Metal	Value £
SY-1905/001	Britannia, Colonial & Indian Exhibition	Legend	RRR	51	Aeg	50
SY-1905/005	Shield shaped C of E Temperance Fete	Legend	R	36x30	Ae	15
			RR	36x30	Ar	30
SY-1905/010	Crystal Palace Indoor Bowls Club badge	Blank	R	27	Br	10
SY-1905/015	British Bulldog Club	Legend in wreath	RRR	45	Ae	40
SY-1905/020	John Pinches bust R	Legend	N	32x25	Ae	20

1906

Cat.No.	Description		Rarity	Size mm	Metal	Value £
SY-1906/001	Shield shaped C of E Temperance Fete	Legend	R	36x30	Ae	15
			RR	36x30	Ar	30
SY-1906/005	Shield shaped Kennel Club Ladies Branch	Blank	RRR	99x70	Ar	100

1907

Cat.No.	Description		Rarity	Size mm	Metal	Value £
SY-1907/001	Edward & Alexandra busts L	Balloon School	S	32	Wm	10
			R	32	Ae	15
			R	32	Aes	20
			R	32	Aeg	30
SY-1907/005	Int Ex of Artistique Furniture	Britannia	RRR	56	Aeg	50
			RRR	56	Aes	40
SY-1907/010	Shield shaped Kennel Club Ladies Branch	Blank	RRR	99x70	Ar	100
SY-1907/015	John Curwen bust	Tonic Sol-fa Jubilee Festival	R	39	Wm	10
			RR	39	Ae	20
SY-1907/020	Crystal Palace	L & POS Cage Bird Show	RR	38	Ae	30
			RRR	38	Ar	60
SY-1907/025	Shield shaped C of E Temperance Fete	Legend	R	36x30	Ae	15
			RR	36x30	Ar	30
SY-1907/030	Dandie Dinmont Terrier	Legend	RRR	51	Ae	40

1908

Cat.No.	Description		Rarity	Size mm	Metal	Value £
SY-1908/001	National Crysanthemum Show	Britannia opens doors	RRR	42	Ar	60

1909

Cat.No.	Description		Rarity	Size mm	Metal	Value £
SY-1909/001	Crystal Palace 50th Cage Bird Show	Legend	RR	38	Ae	30
SY-1909/005	Dandie Dinmont Terrier	Legend in wreath	RRR	51	Ae	40
SY-1909/010	Shield shaped C of E Temperance Fete	Legend	R	36x30	Ae	15
			RR	36x30	Ar	30
SY-1909/015	Universal Cookery & Food Exhibition	Beehive	RRR	44	Ae	35

1910

Cat.No.	Description		Rarity	Size mm	Metal	Value £
SY-1910/001	Brass Band Championship	1000 guinea Trophy	RRRR	32	Ae	50
SY-1910/005	School Orchestras — Intermediate	St Celia	S	32	Al	8
SY-1910/010	Advanced		S	32	Al	8

1911

Cat.No.	Description		Rarity	Size mm	Metal	Value £
SY-1911/001	George & Mary busts L	Coronation commemoration	N	39	Wm	8

Festival of Empire Exhibition & Pageant of London

Cat.No.	Description		Rarity	Size mm	Metal	Value £
SY-1911/005	Britannia with trident etc	Laurel wreath	RRR	38	Ae	25
SY-1911/010		Border of roses	RRR	38	Ae	30
SY-1911/015			RRR	63	Ae	75
			RRR	63	Ar	200
SY-1911/020		Laurel wreath	RRR	63	Ae	50
			RRR	63	Ar	80
	cased pair		RRRR	63	Arg	200
SY-1911/025	Geo & Mary busts L Britannia with trident etc		RRR	38	Al	25
			RRR	38	Ae	35
SY-1911/030			RRR	63	Ae	60
SY-1911/035	Cardboard badge used by Welsh National reps		RRR	64x54	Board	50
SY-1911/040	1st Gymnastic Festival — lapel badge		RR	29x22	Br	15
SY-1911/045	School Orchestras — Intermediate	Music stand etc.	S	31	Al	8
SY-1911/050		Advanced	S	31	Al	8
SY-1911/055	Crystal Palace L L & POS Cage Bird Show	Legend	RR	38	Ar	60
SY-1911/060	Shield shaped C of E Temperance Fete	Legend	R	36x30	Ae	15
			RR	36x30	Ar	30
SY-1911/065	L & POS Cage Bird Show	Legend in wreath	RR	32	Ae	20
			RRR	32	Ar	40
SY-1911/070	Tug of War, 7 line legend	Adonis pulling on rope	RRR	41	Ar	60

1912

Cat.No.	Description		Rarity	Size mm	Metal	Value £
SY-1912/001	Monogram	Gas Light & Coke Co. Centenary	S	35	Ae	10
			RR	35	Aes	30
SY-1912/005	Shield shaped C of E Temperance Fete	Legend	R	36x30	Ae	15
			RR	36x30	Ar	30
SY-1912/010	Crystal Palace	N.T.C.U. Jubilee Festival	RR	38	Wm	20
			RR	38	Al	20
			RRR	38	Ae	30
SY-1912/015	School Orchestras — Intermediate	Harp, book, violin	S	31	Al	8
SY-1912/020	Advanced		S	31	Al	8
SY-1912/025	Shield shaped Kennel Club Ladies Branch	Blank	RRR	99x70	Ar	100

1913

Cat.No.	Description		Rarity	Size mm	Metal	Value £
SY-1913/001	Canary on perch	Legend	RR	39x24	Ar	35
SY-1913/005	Shield shaped C of E Temperance Fete	Legend	R	36x30	Ae	15
			RR	36x30	Ar	30
SY-1913/010	School Orchestras — Intermediate	St Celia	S	31	Al	8
SY-1913/015	Advanced		S	31	Al	8
SY-1913/020	Crystal Palace Gymnastic Display	Legend	RR	34x27	Wm	15

1914

Cat.No.	Description		Rarity	Size mm	Metal	Value £
SY-1914/001	Crystal Palace Trustees pass	Name of Trustee	RRRR	28	Arg	150
SY-1914/005	Shield shape C of E Temperance Fete	Legend	R	36x30	Ae	15
			RR	36x30	Ar	30
SY-1914/010	School Orchestras — Intermediate	Apollo with violin	S	31	Al	8
SY-1914/015	Advanced		S	31	Al	8

1922

Cat.No.	Description		Rarity	Size mm	Metal	Value £
SY-1922/001	Daily Mail Fruit Show	Ceres with laden basket	RRR	74	Ae	70

1925

Cat.No.	Description		Rarity	Size mm	Metal	Value £
SY-1925/001	Crystal Palace Bees & Honey Show	Legend	RRR	41	Ae	35
			RRR	41	Ar	60

1926

Cat.No.	Description		Rarity	Size mm	Metal	Value £
SY-1926/001	Crystal Palace Poultry Pigeons & Rabbits	Legend	RR	51	Ae	35
			RRR	51	Ar	75
SY-1926/005	Crystal Palace Bees & Honey Show	Legend	RRR	41	Ae	35
			RRR	41	Ar	60

1928

Cat.No.	Description		Rarity	Size mm	Metal	Value £
SY-1928/001	Crystal Palace Poultry Pigeons & Rabbits	Legend	RR	51	Ae	35
			RRR	51	Ar	75
SY-1928/005	Crystal Palace Cage Bird Show	Legend	RR	45	Ae	30
			RRR	45	Ar	60
SY-1928/010	Crystal Palace Bees & Honey Show	Legend	RRR	41	Ae	35
			RRR	41	Ar	60

1929

Cat.No.	Description		Rarity	Size mm	Metal	Value £
SY-1929/001	Crystal Palace Poultry Pigeons & Rabbits	Legend	RR	51	Ae	35
			RRR	51	Ar	75
SY-1929/005	Crystal Palace Bees & Honey Show	Legend	RRR	41	Ae	35
			RRR	41	Ar	60

1930

Cat.No.	Description		Rarity	Size mm	Metal	Value £
SY-1930/001	Brass Band Championship	1000 guinea trophy	RRR	32	Ar	100
SY-1930/005	A pigeon	Legend	RRR	39	Ar	50
SY-1930/010	Crystal Palace Bees & Honey Show	Legend	RRR	41	Aeg	40
SY-1930/015	Crystal Palace Poultry Pigeons & Rabbits	Legend	RR	51	Ae	35

1931

Cat.No.	Description		Rarity	Size mm	Metal	Value £
SY-1931/001	Crystal Palace Cage Bird Show	Legend	RR	39	Ae	25
			RRR	39	Ar	50
SY-1931/005			RR	45	Ae	30
			RRR	45	Ar	60
SY-1931/010	London Transport Tag	-	RRR	39x33	Brass	15

1932

Cat.No.	Description		Rarity	Size mm	Metal	Value £
SY-1932/001	Crystal Palace Cage Bird Show	Legend	RR	29	Ae	15
			RRR	29	Ar	30
			RR	39	Ae	25
			RRR	39	Ar	50

1933

Cat.No.	Description		Rarity	Size mm	Metal	Value £
SY-1933/001	Crystal Palace Cage Bird Show	Legend	RR	29	Ae	15
			RRR	29	Ar	30
SY-1933/005	Canary on perch	Legend	RRR	31x26	Ar Enamel	50
SY-1933/010	Brass Band Championship	1000 guinea trophy	RRRR	32	Ae	50
SY-1933/015	Crystal Palace Poultry Pigeons & Rabbits	Legend	RR	51	Ae	35
			RRR	51	Ar	75

1934

Cat.No.	Description		Rarity	Size mm	Metal	Value £
SY-1934/001	Beehives	Legend	RR	43	Ae	25

1935

Cat.No.	Description		Rarity	Size mm	Metal	Value £
SY-1935/001	Crystal Palace Cage Bird Show	Legend	RRR	45	Ar	50

1936

Cat.No.	Description		Rarity	Size mm	Metal	Value £
SY-1936/001	Brass Band Championship	1000 guinea trophy	RRRR	32	Ae	50
SY-1936/005	Crystal Palace Poultry Pigeons & Rabbits	Legend	RRR	51	Ar	75

1937

Cat.No.	Description		Rarity	Size mm	Metal	Value £
SY-1937/001	Brass Band Championship	1000 guinea trophy	RRRR	32	Ae	50

1938

Cat.No.	Description		Rarity	Size mm	Metal	Value £
SY-1938/001	Brass Band Championship	1000 guinea trophy	RRRR	32	Ae	50

Cat.No.	Description		Rarity	Size mm	Metal	Value £
SY-1938/005	Crystal Palace Cage Bird Show	Legend	RRR	45	Ar	50

1939

Cat.No.	Description		Rarity	Size mm	Metal	Value £
SY-1939/001	Crystal Palace Cage Bird Show	Legend	RRR	45	Aeg	30

1940

Cat.No.	Description		Rarity	Size mm	Metal	Value £
SY-1940/001	Crystal Palace Cage Bird Show	Legend	RRR	45	Ar	50

1984

Cat.No.	Description		Rarity	Size mm	Metal	Value £
SY-1984/001	John Logie Baird bust R	Radio Rentals	N	39	Ae	5

1987

Cat.No.	Description		Rarity	Size mm	Metal	Value £
SY-1987/001	National Cat Club Centenary	Blank	N	39	Br enamel	10

Undated Pieces

Cat.No.	Description		Rarity	Size mm	Metal	Value £
SY-ND/001	Crystal Palace Trustees Pass	No. 48	RRRR	22	Ar	75
SY-ND/005	Victoria head L	Crystal Palace, Robert Holt	RRR	23	Br	35
SY-ND/010	Crystal Palace Stables	Blank	RRR	36	Wm	50
SY-ND/015	Crystal Palace	John Betjeman's Bygone Britain	RR	39	Ar	25
SY-ND/020	Refreshment Department pass	No. 350	RRR	42	Ae	75
SY-ND/025	Crystal Palace Dog Show	Blank	RRR	51	Ae	40
SY-ND/030	Britannia & Fame etc.	Wreath	RRR	63	Wm	60
SY-ND/035	Prince & Princess of Wales heads L	Peters Rifle Ground -	RRR	23	Wm	25
SY-ND/040	Crystal Palace Company	No. 381	RR	28	Wm	15
SY-ND/045	No. 458	Blank	RR	35	Wm	20

1857 Exhibition of Art Treasures

The Inauguration
by Ottley

Cat.No.	Description		Rarity	Size mm	Metal	Value £
MA-001	Prince Albert head L	Ex building	RRR	51x41	Wm	75
			RRR	51x41	Ae	120

by Pinches

Cat.No.	Description		Rarity	Size mm	Metal	Value £
MA-005	Brass case — Manchester Arms	Legend — empty	R	45	Br	10
		empty	R	67	Br	20
MA-010	Victoria diademed bust L	Exhibition building	RRR	42	Ae	40
			RRR	42	Wm	30
MA-015	Exhibition building	3 Muses	S	42	Wm	12
	in leather case		S	42	Wm	15
	in brass case		RR	42	Wm	25
			RR	42	Ae	30
			R	42	Ae	35
MA-020	bushes in front		R	42	Wm	15
	in leather case		R	42	Wm	18
			RR	42	Ae	35
MA-025	8 line legend		S	42	Wm	12
	in leather case		S	42	Wm	15
	in brass case		S	42	Wm	25
	in leather case		R	42	Ae	20
MA-030			S	63	Wm	30
			R	63	Ae	40
MA-035	Ex building in wreath		R	63	Wm	40
	in brass case		RR	63	Wm	60
			RR	63	Ae	60

Royal Visit
by Ottley

Cat.No.	Description		Rarity	Size mm	Metal	Value £
MA-040	Prince Albert head L	14 line legend	RRR	51x41	Wm	75

by Pinches

Cat.No.	Description		Rarity	Size mm	Metal	Value £
MA-045	Victoria diademed bust L	Exhibition building	R	42	Wm	20
			RR	42	Ae	30
MA-050	Exhibition Building		RR	42	Wm	—
MA-055		3 Muses	RR	42	Wm	25

1862 International Exhibition

A. Official Medals

Cat.No.	Description		Rarity	Size mm	Metal	Value £
SK-A001	Prize medal	unawarded	S	77	Ae	40
		awarded	S	77	Ae	60
SK-A005	different signature	unawarded	S	77	Ae	40
		awarded	R	77	Ae	60
SK-A010	Jurors Medal		RRR	77	Ae	90
SK-A015	For Services medal	unawarded	RRR	55	Ae	60
		awarded	RRR	55	Ae	100
SK-A020	Entertainments Committee		RRRR	72x64	Arg	200
SK-A030	Works Pass		RRRR	35	Ivory	150

B. Unofficial Medals
by Allen & Moore

Cat.No.	Description		Rarity	Size mm	Metal	Value £
SK-B001	Victoria Gothic bust L	Exhibition building	R	39	Wm	15
SK-B005	Napoleon III & Victoria vis-a-vis		S	39	Wm	15

by A. Bovy

Cat.No.	Description		Rarity	Size mm	Metal	Value £
SK-B010	Victoria Laureate head L	Ex building	S	50	Wm	20
	in circular card case		R	50	Wm	25
			R	50	Ae	30
	in circular card case		RR	50	Ae	40
	in circular leather case		RRR	50	Ae	50
			S	50	Aes	20
	in circular card case		R	50	Aes	25
			RR	50	Aeg	30
	in circular card case		RR	50	Aeg	40
	in circular leather case		RRR	50	Aeg	50
			RR	50	Ar	50
	in circular leather case		RRR	50	Ar	60
SK-B015	Shadowed design		S	50	Wm	25
	in circular card case		R	50	Wm	30
			S	50	Aes	25
	in circular card case		R	50	Aes	30
SK-B020	French script		RR	50	Wm	30
	in circular card case		RR	50	Wm	35
	in leather case		RR	50	Wm	40
			RR	50	Ar	60
	in circular card case		RR	50	Ar	65
	in leather case		RRR	50	Ar	75

by H. Brown

Cat.No.	Description		Rarity	Size mm	Metal	Value £
SK-B025	Exhibition building	Sydenham Crystal Palace	RRR	42	Wm	50

by G. Dowler

Cat.No.	Description		Rarity	Size mm	Metal	Value £
SK-B040	Exhibition building	Terrestrial globe	S	26	Wm	10
SK-B045	Victoria Gothic bust L	Ex building	RRR	36	Wm	—
SK-B050	Brass case-Albert bust L	Legend — empty	R	41	Br	10
		empty	RRR	68	Br	25
SK-B055	Exhibition building	Terrestrial globe	S	37	Wm	12
	in brass case		RR	37	Wm	25
SK-B060	Exhibition building	12 line legend	S	38	Wm	12
			R	38	Wms	15
SK-B065	Exhibition building	Terrestrial globe	RRR	42	Wm	—
SK-B070	Victoria diademed head L	Exhibition building	RRR	42	Wm	40
SK-B075	Victoria Gothic bust L		RR	52	Wm	30
SK-B080	Victoria diademed bust L		RRR	52	Wm	45
SK-B085	Prince Albert head R		RR	52	Wm	30
SK-B090	Exhibition building	5 line legend	RR	52	Wm	30
SK-B095		Sydenham Crystal Palace	R	52	Wm	25
SK-B100	Victoria diademed head L	Exhibition building	RRR	61	Ae	—
SK-B105	Exhibition building	Terrestrial globe	RRRR	61	Wm	100
	in brass case		RRRR	61	Wm	125
SK-B110	Victoria diademed bust L	Exhibition building	RRR	75	Wm	75
SK-B115	Exhibition building	Britannia standing on shore	RRR	75	Wm	75
SK-B120	Exhibition building	Sydenham Crystal Palace	RRR	75	Wm	75

by G.L.

Cat.No.	Description		Rarity	Size mm	Metal	Value £
SK-B130	Prince Albert in frame etc	Exhibition building	RRRR	69	Wm	120

by J. Moore.

Cat.No.	Description		Rarity	Size mm	Metal	Value £
SK-B140	Victoria crowned bust L	Exhibition building	RRR	52	Wm	—

by T. Ottley.

Cat.No.	Description		Rarity	Size mm	Metal	Value £
SK-B150	Victoria Gothic bust L	Exhibition building	RRR	42	Wm	30
SK-B155	Exhibition building	Britannia with globe	RR	42	Wm	20
SK-B160	Princess Alice & Louis of Hesse	Exhibition building	RRR	51	Wm	50
SK-B165	Victoria Gothic bust L		RR	54	Wm	30
SK-B170	Exhibition building	Four seated figures	RR	54	Wm	30
SK-B175	Victoria diademed bust L	Exhibition building	RRR	65	Wm	60
SK-B180			RRR	65	Wm	—
SK-B185			RRR	70	Wm	—
SK-B190	Exhibition building	Angels around globe	RRR	74	Wm	75
SK-B195		Britannia with globe	RRR	74	Wm	75

by Pinches

Cat.No.	Description		Rarity	Size mm	Metal	Value £
SK-B200	Building inscribed West Front	Two seated females	N	42	Wm	10
	in leather case		S	42	Wm	15
	in paper packet		RR	42	Wm	30
			RR	42	Wmg	20
	in leather case		RR	42	Wmg	25
	in paper packet		RRR	42	Wmg	40
			R	42	Al	20
	in leather case		R	42	Al	25
	in paper packet		RRR	42	Al	35
			S	42	Ae	20
	in leather case		S	42	Ae	25
SK-B205	Flag incuse		R	42	Wm	15
SK-B207	not inscribed		RRR	21	Aeg	30
SK-B210			N	42	Wm	10
	in leather case		S	42	Wm	15
	in paper packet		RR	42	Wm	30
			S	42	Ae	15
	in leather case		S	42	Ae	20
SK-B215	Flag incuse		R	42	Wm	15
SK-B220	inscribed West Front		R	51	Wm	15
	in leather case		R	51	Wm	20

Cat.No.	Description		Rarity	Size mm	Metal	Value £
	in paper packet		RR	51	Wm	40
			RR	51	Ae	25
	in leather case		RR	51	Ae	30
			RR	51	Al	25
	in leather case		RR	51	Al	30
	in paper packet		RRR	51	Al	50

by Uhlhorn

Cat.No.	Description		Rarity	Size mm	Metal	Value £
SK-B230	Prince Albert head L	Exhibition building	N	41	Ae	20
			N	41	Aes	15
	in circular card box		R	41	Aes	20
			R	41	Aeg	20
	in circular card box		R	41	Aeg	25
			R	41	Ar	60
SK-B235		Interior view	S	41	Ae	20
			S	41	Aes	15
	in circular card box		R	41	Aes	20
			R	41	Aeg	20
	in circular card box		R	41	Aeg	25
			R	41	Ar	60
SK-B240	Exhibition building		R	41	Ae	20
			R	41	Aes	15
	in circular card box		RR	41	Aes	20
			R	41	Aeg	20
	in circular card box		RR	41	Aeg	25
			R	41	Ar	60
SK-B245			R	41	Ae	20

All the silvered specimens seen by the Author were most unattractive because the bronze was showing through the silver on at least one side, if not on both. This is undoubtedly a manufacturing defect common to this particular version, therefore these pieces have been priced lower than bronze. Naturally, If there are any specimens not affected in this way, they will fetch a similar or slightly higher price than bronze.

by JS & AB Wyon

Cat.No.	Description		Rarity	Size mm	Metal	Value £
SK-B250	Six plants in a roseace	Britannia seated etc	RRR	64	Ae	85

by ?

Cat.No.	Description		Rarity	Size mm	Metal	Value £
SK-B260	Victoria Bare head L	Exhibition building	S	22	Brg	8
SK-B265			RR	22	Brg	10
SK-B270			N	22	Aeg	6
			N	22	Brg	6
SK-B275			N	22	Brg	6
			RR	22	Brs	10
SK-B280			RR	22	Br	—
SK-B285	Prince Albert head R		RRR	32	Br shell	25
SK-B290	Exhibition building	12 line legend	RRR	38	Wm	30

C. Trade Tokens

Cat.No.	Name	Location	Rarity	Size mm	Metal	Value £
SK-C010	R. Jeary,	Norwich	RR	22	Br	35
SK-C020	W. Kibble,	London	RRRR	54	Wm	70
SK-C030	M. Lyons,	Birmingham	R	35	Br	20
			R	35	Brs	20
			R	35	Ae	20
			R	35	Aeg	20
			R	35	Aes	20
SK-C035			RR	35	Ae	25
SK-C040	Piesse & Lubin,	London	R	22	Brg	25
SK-C050	D. Uhlhorn -	Prince Albert head L / 6 line legend	RRR	21	Br	25
SK-C055		/ 7 line legend	RRR	21	Aeg	25
SK-C060		7 line legend / 6 line legend	RRR	21	Ae	25
SK-C065		7 line legend / 6 line legend	RRR	21	Ae	25

D. Associated Pieces

Cat.No.	Description		Rarity	Size mm	Metal	Value £
SK-D001	Prince Albert head R	Parksine Exhibition	RRR	42	'Parksine'	60
SK-D010	Francis Fowke bust L	Legend	R	58	Ae	75
			RRR	58	Ar	200
SK-D020	Prince Albert head L	Legend in wreath	R	68	Ae	60
SK-D025	Prince Albert head L	Legend in wreath	R	68	Ae	60